LOGIC AND PROLOG

LOGIC AND PROLOG

Richard Spencer-Smith

HARVESTER
WHEATSHEAF

New York   London   Toronto   Sydney   Tokyo   Singapore

First published 1991 by
Harvester Wheatsheaf
66 Wood Lane End, Hemel Hempstead
Hertfordshire HP2 4RG
A division of
Simon & Schuster International Group

Printed in Great Britain at the
University Press, Cambridge

British Library Cataloguing in Publication Data

Spencer-Smith, Dr Richard
  Logic and Prolog
  1. Prolog Programming Language
  1. Title
  005.13

  ISBN 0-7450-1022-9

  2 3 4 5 95 94 93

Contents

Preface

In the production of this book, I owe a debt of gratitude in many quarters. First and foremost, to the University Grants Committee, without whose financial support it would not have been possible. The U.G.C, through its Computers in Teaching Initiative, provided funding for the development of a course combining Logic with Prolog.

In help with Prolog, I am particularly indebted to two people: Steve Torrance and Don Smith. I have been fortunate enough to have Steve as a close friend, and collaborator on other projects. Steve has shown me many things about Prolog, especially in relation to second order programming and production systems. He has been generous in supplying ideas for the book (e.g. the basis of Appendix 3), and has made many valuable comments on earlier drafts. I have also benefited enormously from the expert eye of Don Smith, who is responsible for the tail recursive definition of cumulative interest in section 5.2, and for a backwards chaining system which gave me the idea for the illustrative expert system of section 5.4. Amongst many who have given me help and encouragement, I would especially like to thank Ruth Crocket, Tony Drapkin, David Over and Alan Lacey for their comments.

I would also like to thank all those students at London, and latterly at Middlesex, who have suffered my various attempts to get this material right. On occasions they have shown me more elegant solutions than my own - both proofs and programs. Their solutions than my own - both proofs and programs. Their criticisms have been the most valuable - of my mistakes, and incomprehensible formulations.

I have produced an Instructor's Manual to accompany the text. This arose initially out of my own need for a record of answers when marking - including acceptable alternative solutions to exercises, and common mistakes. Its development was further encouraged when I had postgraduate assistants to help with marking. Since many lecturers will have such assistance, I believe it is useful to make this material more widely available - but not so accessible as simply appearing in the back of the book. Any lecturer can obtain a free copy of this Manual from the publishers.

London, 1990.

Chapter 1
Introduction

1.1 Background to logic

What exactly is logic? Some will say that logic is centrally concerned with defining the notion of *proof* - an account of the inferential transformations that can lead to the derivation of a conclusion from a set of assumptions. Others may say that *logical truth*, and related notions involving meaning and truth, are central. Others may say that the definition of consistency is what logic is really all about. All of these concerns are important, but it is misleading to suggest that one is more fundamental than the others. One could equally well say that logic is essentially concerned with characterizing a few special expressions, known as the logical constants. It studies them from two angles: what they mean, and what inferential properties they have. This dual characterization of the logical constants only makes sense in the context of a general conception of meaning and of proof - that is, a context which includes those general relationships of truth, proof, consistency, etc.

Logic is relevant to any area of thinking or talking where the logical constants are used. Since these words are of the highest generality, that is really all areas. From theoretical physics to everyday talk of mundane matters, we make assertions and reason with sentences employing these words. This fact is sometimes expressed in the thesis that logic is *topic-neutral*; it applies to all topics, and is partial towards none. But with some fields of inquiry logic enjoys a special bond. With linguistics there is a common interest in the structure of ordinary language, and the extent to which that is a logical structure. Psychologists are concerned with the nature of cognition; reasoning (however well or badly we ordinarily do it) is a cognitive process of central importance. To a

1

logical structure. Psychologists are concerned with the nature of cognition; reasoning (however well or badly we ordinarily do it) is a cognitive process of central importance. To a mathematician, symbolic logic is a branch of the subject like any other. Logical systems can be the object of mathematical investigation, and some of the most important theorems this century have concerned what can and cannot be done within them.

Computer science uses logic at its lowest level, in the switching of its circuitry, and at the highest level, in logic programming languages such as Prolog. However, with philosophy the link is at its most venerable. Philosophy gave birth to logic as a discipline, and still accords it a central place. Philosophy needs logic as a tool for the analysis of concepts and problems, and because its principal mode of demonstration is reasoned argument. Moreover, concepts such as truth, necessity and existence require both philosophical and formal investigation. What this list of disciplines indicates is that there are many different facets to the study and application of modern logic - so much so that it is impossible to begin to cover them all in a single work. This book is concerned with the *use* of logic, and especially its application in these last two subject areas.

Rather than launch straight in to the formalities, I will begin with some informal reasoning tasks. There is more to these exercises than appears at first sight, and we shall return to them in due course. You may have already encountered variants of the problems before. The kind I shall now describe are developed most fully in some books by Raymond Smullyan. In tribute to Smullyan's formulation, I shall call these **knights** and **knaves** problems. A knight is *honest*, in this very strict sense: everything he says is true. Knaves are correspondingly *dishonest*: anything a knave says is false. There is also the possibility of encountering a **normal**: someone who, like normal people, sometimes speaks truly, sometimes falsely. There is a group of islands notorious for these characters. Some islands are populated only by knaves, others by knights, while some may even contain normals. People occasionally get washed up amongst these islands, and the locals are wont to have a little fun with them by venturing information about themselves - or disinformation, as the case may be. We shall assume in what follows that we are on the island of knights and knaves, i.e. that we will encounter both of these types, but no normals. (This is only an assumption, and may need to be revised later.)

A typical case is this. We come across two of the locals - let's call them 'a' and 'b'. a tells us that at least one of them is a knave. So the problem is: what, if anything, can we deduce about these characters, from the information that a said this? Before proceeding to my account of the matter, you may like to stop and work out the solution for yourself.

Well, here's my version:

a says that at least one of a and b is a knave.
Suppose that a is a knave.
Then anything he says is false.
So it's false that at least one of them is a knave.
In other words, neither a nor b is a knave.
But then, in particular, a is not a knave.
This contradicts our initial hypothesis - so he can't be a knave.
If every islander is either knight or knave, a must be a knight.
If he's a knight, then what he said is true: at least one of them is a knave.
If at least one of them is a knave, and it isn't a, it must be b.
So we conclude: a is a knight and b a knave.

This sort of problem is in a sense rather artificial. In the present context this is an advantage, because it means that they are very self-contained. The assumptions which are relevant to the problem are few. A problem involving a more realistic example would tend to get us side-tracked into questions about what assumptions were correct and appropriate. With an artificial example we can concentrate on the reasoning, not the assumptions. It's better if there are a small number which can be agreed upon, for what's important is how one reasons *from* those assumptions. Many of the key words in the little specimen of reasoning above - 'suppose', 'if', 'not', 'every', 'and', 'so', 'true', 'or', 'false' - might occur in any piece of reasoning. They are the logical hinges on which an argument can turn, no matter what its topic. These are the sorts of words which logic is concerned to characterize, and thus our subject matter in what follows.

1.2   Background to Prolog

In order to do anything at all, a machine needs to be told what to do - either through some form of external control, as when operated by a person, or by containing within it a sequence of instructions which direct it - a *program*. A machine might, for instance, compute the inference 'Socrates is human. Therefore: Socrates is mortal'. It can't do this without being programmed in some way to do so, e.g. by containing the instruction 'To prove that something mortal, show that it is human'. For any computing machine it is customary to distinguish between its *software*, the instructions and information which guide it, and its *hardware*, the collection of devices which is the physical machine. The two are mutually independent. The same set of instructions may be physically embodied in totally different ways, in different machines. And the same machine may be able to follow many different kinds of instructions.

Instructions need to be formulated in a language. There are many computer languages, and different ones are suited to different tasks. They can be graded from ease of comprehension to humans (*high-level*), to ease of comprehension to computers (*low-level*). For every computer there is a fundamental language, its *machine code*, the instructions of which correspond to the basic operations which it can perform (looking at the number stored in a certain memory location, say). At the other end of the scale are high-level languages like Prolog, which are relatively close to natural language. If a computer is running a Prolog program, in addition to the low-level description of what is going on, in machine code terms, there will also be a high-level description of what it is doing (drawing a certain inference, for example.).

A computer *file* can be a program, e.g. which tells the computer how to perform some function, such as word processing. Or a file could contain the data which such a program manipulates, e.g. the text of a document created by someone using the word processor. Some tasks which computers perform - airline bookings, say - require many particular items of data (flight details, passenger reservations, etc.) to be recorded in a very structured way, so that information can be accessed and manipulated in certain set ways - a *database*. So a file might consist of a database of information. Or a file might contain the instructions which make it possible for the machine to be programmed in a particular language. Such a file would need to contain some means of translating a program written in that language, a *source* program, into the machine code of the computer, an *object* program. A file can be stored on whatever storage medium the machine uses - or by being written down on a piece of paper. Since a file is essentially a quantity of information, files are capable in principle of being transferred from one machine to another, e.g. over a telephone line.

One can distinguish two ways of approaching a programming task, two different programming styles: the *imperative* (or *procedural*), and the *descriptive* (or *declarative*). The imperative approach is epitomized by the question: how am I going to get the computer to do this task - what sequence of instructions should I give it?

This approach fits naturally with an imperative programming language - one in which many of the primitive expressions are *commands*. Most traditional computer languages have been imperative. The descriptive approach is characterized by a different attitude: how can I analyse and *describe* the matter in hand - the description to be in a form which the computer can use? The difference between the two styles can be illustrated by the kind of conditionals typically found in the corresponding programming languages. In an imperative language, they are like the conditional imperatives of ordinary language (e.g. 'If it's raining, put your coat on'). In a descriptive language, conditionals are like ordinary declarative conditionals (e.g. 'If it's raining, the pavements will be wet').

The logic programming language Prolog is typical of a descriptive language. However, even a descriptive language like Prolog has some imperative features. (In order to get the computer to display messages, for instance, we need something which is in effect an *instruction* to print.) This is why I prefer to draw the contrast primarily in terms of programming styles, rather than languages. Prolog counts as a descriptive language because it is suited to the descriptive attitude. Programming in it is an extension of our techniques for logical analysis and description. A problem is tackled by writing an analysis of it as a set of sentences in Prolog (a version of first order logic), which the machine can use like a set of axioms, to prove conclusions. A program is used not by telling it to run, but by putting questions to it - can a particular conclusion be derived? The overall approach, then, is one of description and deduction. But since we also have to pay attention to controlling the way deductions are carried out, and to producing side-effects like messages being printed out, there will usually be a procedural element too.

There is one other general contrast which is worth drawing - between two ways computers can be set up for programming. These ways are independent of the kind of language being used; rather, they are environments in which programming can take place. I shall say that the distinction is between *prompt*-based systems, and *windows*-based systems. The point of making this contrast is merely to indicate that there are different ways of entering, testing and changing a program, for it has a slight impact on the syntax of the language being used. A prompt-based system essentially allows just one point of contact with the language: the prompt. A multi-windows environment presents a more flexible interface to the user. Being easier to use, they generally require more sophisticated hardware on which to run. The distinction is neither exclusive (combinations of the two are possible) nor exhaustive (in the future, one might be able to give instructions to a computer by speaking to it in ordinary language).

The standard prompt in Edinburgh Prolog is the combination '?-'. When the prompt shows, one may interact with Prolog - telling it to add a certain sentence to its logical database, for instance, or asking it a question. Here is a short illustration of an interaction on a prompt based system:

```
?-      listing.
mortal(X) :- human(X) .
human(socrates).
yes
?-      mortal(socrates).
yes
?-
```

On the first of these lines, Prolog is told to show everything in its current program - to list all the sentences. There are just two: any X is mortal if it is human, and: Socrates is human. After these are displayed, the prompt reappears, and this time Prolog is queried: is it deducible that Socrates is mortal? Prolog makes the inference, gives the answer, and then returns the prompt, ready for the next interaction.

A multi-window environment is easier to use, because it can separate out some of these different aspects of programming into different windows. Here is roughly the same interaction in a windows system:

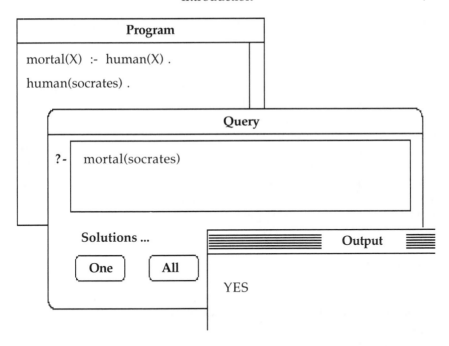

In the Program window at the top left, the program can be written - and edited like an ordinary piece of text on a word processor. This makes editing far simpler than having laboriously to enter edit instructions through the prompt. The middle window allows queries to be entered. The Output window, at the front, is where the solution to the query is displayed.

Lecturers at a university or college are likely to have access to a computer advisory service; those wishing to try out Prolog for the first time should consult the service as to whether their institution already has a licence for some version of Prolog; if not, whether it can be provided for the available machines; if not, which combination of hardware and software they would recommend. Those without access to a computer advisory could try looking in computer magazines for reviews of, and adverts for, implementations of Prolog; bear in mind that most commercial software (and hardware) is available to educational users at a substantial discount. It may be possible to obtain a demonstration version of the software for evaluation. In view of the above, one point to look out for is general ease of use - it's important that, for example, the business of editing doesn't get in the way of the more important task of working out what needs to be edited. Another valuable feature in an educational context is the provision of detailed and intelligible error messages.

For those used only to teaching pure logic, the value of 'hands on' classes or workshops cannot be stressed enough; students need not only to have the general system demonstrated while they are sitting at a computer terminal, they also need practical sessions in Prolog programming and debugging. If the students are new to computers - or just new to the machines they will be using for Prolog - it is advisable to spend some time getting acquainted with the general environment before launching into Prolog. In particular, one should know how to edit, save, load and print out a file. A suitable exercise would be to use a word processing program with the same kind of interface as the Prolog implementation, to prepare some text - a letter, or an essay - and print it out.

1.3   Logic and Prolog

Many students of both logic and Prolog have great difficulty mastering the abstract concepts and techniques of these two subjects. This book attempts to explain these abstract concepts in an intuitively comprehensible way. It is thus aimed especially at those who are not well-versed in the use of formal or symbolic languages (unlike for example mathematicians and computer scientists) - students of philosophy, or cognitive science, or anyone studying Prolog as a first computer language. Despite their theoretical affinity, logic and Prolog are often not studied together. Nevertheless, studying one will enhance the learning of the other. The book is intended to provide a comprehensive grounding in both subjects, taking students from introductory level through to advanced features of Prolog, including some basic applications to artificial intelligence (A.I.). The relationship between logic and Prolog is developed from a practical, rather than theoretical perspective.

One component of philosophy, ancient and modern, is the analysis of concepts. Frege, the discoverer of modern formal logic, called it a *Begriffsschrift*, a concept notation. The analysis of a concept might involve attempting to get straight the conditions necessary and sufficient for its correct application, or seeing where such an attempt fails. For a simple example, see the analysis of knowledge, exercise 2.4, D. An analysis of knowledge involves a theory of the kind of thing which knowledge is, and may issue in a proposed definition of that concept. Logic serves the analysis and statement of such definitions and theories, making their content precise, e.g. by laying bare the different readings of an ambiguous formulation, or showing exactly where qualifications or amendments are needed. One could say that philosophers have been using logic as a knowledge representation language longer than anyone. Analysis is one of the most important applications of logic in modern philosophy, yet most courses in logic do not seriously address it. At best they contain exercises in formalizing English sentences into logical formulae. But real problems do not come already packaged into a neat set of sentences; they are specified informally, and the difficult task is to produce a precise analysis from that informal description.

I have tried to design a number of logic exercises which give the student practice and confidence in applying logic to the analysis of problems. But problem solving is one area where logic *programming* has a great deal to offer the teaching of logic. In Prolog, you can work right through from an informal specification of a problem to a working analysis of it. You are not presented with a number of statements in English to translate into logical notation - getting a propositional description is half (or maybe much more) of the problem. You have to decide what the basic facts are, and what vocabulary you should use to describe them with, and then work out how to define other relationships in terms of that vocabulary - define the logical connections between these concepts. The computer makes the process of logical analysis interactive, providing very direct feedback in a way one simply cannot get if the sentences are just written down on paper. A student can see his or her logical definitions at work, and can get an idea from the answers of whether for example a defining condition needs to be added to or altered. Does the program prove fewer consequences than were intended - or more? Perhaps it works partially, answering some queries correctly but not others. One can experiment with it, and see the consequences of altering it in different ways.

Other examples of the pedagogical symbiosis between logic and Prolog are worth citing. Prolog can help to bring to life some aspects of the language of logic, for instance by showing that a variable is, precisely, variable: a term which can take various objects as its values. Recursion is another example. In elementary logic students learn techniques which are recursive, such as truth tables and proofs, without being explicitly introduced to the concept of recursion. By learning recursive programming in Prolog, they can come to a deeper understanding of these elementary recursions. Search, which is one of the major topics in A.I., provides another important example. By seeing proof construction as a search problem we can bring to bear some of the understanding of search developed in A.I., to provide students with heuristics and strategies for reasoning. As a final example of the way Prolog can help with logic, I would mention the most important properties which can attributed to a logical system: that it be consistent (that it does not entail anything unwanted), and complete (that it does entail everything it should). I have not attempted to state proofs of any of the fundamental results involving these concepts, e.g. the consistency and completeness of propositional logic - material which, I believe, is neither necessary nor comprehensible to the average beginner. Rather, the approach here is practical: a student can get a much firmer grasp of what these properties really amount to by setting up and interpreting a small logical system of their own. The expert system sketched in sections 5.3 and 5.4 is just that: a simple logical system interpreted within Prolog.

Benefits also accrue in the other direction. At the elementary level, by providing students with a grounding in logic before attempting to program with logic, we can avoid some of the problems of adjusting to the declarative style of thinking typically encountered by those who come straight to Prolog from the traditional, procedural style of programming. Secondly, studying how proofs work (especially inferences involving Modus Ponens, Reductio, Disjunctive Syllogism and Universal Instantiation), helps to make clear what Prolog is actually doing when it solves a query - namely, performing a mechanical derivation according to such rules. As a final example: use of the more explicit notation of logic can help to clarify some of the more advanced features of Prolog - the precise force of such constructs as **not**, **forall** and **setof**.

Given all these potential benefits of studying the two subjects together, the question naturally arises as to how best they can be combined. Already they have grown apart in notation and terminology. This poses a dilemma: adopt a consistent style throughout, or mix the two? I have taken the latter course, since to do otherwise would be unfair to one or the other discipline, and it is my intention that this course should provide students with a firm grounding in both. There is a need for each community of practitioners to stay in touch with the other: for logicians to know about this most important area of application, and for logic programmers to know about the theoretical roots of their practice. Since it would be confusing to switch back and forth between the two disciplines too often, I have grouped them into two chapters apiece.

Texts and courses in logic tend to fall into two sorts. Those in informal logic look at real examples of reasoning, both valid and fallacious, but lack the rigour and generality of formal logic. Those in formal logic present it as a rigorous, abstract discipline, but which may appear to the student to bear little or no relation to real reasoning. What is interesting, I believe, is the interaction between formal and informal, and I have tried to introduce formal concepts by means of examples of their informal application. For instance, by relating natural deduction to everyday reasoning - introducing it via real problem solving examples (such as knights and knaves problems) - it is made comprehensible to those who might otherwise not see the point of it. But in consequence, purists may find that informality and intuition intrude too often. It is a commonplace of the philosophy of mathematics that although Euclid was the founder of the axiomatic method, some of his proofs are vitiated by appeals to intuition, rather than being carried through rigorously. Appeals to intuition were only expunged from mathematics with the development of formal methods in the nineteenth century. From a theoretical point of view, the proper way to present a logical system is first to set out the uninterpreted language, with rules of formation and transformation, and only later perhaps mention an intended interpretation for it. Proof theory (syntax) before model theory (semantics). But conceptual priorities do not necessarily coincide with pedagogical priorities. This is not the best approach for those who are not familiar with formal languages. It encourages the misconception that logic is just a formal game played with abstract symbols, unrelated to the real world. Perhaps the most evident sacrifice of formal rigour for pedagogical clarity is in my system of tracking assumptions within proofs. Assumption tracking is a matter which beginners can find particularly difficult, and my system is deliberately intended as a simplification which gets the essential idea across, by avoiding the complexities of a complete system.

With Prolog, I have tried to separate off into one chapter an introduction to the language for those with little or no computational background. It is intended to keep to the 'programming in logic' ideal - in which the solution to a programming problem takes the form of a logical description of a set of relationships, rather than a set of instructions. It is relatively easy to switch from predicate logic to writing elementary programs in Prolog - essentially it involves only a notational change. But proper understanding of a program requires a grasp not only of its descriptive content but also the way it works as a procedure - how a machine will carry out derivations from it, and how such derivations are controlled. In Kowalski's well-known formula, Algorithm = Logic + Control. In other words, in order to do any serious programming in Prolog, one needs more than pure logic - one needs to understand the pragmatics of a program, its control or procedural aspects. The more advanced the program, the more important this becomes. I have tried to defer these issues as much as possible until the final chapter, which looks at more advanced applications of Prolog.

Exercise 1

A good way to proceed with these two questions is as follows. Firstly, work out your answer, by whatever means suits you. Make sure you consider all the possibilities. Secondly, organize your thoughts into a step by step argument for your conclusion, rather as I have done in the example above. It's important always to aim for the best presentation of your views you can provide - present your reasoning as a clear and concise argument, ending with an explicit statement of your conclusion.

A.   Suppose there are three hats, about which I tell John and Mary the following. Two of them have feathers, one does not. Two of them are red, one is blue. I put one hat on John, and one on Mary. Each can see the other's hat, but neither can see their own. (The spare hat remains hidden.)   Both are honest, and can reason perfectly with the information they are given. I ask Mary: 'What can you deduce about your hat?' She replies that all she knows is that it is red. Given that John can see a feathered hat on Mary, can you work out the colours of the hats which are feathered, and who is wearing which?

B.   On the island of knights and knaves, we come across two more of the locals, c and d. c says something, but we don't hear him. We ask d. d replies: c said, of himself, that he is a knave. First question: what can we deduce about the nature of these characters? Second question: what general principle about the land of knights and knaves do we learn in answering this?

Chapter 2
Logic: the foundation of analysis

2.1 Structure

2.1.1 States of affairs

Consider the sentence

1)   Picasso was not French.

An important question is: In what circumstances would this sentence
be true, and in what circumstances would it be false? In other words,
how would its truth or falsity vary in different possible
circumstances? Truth and falsity are known as **truth values**. So our
question can be reformulated like this: What possible states of
affairs are directly relevant to the truth value of this sentence?
There's a fairly obvious answer: it would be false if Picasso was
French, and true otherwise. We can represent this answer in a table:

Relevant possible circumstances	Truth value of 1)
Picasso French	False
Picasso not French	True

Now let's take a second example. Suppose someone asserts:

2)   Picasso was either French or he was Spanish.
Under what circumstances would this be true or false? In this case
there will be four possibilities, and our table of relevant states of
affairs will look like this:

Under what circumstances would this be true or false? In this case there will be four possibilities, and our table of relevant states of affairs will look like this:

Relevant possible circumstances	Truth value of 2)
Picasso French, Picasso Spanish	True
Picasso French, not Spanish	True
Picasso not French, but Spanish	True
Picasso not French, not Spanish	False

In other words, so long as he was one or the other, or possibly both, the assertion of 2) will be true. The only part of this table which some find objectionable is the first line: can it be true if both possibilities are realized? An 'Either ... or ...' presents us with alternative possibilities, and what seems to be motivating this worry about the first line is that we often use a statement of this form to describe *incompatible* alternatives. But this is not an essential feature of 'Either ... or ...' statements - their meaning does not require that the alternatives be incompatible. In this case, there are certainly possible states of affairs in which both alternatives are realized. Picasso might have been Spanish early on, and changed nationality. Or he might have held a dual passport, if such a thing exists for those countries. An assertion of 2) wouldn't be false under such circumstances - it would still count as true.

These tables may seem an elaborate way of stating the obvious, but what is important is the basis they provide for a far more general account. We can begin to make them more general by introducing some abbreviations: for Truth and Falsity we'll just use the letters T and F. Secondly, to abbreviate whole sentences of English, we'll use capital letters from the beginning of the alphabet: A, B, C, ... For instance, to help with sentences 1) and 2) we can adopt the following scheme of abbreviation:

A   Picasso was French.
B   Picasso was Spanish.

Thirdly, we'll introduce symbols for the *logical constants*: '¬', for *negation*, and 'v', for *disjunction*. That is, '¬' is to symbolize any English phrase which expresses negation: 'not', 'it is false that', 'it is not the case that', and so on. Unlike the English 'not', which tends to be buried in the middle of a sentence, we always place '¬' at the front.

Thus ¬A is our formalization of sentence 1), and its state-of-affairs table can be summed up in a *truth table*:

A	¬A
T	F
F	T

Essentially, this just abbreviates the table for 1) above - it says that for sentence A, the negation of A will be false if A is true, and true if A itself is false. Likewise, 'v' is to symbolize the words 'Either ... or ...', or any other combination which expresses disjunction. We place 'v' between the two sentences it connects, so that 2) formalizes as A v B, and its table becomes:

A	B	A v B
T	T	T
T	F	T
F	T	T
F	F	F

The more general idea which our talk of states of affairs introduces is, therefore, that the truth value of a sentence built up using these logical constants will be determined by the truth values of its component sentences. The tables show just how the determination goes. If you negate a sentence, for instance, you reverse its truth value: you turn a true sentence into a false one, and a false one into a true one. To take another central example, consider the word 'and' as it occurs in

3)   Picasso was French, and Chagall was French.

This contains a new component sentence, for which we need to pick a new letter, e.g.

        C   Chagall was French.

We also need a symbol for *conjunction*: '&', to represent 'and', and anything similar (such as 'but'). As in English, '&' goes between the two sentences it connects. Thus 3) becomes A & C, and its truth table is:

A	C	A & C
T	T	T
T	F	F
F	T	F
F	F	F

Each line of the table can be read both from left to right, and in the opposite direction. The first line, reading from left to right, says that if A is true - in this case, if Picasso was French - and C is true - Chagall too - then the conjunction of these two sentences, A & C, is also true. Reading the table from right to left we see that if, for example, the conjunction is false then it could be one of three cases: C is false (second line), A is false (third line), or both are false (last line). In short, if a conjunction is false, one or other or possibly both its parts must be false. Since the four lines of the table exhaust all the possible states of affairs, one of them must represent the *actual* state of affairs. Which state of affairs is actual is always a matter for empirical investigation, not logic. In this case, it is a matter for art history. As far as I know, the fourth line corresponds to the actual situation; although both artists lived most of their lives in France, one remained Spanish, the other Russian.

2.1.2 Structure

The logical analysis of sentences of English can be considered a two-stage process. In the first stage, the ordinary words which correspond to logical constants are replaced by those constants. That is, the non-logical content of the sentence is left undisturbed, but its composition out of the logical constants is made explicit - for example, 4) becomes 5):

4)   Either John didn't play well, or he won.
5)   (¬ John played well) v John won.

We can think of this as translation from ordinary English to a cleaned-up dialect, the Language of Quasi-English (or Logician's Queer English - anyway, LQE for short). Given that the LQE translation 5) reveals all of the logical connectives in 4), the English sentences which remain in 5),

John played well.
John won.

must be logically simple, or **atomic**. 'Atomic' here means: not logically complex - containing no logical connectives.

In the second stage of the process, the non-logical components are replaced, so that only the **logical form** of the sentence remains - 4) is analysed as 6):

6)   (¬ A) v B

We can think of this as mapping sentences of English into the Language of Pure Form (or the Logically Perfect Formalism, or just LPF). The sentence in LPF displays the logical form of the corresponding English sentence. For brevity, I shall sometimes say that a sentence of LPF is true, possibly true, and so on. This is shorthand for saying that the (or a) corresponding real sentence is true, possibly true, or whatever. Strictly speaking, the expressions in LPF are *forms* of sentences - they're not really true or false.

Syntax is concerned with grammaticality - grammatical role and grammatical structure - independently of considerations about meaning. Meaning is the concern of **semantics**. The logical constants have a quite simple but strict syntax. Essentially, '¬' prefixes to the front of a sentence (whether that sentence is atomic or complex) - it's a **unary** connective. '&' and 'v' combine with any two sentences - they are **binary** connectives. But it's worth being a little more explicit about their syntax than that. We can think of this as the grammar for LPF. I shall use a common abbreviation, 'wff', for well-formed formula, i.e. grammatically correct and complete sentence. We characterize the wffs of LPF in a number of stages.

Rule 1:   A, B, C, ... are wffs.

This rule says that these capital letters, on their own, count as complete sentences of the formal language. It has the following important consequence: when one of these letters is used, it must represent an expression of English which could stand on its own as a grammatically whole sentence. These simple sentences are the atomic sentences of the language.

Rule 2:   If X is any wff, then ¬X is also a wff.

Note that 'X' is not itself a wff of the language, it is a device which enables me to talk about the wffs of LPF. But A is a wff, so Rule 2 says that ¬A is too; and since ¬A is a wff, applying the rule again shows that ¬¬A is. And if ¬¬A is, then so is ¬¬¬A. And so on. This modest rule allows in an endless number of new expressions to the language; ¬¬¬¬A, ¬¬C, ¬¬¬B, etc., will all count as wffs.

Rule 3: If X, Y are wffs, so is (X v Y).

Given *any* two well-formed sentences, you can form their disjunction; the next rule says you can likewise form their conjunction. (Given a pair of English sentences chosen at random, one might well fail to see *why* anyone would want to form their conjunction, but that's not the point here. These are rules of syntax - an arbitrary conjunction will be grammatically well formed, even if we all agree that it would be a pointless thing to say.)

Rule 4: If X, Y are wffs, so is (X & Y).

Some terminology: in (X v Y), X and Y are **disjuncts**; in (X & Y), X and Y are **conjuncts**.

Rule 5: Nothing else is a wff.

In other words, if you are confronted by a sequence of symbols, e.g. 'A ¬', which cannot be classified as a wff by rules 1 to 4, then it isn't a wff.

So, for example, by the rules of this grammar

7)   A & ¬ (¬¬A v B)

counts as a wff. (Strictly speaking it should be (A & ¬ (¬¬A v B)), but we don't really need the outermost pair of brackets.) We can see that it's a wff by tracing through its construction out of its sub-formulae. The *sub-wffs* of a wff are all its sub-parts which are themselves well formed. The sub-wffs of 7) can be enumerated as follows:

By rule 1, its atomic components are wffs:	A, B.
From this and rule 2, the negation of A is a wff:	¬A.
So by rule 2 again, the negation of that is a wff:	¬¬A.
By rule 3, we can form the disjunction:	(¬¬A v B).
From this and rule 2 once more, we get the wff:	¬ (¬¬A v B).
Finally, any wff can be considered a sub-wff of itself; rule 4 is the last rule used in the construction of sentence 7):	A & ¬ (¬¬A v B).

Thus the overall form which 7) has is that of a conjunction. We could say: when we assemble it from its components, the last thing we do is *conjoin* two wffs.

The formulae in this list are just the sub-wffs of 7). Notice what *doesn't* count as a sub-formula - e.g. the initial sequence: A & ¬. This isn't a sub-wff of 7) because it isn't a wff at all - it couldn't stand on its own as a well-formed sentence. There is no way such a string of expressions can be constructed as a wff by the rules of the grammar. But nor is, for example, ¬ ¬¬A a sub-wff of 7). Although it is well formed, it isn't a genuine component of 7). If it were, it would have appeared at one of the stages in our reconstruction of 7). In fact, the nearest thing to ¬ ¬¬A in 7) is the sequence '¬(¬¬A', and this isn't really a wff, because of the odd left bracket.

LPF is a *logically perfect language*, in that the syntactic structure of each of its sentences is also exactly its semantic structure. The way the semantic value of a whole sentence (true or false) is determined precisely mirrors its construction as a syntactic unit. The way to work out what the truth value of sentence 7) would be, in each possible circumstance, is to work out, from the truth values of its atomic components, what the truth values of its sub-wffs would be, working up to the truth value of the whole:

A B	¬A	¬¬A	(¬¬A v B)	¬ (¬¬A v B)	A & ¬ (¬¬A v B)
T T	F	T	T	F	F
T F	F	T	T	F	F
F T	T	F	T	F	F
F F	T	F	F	T	F

Inspection of the column of values under the complete wff shows - what may not have been obvious at the outset - that any sentence of this form will be false come what may. What's most important here, though, is the way that on each line, the truth value of each sub-wff is determined by its composition out of parts, and the truth values of those parts.

2.1.3 Scope

At the beginning of his essay 'Wild Bird Hickok and his Friends', James Thurber quotes the following sentence of E.M. Forster's:

American women shoot the hippopotamus with eyebrows made of platinum.

Thurber comments "I have given that remarkable sentence a great deal of study, but I still do not know whether Mr Forster means that American women have platinum eyebrows or that the hippopotamus has platinum eyebrows or that American women shoot platinum eyebrows into the hippopotamus." The ambiguity which Thurber brings to our attention is created by the various ways that the phrase "with eyebrows made of platinum" can combine with other parts of the sentence. Roughly, the possibilities are "American women", "hippopotamus", or the verb "shoot". It's a question of which bit - or how much - of the sentence that phrase *attaches to*: which bit falls within its scope.

The example is a reminder that we all have an intuitive grasp of differences of scope. Scope distinctions can be very important in logic and philosophy. A full treatment, showing all the possibilities for scope interactions between expressions, would require nothing less than a complete grammar for English. Rather than attempt that, we can study the notion of scope as it bears on our simple logical language. Compare:

8)   John is rich but he's not stupid,
9)   It's not true that John is rich and stupid.

Using A for 'John is rich' and B for 'John is stupid', we see that 8) has the structure A & ¬B, and 9) the structure ¬(A & B). The overall structure in 8) is that of a conjunction; in 9), that of a negation. We say that in 8) '&' is the **dominant connective**, and that it has **wider scope** than the negation. The negation falls within its scope - 8) is like this: (A) & (¬B). 9) is the converse: '¬' is the dominant connective, and has widest scope.

Let's look at the semantic import of this scope difference. We construct the truth tables by looking at the respective construction of 8) and 9) out of their sub-wffs:

8:	A	B	¬B	A & ¬B	9:	A	B	A & B	¬(A & B)
	T	T	F	F		T	T	T	F
	T	F	T	T		T	F	F	T
	F	T	F	F		F	T	F	T
	F	F	T	F		F	F	F	T

Someone who asserted 9) might believe it for one of three different reasons. These are shown in the different ways the remark might be expanded:

9)   It's not true that John is rich and stupid;
                        i) he's rich but not stupid.
                        ii) he's stupid but not rich.
                        iii) he's neither rich nor stupid.

In other words, 9's being the case is consistent with any of the three possibilities expressed by i) to iii). Now look at its truth table: there are three possible states of affairs in which 9) would be true. Do you see how cases i) - iii) correspond to lines 2 to 4 of the table? Compare this with sentence 8), which is far more restricted in the way it can come out true. From these kinds of examples we see that the relative scope of an expression in a sentence can have a dramatic impact on its significance, on the conditions under which the sentence is true.

Ordinary sentences, like the Forster example, sometimes contain *scope ambiguities* - it's not clear what the relative scopes of expressions in them are. As an illustration for LPF, I have contrived a rather ungainly example:

10)   We're going to a restaurant and we're going to a film or we're going to the theatre.

If we abstract from the content of this, it would appear to have the form:

11)   A & B v C.

But this is simply ambiguous. In an ordinary utterance of 10), the ambiguity would be eliminated by suitable pauses and intonations. In a logical language, ambiguity is eliminated by the presence of brackets. Brackets could be inserted in 11) in either of two ways:

11i)   A & (B v C),
11ii)   (A & B) v C.

This is why we need brackets - to eliminate such scope ambiguities. 11i) gives 10) the meaning: we're definitely going to a restaurant, and there's a choice between film or theatre, whereas 11ii) reads it as a disjunction of options: either theatre, or both film and restaurant. Again, we can see that there is a genuine semantic difference by looking at the respective truth tables.

With three atomic wffs, A, B, and C, there are eight lines of the truth table to consider, i.e. eight relevant possible permutations of atomic states of affairs. The reason is this. If we had any one of them on its own, C for example, there would be just two possible states of affairs to consider: that in which C is true, and that in which C is false. With another atomic wff, e.g. B, we have to consider these two possibilities - C true and C false - both in combination with B being true, and also with B being false. The number of possible combinations doubles from two to four. If A now enters the picture, we have to consider each of *these* possibilities twice over: firstly against A true, then against A false. So with each additional atomic wff, the number of combinations doubles.

The standard recipe for ensuring you get all the possibilities in the truth table parallels this explanation. Firstly, work out how many lines there will be; with n atomic wffs there will be 2 multiplied by itself n many times, i.e. 2^n. Next, write out the atomic wffs in their place at the top left of the table. Consider the last of them (in this case C): for its column, repeat the cycle: T on one line, then F on the next, until you get to the final F on the bottom line. For the penultimate atomic wff (i.e. B here), its column will have a cycle of two Ts, then two Fs, down to the bottom. For the wff which precedes that, the cycle will go four Ts, then four Fs. And so on (compare the table at the beginning of section 4.1, which deals with 4 atomic wffs). In the column below the first wff, there will be Ts for half the lines, followed by Fs for the remainder. The table for the two versions of 11) will thus look like this:

A B C	(B v C)	A & (B v C)		(A & B)	(A & B) v C
T T T	T	T		T	T
T T F	T	T		T	T
T F T	T	T		F	T
T F F	F	F		F	F
F T T	T	F		F	T
F T F	T	F		F	F
F F T	T	F		F	T
F F F	F	F		F	F

The table shows that the syntactic ambiguity of 10) corresponds to a genuine semantic ambiguity. The lines marked with an asterisk indicate states of affairs in which its ambiguity makes a difference - that is, a situation in which it will be true on one reading, false on the other. The fifth line, for example, shows that if A is false, B and C true (we don't go to a restaurant, but do go to both film and theatre), then understood as a conjunction, 10) is false, whereas on the alternative reading, it will be true.

One last point. In principle, a wff such as 12) might be structurally ambiguous between the two readings given by 12i) and 12ii):

12)   ¬ A & B
12i)   (¬ A) & B
12ii)   ¬ (A & B).

However, it is a common practice in logic to adopt conventions about the relative scopes of logical connectives, to avoid an unnecessary clutter of brackets. One such convention is: if there is a possibility of a scope ambiguity between some connective and a negation, always give the negation the narrower scope. So in the case of 12) this means: read it as 12i). If you see a negation next to an atomic wff, as in 12), take it that the negation attaches only to the atomic wff. To put it another way: if you want to write a wff with the force of 12i), just write 12). If, however, you want the scope of the negation to encompass the conjunction, then put the brackets in to make it clear - as in 12ii).

2.1.4   Recap - an arithmetical analogy

This sub-section briefly reviews the preceding, for those who would like it re-explaining in slightly different terms (and can therefore be skipped by those who had no difficulty with it). You will have no trouble in saying what number this term denotes:

13) $2 + 3$.

Similarly, if you are asked what

14) $(2 + 3) \times 4$

is. The brackets make it clear that this is the multiplication of $(2 + 3)$ by 4. So to evaluate this, you first evaluate the embedded expression $(2 + 3)$, and then use the value of this in the main calculation - which thus becomes the multiplication 5×4. Addition, multiplication, subtraction, etc. are simple and familiar examples of *functions*. We could represent addition as a sort of black box; feed two numbers into the box and it churns out another number, the result of adding them together:

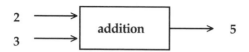

More generally, we can display addition as taking any two numbers x and y as input, and producing their sum as output:

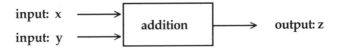

Figure **2.1**   x + y = z

One of the important things you can do with arithmetical functions is
to *compound* them. To continue with this example, the calculation (2 +
3) × 4 can be represented by these black box diagrams as:

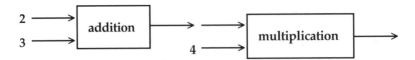

We first perform the addition on 2 and 3.   The output of this
calculation, 5, then becomes the input to the multiplication - so that
the whole complex outputs the value 20.
        We can take the multiplication 14) and embed it within an
even larger context, e.g:

15)   [(2 + 3) × 4] - 10.

As always, evaluation of such a complex term works outwards, from
the innermost expressions to the arithmetical operation which has
widest scope.   In this case, subtraction dominates: 20 - 10.   Clearly,
there is no end to this process - we can ask for the value of, say,

16) $([(2 + 3) \times 4] - 10)^2$,

and we would arrive, by this sequence of calculations, at $(20 - 10)^2$,
which is 10^2, which is 100. We can abstract from 16) the form

17) $([(x + y) \times z] - w)^n$.

This gives the general structure of endlessly many arithmetical
calculations, of which 16) is just one particular instance. So that if I
now set the problem: evaluate the expression 17), giving x the value 2,
y the value 3, z the value 4, w the value of 10, and setting n to 2, we now

have a definite problem. With these values, it is exactly the same as 16), the specific problem we have been working through.

Some numerical functions take a just one number for their input - squaring, for instance. The square of 2 is 4, the square of 10 is 100, and so on. Diagrammatically:

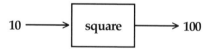

The functions we first considered are binary, they take two numbers for their input. To represent a function by this sort of box

is to reveal its *syntax*. It's to say that it's a function on two numbers, and thereby shows the way it can fit together with other numerical expressions to form a more complex whole. Likewise, there can be functions which take three numbers as input. We have in effect already seen one - the complex function which results by combining addition and multiplication thus:

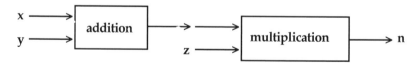

Figure 2.2 $(x + y) \times z = n$

There are two significant respects in which elementary arithmetic is similar to elementary logic, and one respect in which they differ. Firstly, there is no end in principle to our ability to combine *sentences* with the logical connectives 'and', 'or' and 'not'. Working through example 7) showed how the rules of the logical grammar allow us to form sentences (wffs) out of sentences. Secondly, given a specific form - for instance 11i), A & (B v C) - and given a particular assignment of truth values to its components, e.g. A true, B and C false, we can then work out the value of the whole. With an arithmetical term like 17), the value of the whole will be a number; with a sentence, it will be either True or False. This brings us to the point of disanalogy: there are infinitely many numbers, and so infinitely many values which 'x', 'y', ... in 17) could be assigned. We can't give the meaning of multiplication by drawing up a table which shows, for every pair of numbers, the result of multiplying them together. We would need an infinitely large piece of paper. By contrast, in elementary logic there are only two truth values, and so we can draw up tables for 'and', 'or' and 'not', which give all the possible combinations. We can fully represent the function which negation embodies, for instance, in terms of this diagram:

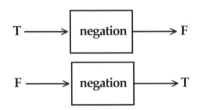

This is just another way of presenting the truth table for 'not'.

Exercise 1

A.   Reveal to the fullest extent possible the form of the following sentences - firstly, by translating into LQE, and secondly, into LPF. (When translating into LQE, remember that &, v and ¬ connect *whole* sentences, i.e. what they connect must be capable of standing on their own as complete sentences of English.)

1)   Not only is it raining hard, it's also very cold.
2)   It is not true that black holes do not exist.
3)   It is false that John drinks but doesn't smoke.
4)   Neither are whales fish, nor are dolphins fish.
5)   Either we go to Spain this year and France the year after, or we go to France this year and Spain the year after.

B.   State what the dominant connective is in these two wffs, and list all their sub-wffs.

6)   ¬(¬A v B).
7)   (A & B) v C.

C.   Here is a sentence which might describe two individuals
Anthony and Brian: Not more than one of them is dangerous.
Supposing that we choose the scheme of translation:

A   Anthony is dangerous,
B   Brian is dangerous,

we could put this sentence into propositional form as: ¬(A & B). For if
there are just two of them, to say that at most one of them is dangerous
is to say that they're not both dangerous. Below are five more possible
sentences describing these putative desperados:

8)   Both of them are dangerous.
9)   Neither of them is dangerous.
10)   At least one of them is dangerous.
11)   Either both or neither of them is dangerous.
12)   Exactly one of them is dangerous.

Using A, B, and the connectives ¬, & and v, formalize 8) to 12). Give
the truth tables for each of the resulting wffs. Is there any possible
state of affairs in which 10) is true but 12) is not? Is there any state of
affairs in which 8) is true but 10) is not? If the answer to either of
these is affirmative, explain what this state of affairs is in terms of
Anthony and Brian (rather than A and B), and why it makes one
sentence true but not the other.

D.   John recently went to a party.   We hear the following
ambiguous report:

13)   He either went with his wife or he didn't go with his wife and
he had a good time.

Give the two wffs in LPF which formalize the two readings of it, and
then construct their truth tables. In which state of affairs is one true
but not the other? Explain briefly what this state of affairs is, and
why it makes a difference to the truth value.

E.   Show that the wffs 14) and 15) are equivalent semantically:
they come out true under exactly the same circumstances (on the same
truth table lines).
14)   ¬A v (A & B)
15)   ¬(A & ¬B).

2.2 Logical status

2.2.1 Sentences

A sentence is *necessarily true* if it couldn't be other than true. Or we could say: a sentence states a necessary truth if there is no real possibility of it being false. A plausible example is

1)   All bachelors are unmarried.

Not only is this actually true, but there *could* not be a circumstance in which it is other than true - it is not possible for there to be a bachelor who is married. The truth of 1) is guaranteed by what its component words mean, and the way they are put together. Such necessary truths are traditionally classified as *analytic* - true in virtue of meaning alone. Other plausible candidates for the status of necessary truth are provided by pure mathematics, e.g.

2)   9 is greater than 7.

Our inability to conceive of a state of affairs in which this sentence is false has nothing to do with a failure of knowledge or imagination on our part, it's in the nature of things - 9 could not fail to be greater than 7.
      Some sentences are guaranteed to be true in virtue of their logical structure. They are a special case of analytic truth - those which are true in virtue of the meanings of their *logical* words. They could be said to be *logically necessary*, or *tautologous*. Consider this instance of the *Law of Excluded Middle*:

3)   Either Budapest is the capital of Roumania or it isn't.

This sentence is true in virtue of its logical structure. It has the form $A \vee \neg A$, and every other instance of that form will also be true. We can show this in either of two ways. i) By substitution. Choose any English sentence and substitute it for A - the resulting complex $A \vee \neg A$ will be true. Take a false sentence, e.g. 'Coal is white', and you get:

4)   Either coal is white or it is not white,

which is true. Or you can substitute a true sentence, e.g. 'Coal is black':

5)   Either coal is black or it is not black,

and again, the whole is true. ii) By truth table. No matter what truth value the component wff A has, the disjunction A v ¬A will be true:

A	¬A	A v ¬A
T	F	T
F	T	T

Both methods i) and ii) amount to the same thing, as far as we are here concerned, viz.: no matter whether the atomic component is true or false, the sentence as a whole comes out true. But ii) provides us with a very convenient method: construct the truth table for the wff; if it comes out true on every line, it's logically necessary.

In sum, a sentence X is logically necessary if (and only if) as a matter of logic X couldn't be other than true, i.e. X is true in every possible state of affairs. We can see that 3) is true without knowing any geography - we don't have to get out an atlas to check its truth. It is true *a priori* - it can be known to be true without any empirical investigation of how things actually are. You *could* test its truth empirically, but you don't *have* to - you can tell that it is true just by reflecting on its logical structure.

It is **logically impossible** that X, or: X is **contradictory**, if X couldn't be true. So for a sentence which can be treated in terms of truth tables: if it comes out false on every line of its truth table, e.g.: A & ¬A

A	¬A	A & ¬A
T	F	F
F	T	F

Suppose you said, instead of the last example,

6)   Budapest is the capital of Roumania and it isn't.

How could this be literally true? You would describe the world as being a certain way, and in the same breath say that this isn't so. It's a logically self-defeating assertion - you would contradict yourself. Notice the following connection between impossibility and necessity:

It's impossible that X if, and only if, it's necessary that not X. So, if X is logically contradictory, ¬X will be necessarily true - by negating a logically impossible sentence one produces a necessary one.

Taking the negation of this example, we get the *Law of Non-Contradiction*: ¬(A & ¬A).

A sentence X states a *possible truth*, or it is *logically possible* that X, if as far as logic is concerned X could come out true. Thus consider

7)   Brutus stabbed Caesar.

We could say this is logically possible because it is actually true, and whatever is actual must be possible. But this isn't the essential point, for the following is equally possible:

8)   Brutus didn't stab Caesar.

This is logically possible because nothing in logic precludes it being true. As mentioned with necessity, the notion we are dealing with here has nothing to do with what we know or can imagine. In ordinary conversation, if we say that something is possible we often mean that we don't know whether or not it is so. Such a notion is not our concern here. We are dealing with a purer, more abstract notion of possibility: a sentence is logically possible if its logical structure does not preclude it being true.

Thus, it is logically possible that X if X is not logically bound to be false, i.e. if it's not impossible that X. In terms of truth tables: if on some line of its truth table, it comes out true. The simplest case is an atomic sentence like 7):

$$
\begin{array}{cc}
\underline{A} & \underline{A} \\
T & T \\
F & F
\end{array}
$$

(If A is atomic, we have this trivial case of a truth table, where the left column, giving all possible assignments of truth values to atomic components, is identical to the right column, giving the truth value of the whole, as determined by those assignments.) Notice also this important connection between possibility and necessity:

9)   A sentence X is necessarily true exactly when it's not possible that ¬X.

Consider it semantically: it's necessary that X if X is true in every possible state of affairs, which is to say that there's no possible state of affairs in which its negation is true.

A sentence X is *logically contingent* if it's neither impossible nor necessary that X. Equivalently, we can say that X is contingent if it's both possible that X and possible that ¬X. In truth table terms: if X is true on some line of its truth table, and also false on some line. The preceding example is an obvious case. It is contingent that Brutus stabbed Caesar, because it is logically possible that he did, and logically possible that he didn't. By contrast, it is possible that 9 is greater than 7, but not contingent. It is possible that 9 > 7 because it is necessary, and since it is necessary, it is not contingent. Contingency requires *more* than just possibility - it requires non-necessity too.

It is worth emphasizing this difference between contingency and possibility. A principle which distinguishes them is this:

10)   If it's contingent that X, it's contingent that ¬X.

This is true, but the corresponding principle does not hold for possibility, viz.:

11)   If it's possible that X, it's possible that ¬X.

For the following is certainly true:

12)   If it's necessary that X, it's possible that X,

(since if X is true in all situations, it's true in at least one.) So if 11) were true, we would have, by putting 12) together with 11):

13)   If it's necessary that X, it's possible that ¬X.

This is clearly false, for to say that X is necessary is to say that it's *not* possible that ¬X. Aristotle was perhaps the first to recognize that possibility does not obey principle 11).

It's *contingently true* that A, or: A expresses a contingent truth, if A is contingent, and actually true. Logic can't tell us whether a sentence is contingently true, because it can't tell us whether a contingent sentence is actually true. To know whether some contingent sentence is actually true is just to know some contingent, empirical fact about the world, e.g. that Bucharest is the capital of Roumania.

Possibility is a property which a single sentence, whether atomic or structured, may either possess or fail to possess. But there is a related notion which generalizes it to pluralities of sentences. We can say that a number of sentences are **consistent** if there is at least one state of affairs in which they are all true. In other words, several sentences are consistent with each other if it's possible for them all to be true together. (We can then think of possibility as a special limiting case, of a single sentence being *self*-consistent; the sentence does not contradict itself.) To use truth tables to test several wffs X, Y, Z, ... for consistency with each other, we need to construct one table for them all. So long as we find at least one line in which they all come out T, it is possible for them all to be true.

Thus consider the sentences

14)   Socrates didn't teach Aristotle,
15)   Either Socrates taught Plato or Plato taught Socrates,
16)   Socrates didn't teach Plato.

Is it possible for them all to be true at once? Formalizing them by ¬A, (B v C), ¬B respectively, the truth table for the three together is:

A	B	C	¬A	B v C	¬B
T	T	T	F	T	F
T	T	F	F	T	F
T	F	T	F	T	T
T	F	F	F	F	T
F	T	T	T	T	F
F	T	F	T	T	F
F	F	T	T	T	T
F	F	F	T	F	T

We can immediately see from the column for ¬A that none of the first four lines will help, for ¬A comes out false in each. In the next two lines ¬B is false. It is the seventh line which shows that there is a state of affairs in which our three sentences would all be true, and thus shows that they are consistent.

A number of sentences are mutually inconsistent, therefore, if there is no possible state of affairs in which they are all true. For pairs of sentences, the notion of inconsistency covers two interestingly different sub-cases, and it is to these we now turn.

2.2.2 Pairs of sentences

Traditional Aristotelian logic recognized four kinds of general statement, and various logical relationships between them. These are often conveniently summarized in the *square of opposition*:

All swans are white   <--- CONTRARY ---> No swans are white

Some swan is white   Some swan is not white

We shall say that a pair of sentences are *contraries* if it is not possible for them both to be true. They are mutually exclusive: if one is true, the other must be false, and vice versa. Thus with the pair of sentences at the top of the square: it cannot both be that all swans are white and that all swans are not white. If no swan is white, then it is false that all swans are white; and conversely.

   These two sentences are exclusive, but they are not exhaustive, they do not exhaust all the possibilities. Suppose, as is the case, that some swans are white, and some are black. Then neither of these generalizations is true. It is neither the case that no swan is white (for some are), nor the case that all swans are white (for some are black). So there is room for a stronger relation between sentences - when they are not only exclusive, but also exhaustive. We shall say that a pair of sentences are *contradictories* just when they cannot both be true, and they cannot both be false. Thus 'All swans are white' and 'Some swan is not white' together exhaust the possibilities: either every swan is white, or at least one isn't. We could sum up our definitions thus:

A, B are contraries if, and only if, necessarily not both A and B.
A, B are contradictories if and only if they are contraries,
                                     and necessarily: either A or B.

   It is natural to extend these relations to predicates, words like 'black' and 'white' which are contained within these generalizations. 'White' and 'black' are contrary predicates, in that if one truly describes a surface, then the other does not. They are not contradictory, of course, for a surface may be neither, if for example it is red. 'White' and 'not white' are contradictory. These facts are part of the reason why the general statements just discussed are related as shown in the square of opposition, but a full explanation must await an analysis of the logic of 'all' and 'some'. For the moment, we can only test for sentences which stand in these relations in virtue of their propositional form. Consider, for instance,

17)   John is either not a catholic or not a socialist.
18)   John is a catholic and a socialist.
19)   John is not a socialist.

If we compare their truth tables:

A	B	¬A v ¬B	A & B	¬B
T	T	F	T	F
T	F	T	F	T
F	T	T	F	F
F	F	T	F	T

we find that 17) and 18) are contradictory; in no possible state of affairs are they both true, but in none are they both false. 18) and 19), by contrast, are just contraries; if John is a socialist but not a catholic, they are both false.

It's important to be clear whether two sentences or predicates which are contraries are also contradictory, because it makes a difference to how we may reason with them. Those who would polarize a debate by arguing 'If you're not for X, you're against it', make the mistake of confusing contraries for contradictories. *For* and *against* are exclusive attitudes, but they are not exhaustive. (Whether because you do not consider yourself appraised of all the facts, or you do, but see both good and bad in X, you may decline to be either for or against it.) If A and B are contraries, from A one may validly infer not B (So: if you're for it, you're not against it). But only when A and B are contradictories is it correct to infer from not A to B.

2.2.3 Functions and truth functions

In section 2.1.4, comparison was made between truth functions and arithmetical functions. But not all functions concern abstract objects like truth values and numbers - there are functions which are defined over tangible, physical objects. The relation of *being the father of* is a function on people. According to the Bible, its first human application is this:

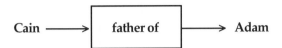

What makes fatherhood a function is that for a given input, *the output is unique*. In other words, it's a function because Cain couldn't have had two (or more) fathers. Likewise, addition is a function on numbers: given any two numbers, e.g. 2 and 3, adding them together produces a unique number, 5. That's just what it means to say that addition is a function - the result, 5, is wholly determined (is unique) once the arguments, 2 and 3, have been specified. And '¬', 'v' and '&' all express truth functions: the truth value of a negation, disjunction or conjunction is wholly determined by (is a *function of*) the truth values of its parts.

Note that a function can take two or more inputs to share the same output, as in the case of fatherhood:

What prevents something being a function is the possibility of one input being taken to two or more outputs - which spoils the chances of the *son of* relation being functional:

We cannot properly speak of *the* son of Adam.

Truth functions are precisely the concepts we can express by means of truth tables. In all, there are 16 possible binary truth functions, like conjunction - functions which, when applied to two truth values, return a unique truth value. That is, there are 16 different ways you can combine two sentences A and B in such a way that the truth value of the combination is always completely fixed, given the truth values of A and B. We can draw them up in a table:

	1	2	3	4	5	6	7	8	9	10	11	12	13	14	15	16
A B																
T T	T	T	T	T	T	T	T	T	F	F	F	F	F	F	F	F
T F	T	T	T	T	F	F	F	F	T	T	T	T	F	F	F	F
F T	T	T	F	F	T	T	F	F	T	T	F	F	T	T	F	F
F F	T	F	T	F	T	F	T	F	T	F	T	F	T	F	T	F

Each of these columns defines a possible truth functional connective. You should be able to pick out the columns which define disjunction and conjunction: 2 and 8, respectively. Column 1 gives the truth table of any tautologous combination of A with B, and column 16, any contradictory combination.

Syntactically, there are endless ways to express each of these 16 truth functions using connectives &, v and ¬. Exercise 2.1 E, for example, showed that the combinations ¬(A & ¬B) and ¬A v (A & B) express the same underlying truth function - the one given by column 5. Notice that column 9 defines exactly the opposite function to 8 - it gives T when, and only when, the conjunctive function gives F. So it could be expressed by 'Not both', i.e. the exact negation of a conjunction, ¬(A & B). It is sometimes symbolized by the Sheffer stroke: A | B. By saying that ¬(A & B) can be written A | B, I in effect define a new symbol in terms of already familiar ones. We can also do the opposite: take the Sheffer stroke as primitive, and define '¬' and '&'. Firstly, we define ¬A as A | A, i.e. not both A and A. We then take A & B as ¬(A | B) or, just using the stroke: (A | B) | (A | B).

Our semantic theory is the simplest one possible. It essentially employs just the notions of truth and falsity. They are perhaps the most central semantic concepts, but only a very restricted portion of language can be explained with reference to them alone. For instance, there is more to the explanation of necessity, possibility, contrariety, etc. than just the notions of truth and falsity. It is important to appreciate that necessity and these related notions are not truth functional, even though truth tables can be used to *help* explain what they are. The point can be introduced with a slightly different example. John, like all of us, has many true beliefs, and some false ones. Suppose that he correctly believes that Paris is in France, but mistakenly thinks that Budapest is not in Hungary. The two sentences 'Paris is in France' and 'Budapest is in Hungary' suffice to show that the context 'John believes that' is not a truth function. Both these sentences are true, but whereas 'John believes that Paris is in France' is true, 'John believes that Budapest is in Hungary' is false. One cannot tell, simply from the truth value of a sentence, whether or not John believes what it says. The truth value of the complex 'John believes that A' depends on factors other than the truth value of A.

Similar consideration apply to necessity and possibility. To judge that 'Not X' is true, you need only know that X is false, but to judge that 'Necessarily X' is true, it does not suffice to know the truth value of X. You need to know the truth value of X across *all* possible states of affairs. Consider the following pair of sentences, which are both actually true:

20) Tigers exist.
21) $7 + 5 = 12$.

What about the corresponding claims that they hold of necessity?

22) Necessarily, tigers exist.
23) Necessarily, $7 + 5 = 12$.

Sentence 22) is false. It's a biologically contingent fact that tigers exist - one can imagine evolution having taken a different turn. Tigers don't exist in every conceivable state of affairs. But 23) is true. Mathematical facts are not contingent - it's simply impossible that 5 and 7 could add up to anything other than 12. Doubtless, a lot more could be said about these claims, but their purpose here is essentially illustrative. The point they illustrate is that in one case, adding 'Necessarily' to a true sentence produces a falsehood, but in another, it produces a truth. If we tried to draw up a truth table for necessity, the best we could do would be something like this:

X	Necessarily X
T	Sometimes T, sometimes F
F	F

And this amounts to admitting that necessity is not a function on the truth value of a sentence.

Exercise 2

Note that Appendix 1 contains a summary of logical status.

A. Give the LPF forms of these sentences:

1)   I don't remember a lot about Plato, but he was either a philosopher or an ancient Greek.

2)   Either you go on a diet and stop smoking, or you either don't go on a diet and have a heart attack, or don't stop smoking and get lung cancer.

3)   Either Bucharest is the capital of Roumania and Belgrade is in Hungary or Bucharest is not the capital of Roumania and Budapest is in Hungary.

Construct the truth table for 3). From your truth table: is it necessary, impossible, contingent, ..? From your atlas: which line of the truth table corresponds to the actual state of affairs?

B.   Draw up a truth table for these wffs, and thus determine which of 5) or 6) is semantically equivalent to 4) (i.e. expresses the same truth function):

4)   A v (B & C).
5)   (A & B) v (A & C).
6)   (A v B) & (A v C).

C.   Formalize the following four sentences:

7)   Either Mark will get inoculated or he won't go to Mexico.
8)   It's not true that Mark will visit America and not go to Mexico.
9)   Mark will get inoculated but he won't visit America.
10)   Mark will visit America but he won't get inoculated.

Construct a truth table for all four. Are 7), 8) and 9) consistent? Are 7), 8) and 10) consistent?

D.   If you believe that events in the future are already determined, you could be said to be a *realist* about the future, and you would be inclined to view statements about the future as definitely true or false. Opposed to this is the view that much of the future is as yet undetermined. One might think, to take Aristotle's example, that at the moment it's not inevitable that a sea battle will take place tomorrow, nor inevitable that one won't take place. Although things must eventually turn out one way or the other, *which* of these outcomes has yet to be determined. On this view, it's determined that (A v ¬A) - it must be that a sea battle either will, or will not, take place tomorrow - but not this: it's determined that A v it's determined that

¬A. (This distinction illustrates how important it can be to pay attention to differences of scope.)

Is the following a plausible way to formulate this opposition to realism about the future? Statements about undetermined future events are neither true nor false, but have a third truth value: Undetermined. With three values, we need to restate the definition of negation:

X	¬X
T	F
U	U
F	T

Develop the view further, by giving corresponding tables for '&' and 'v' (a table defining a binary connective using three values will have nine lines in all). Remember that statements with the third value are held to be neither true nor false at present, but may *become* either true or false later.

On this three-valued account, do wffs 10) and 11) still count as necessary? In answering this question, bear in mind two points. Firstly, with two truth values, we can define necessity either as: on all lines true, or equivalently as: on no lines false. Is 'always true' still equivalent to 'never false' when there is a value intermediate between truth and falsity? Secondly, be careful to distinguish two questions: i) What status do we (and the Anti-Realist considered here) *expect* these two wffs to have? ii) What results do the three-valued semantics actually deliver? (The shift to three values does not affect the assumption of truth functionality: the truth value of a complex (whether T, F or U) is determined solely by the truth values of its parts.)

10)   A v ¬A.
11)   ¬(A & ¬A).

2.3   Conditions and conditionals

2.3.1   Conditionals

Conditionals are a very important kind of sentence. In logic, for instance, we may be able to sum up a lengthy piece of reasoning, from a supposition A to some consequence B, as a conditional 'If A then B'. Most of our beliefs predicting the future are - tacitly or explicitly -

conditional in form ('This will happen, *if* things go on they way they have'). Planning - our plans for the future - also requires conditionals ('If this happens, we will do such and such, and if not, ...'). In Prolog and other AI formalisms, conditionals are central to the axiomatization of many diverse bodies of knowledge. Classificatory information can be put in conditional form ('If a thing has these properties, it is of this type'). Legal expertise, for instance, involves knowing how the law classifies various cases. Diagnosis is a form of classification ('If a thing manifests these symptoms, it is likely to have this fault'), and diagnosis is central to many areas of expertise - medicine, agriculture, mechanical repair, and so on.

Many people find difficulty with the logic of conditions and conditionals at first. One reason for this may be that our ordinary use of conditionals is quite flexible and loose, in contrast to the strict rules of the formal system. For example, I doubt that a parent would give much thought to whether the following two statements differ in content:

1)   You may watch TV, if you do your homework.
2)   You may watch TV, only if you do your homework.

Can you detect a difference - can you think of circumstances when it would be right to say one but not the other? In logic, there is an important difference between 'if' and 'only if', which needs to be rigorously observed.

Another feature of our everyday use of conditionals is their use in probabilistic, causal reasoning. Suppose, on returning from a fortnight's holiday, you are worried that there may have been a power cut. If you reason as follows:

3)   If there has been a power cut, everything in the fridge will be
        mouldy,
4)   There has been a power cut,   Therefore:
5)   Everything in the fridge is mouldy.

then your reasoning is deductively correct. Assuming 3) and 4) are true, 5) must be also true. But you might instead have reasoned with the conditional in a different way - assuming 3) and 5), and inferring 4). This would be an inference from an effect to its most probable cause: inference to the best explanation, or **abduction**. Although plausible and often reliable, such reasoning is not strictly acceptable by the standards of deductive logic. That is to say, 3) and 5) could be true, and although 4) would be probable in the circumstances, it might nevertheless not be true. The fridge's mould might be due to some other factor. One aspect of the flexibility of our ordinary use of conditionals, then, may be our propensity to slip between deductive and abductive reasoning with them.

Let us begin developing the logic of conditionals with a fairly simple and ordinary example. Suppose John and Bill are playing tennis, and I assert

6)   If John plays well then he will win.

We will symbolize conditionals using an arrow. A sentence of the form 'If A then B' will be written: A → B. So 6) goes into LQE as:

7)   John plays well → John will win.

The sentence which goes with the 'if' part of the conditional is known as the *antecedent* of the conditional. Intuitively, the antecedent is that part which introduces the possibility or supposition which the conditional is concerned with. The sentence which describes the consequences of that supposition is known as the *consequent*. It is important to realize that the distinction between antecedent and consequent is a logical one - it does not concern the grammatical order of the components. It is perfectly possible for the logical antecedent of a conditional to be placed grammatically after the consequent:

8)   John will win, if he plays well.

6) and 8) say the same thing. 'John plays well' is the antecedent of 6), 7) and 8) - it's *if* this happens - and 'John will win' is the consequent - *then* that will follow.

There are other ways of re-formulating this conditional, paraphrases using 'and', 'or' and 'not' which reflect the truth table definition of →. I assert 6) because I believe that on a good day, John is clearly superior to his opponent. Sometimes he doesn't play very well, but when he does, he always beats Bill. Roughly, I could be said to envisage a disjunction of cases:

9)   Either John doesn't play well, or he does, and wins.

This disjunction, ¬A v (A & B), can be more succinctly expressed as ¬A v B:

10)   Either John doesn't play well, or he wins.

This is how we will treat the conditional A → B: as equivalent to the disjunction ¬A v B. The truth table is therefore:

A	B	A →B
T	T	T
T	F	F
F	T	T
F	F	T

Recall from exercise 2.1 E that ¬A v (A & B) is also equivalent to ¬(A & ¬B):

11)   This will not happen: John plays well, and doesn't win.

In asserting 6), one thing I am claiming *won't* happen is that he will play well, yet not win. To put it another way, my assertion of the conditional 6) will be definitely false if John plays well, and doesn't win. As the truth table shows, the one situation in which a conditional A → B is false is when the antecedent is true and the consequent is false. If you are in any doubt about these equivalences, check that this table is also the table for ¬A v B, and for ¬(A & ¬B).

        The → connective defined by this table is known as the *material conditional*. There has been considerable controversy over how close the material conditional corresponds to the conditional of ordinary language - that is, how accurate this truth table is to the meaning of the ordinary 'if'. I shall not attempt to justify this account, beyond pointing out that the paraphrases of A → B as ¬A v B and ¬(A & ¬B) are usually reasonable, as in the above example.   The controversy is not something new; it goes back to the earliest debate on the nature of the conditional. William and Martha Kneale give this passage from Sextus Empiricus, reporting the views of the dialectician Philo of Megara:

> So, according to him there are three ways in which a
> conditional may be true, and one in which it may be false. For a
> conditional is true when it begins with a truth and ends with a
> truth, like "If it is day, it is light"; and true also when it begins
> with a falsehood and ends with a falsehood, like "If the earth
> flies, the earth has wings"; and similarly a conditional which
> begins with a falsehood and ends with a truth is itself true,

like "If the earth flies, the earth exists". A conditional is false only when it begins with a truth and ends with a falsehood, like "If it is day, it is night". (*Adversus Mathematicos*, viii, 113)

As the Kneales point out (*The Development of Logic*, p. 130), this is a clear statement of the truth functional definition of the material conditional.

Does an 'if' really differ from an 'only if'? To make the difference as clear as possible, it will help if we compare two conditionals about which we have fairly clear intuitions. Consider this pair, and before reading on, decide what you think the truth value of each actually is:

12)   It snows if it is cold.
13)   It snows only if it is cold.

The actual truth values of such contingent sentences as these are normally of no concern to logic. But if we establish that they actually have different truth values, then it will be clear that they are not equivalent - they say distinct things. 12) says that if it's cold, it snows. To use a different sort of paraphrase, this is to say that the weather's being cold *suffices* for there to be snow. Is this actually true - is the presence of cold weather sufficient for it to snow? The answer is surely "No" - there are plenty of cold days when there is no snow. So 12) is false. What about 13)? Paraphrasing again, we could say that 13) asserts that cold weather is *required for*, or *necessary for*, the occurrence of snow: only if it's cold does it snow. This is true: the temperature has to drop before there is snow. In short, the presence of cold weather is required for, but does not suffice for, the occurrence of snow.

We have seen how to formalize a conditional like 12). Since its 'if' part, the antecedent, is 'it is cold', it has the form:

14)   It is cold $\rightarrow$ it snows.

How should we formalize the 'only if' conditional 13)? The following paraphrase will point us towards the answer. 13) amounts to:
        This won't happen: it snows, and it's not cold.
As we have already established, $\neg(A \ \& \ \neg B)$ is equivalent to the conditional $A \rightarrow B$, so 13) is in fact equivalent to this conditional:

15)   It snows → it is cold.

To say that it snows only if it's cold is to say that you can't have snow without it being cold, which is to say that if it snows, it must be cold. So now we have a better appreciation of the difference between 12) and 13) - 12) is the conditional 14), and 13) is the *converse* conditional 15).
        To summarize, we have seen that

'A → B' formalizes 'If A then B', 'A only if B', and 'B if A'.

This has the counter-intuitive consequence that, at least as far as we are concerned in elementary logic, a conditional such as 16) shares the same underlying form as 17), namely 18):

16)   If John marries he will be happy,
17)   John will marry only if he will be happy,
18)   John marries → John is happy.

Ordinarily, we would use 16) and 17) to say different things: 16), to say that John's happiness will be a *consequence* of his marrying; 17), that it is a *precondition* of his marrying. This is because of the interaction between tense and the ordinary English conditional. The 'If A then B' form is usually reserved for cases where the situation A describes occurs before the one which B describes, whereas 'A only if B' tends to favour the opposite temporal order. But in elementary logic we abstract from such temporal considerations. If we put aside questions of temporal priority, there is indeed a level at which 16) and 17) can be seen to be equivalent:

19)   This won't happen: John marries, and is not happy.

That is, both 'If A then B' and 'A only if B' amount to: you can't have A without also having B, whether the state of affairs described by A comes before, after, or at the same time as that described by B - or indeed whether the notion of temporal ordering applies to A and B at all.

2.3.2 Biconditionals

Returning to example 8), we see that although it commits me, if I assert it, to what will happen if John plays well, nothing has been said about what might happen if he *doesn't* play well. Without fear of contradiction, I could append to it "and for that matter, he can even win if he plays terribly". I may believe that the opponent is so awful that John can beat him if he doesn't play well. But it's also possible that I may not. I may think that the *only* way for John to win is for him to play well. If I do think this, I could assert the converse conditional:

20)   John will win only if he plays well.

This says that if John wins, this could not have come about except by his playing well; if he wins, he must have played well. Whereas 8) says of John that playing well suffices for a win, 20) says that it is necessary. Since they are distinct, one could believe either one of them without believing the other. But equally, one might believe *both*. If you believe both, you could of course express this by uttering their conjunction. A shorter means is available; we can compress the conjunction of 8) and 20) into a **biconditional**:

21)   John will win if, and only if, he plays well.

This says that the direction of conditional dependence holds both ways, and we formalize it with a double arrow:

22)   John wins ↔ John plays well.

Naturally, the *material biconditional* has the table of $(A \rightarrow B)$ & $(B \rightarrow A)$:

A	B	$A \leftrightarrow B$
T	T	T
T	F	F
F	T	F
F	F	T

$A \leftrightarrow B$ is also read: 'A just in the case that B', or 'A just in case B', or 'A when, and only when B'. 'iff' often abbreviates 'if and only if'. $A \leftrightarrow B$ is true just when its two sides A and B are *materially equivalent* - when they have the same truth value. That is, a material biconditional is true iff its two sides are either both true, or both false. This is an extremely weak notion of equivalence. 'Tigers exist' and '7 + 5 = 12', for example, are materially equivalent. That is, it's true to say

23)   Tigers exist ↔ 7 + 5 = 12,

for both sides of the biconditional have the same truth value. But that's about all they have in common.

Just as we have seen how conjunctions and disjunctions can be conjoined and disjoined with other wffs, so conditionals and biconditionals can be components of larger complexes. It is important to notice the different forms of compounding in, say,

24)   If England qualify only if Germany lose, then England won't qualify.
25)   England will qualify if and only if Germany lose.

The former has the overall form 'If ... then ...', and so is a conditional. Within the antecedent of that conditional occurs the phrase 'only if', which shows that the antecedent is itself a conditional. Paraphrasing loosely, 24) says that *if* a certain conditional connection holds - viz., that England qualify only if Germany lose - *then* England won't qualify. In other words,

26)   (England qualify $\rightarrow$ Germany lose) $\rightarrow$ $\neg$ England qualify.

By contrast, the latter is an 'if *and* only if', and so is a straightforward biconditional:

27)   England qualify $\leftrightarrow$ Germany lose.

A biconditional will be false when the two sides have different truth values. In other words, $\neg(A \leftrightarrow B)$ will be true just in case either A is true and B false, or vice versa. It would therefore do as a formalization of the *exclusive* sense of 'or' - either A, or B, but not both, i.e. which excludes the case where both disjuncts are true. Our 'v' is *inclusive* disjunction. To show that $\neg(A \leftrightarrow B)$ amounts to exclusive disjunction, we can show that it expresses the same truth function as (A v B) & $\neg$(A & B) (i.e. A inclusive-or B, but not both). I shall now adopt the following short-cut in writing out truth tables. Our procedure for evaluating the truth value of any complex wff has been to work up to the truth value of the whole by writing out all its sub-wffs, and writing their truth values beneath them. Instead of this, we can save some effort, shortening the table by just writing out the whole wff, and writing down the truth values of its sub-wffs underneath the logical connective which dominates that sub-wff. So in this case:

A	B	¬	(A ↔ B)	(A v B)	&	¬	(A & B)
T	T	F	T	T	F	F	T
T	F	T	F	T	T	T	F
F	T	T	F	T	T	T	F
F	F	F	T	F	F	T	F

Since ¬(A ↔ B) is a negation overall, the column which gives its truth value in each possible situation is the one under its negation sign. The column beneath the biconditional sign gives the truth value of the sub-wff (A ↔ B) which is embedded within that larger wff. Since (A v B) & ¬(A & B) is a conjunction, the column to look at for that wff is the one under the dominant &. We see that on each line, the truth value in this column is the same as that under the negation of ¬(A ↔ B). We shall say that two sentences are *logically equivalent*, as these are, if as a matter of logic they have the same truth value in every possible situation, i.e. if it's not possible for one to be true and the other false. Or, what comes to the same thing: if the sentence formed by linking them with a biconditional is a necessary truth. In other words, it's necessarily true that

$$\lnot(A \leftrightarrow B) \leftrightarrow ((A \lor B)\ \&\ \lnot(A\ \&\ B)).$$

Ordinary biconditionals, like 21) and 23), may be true, but they are not necessary truths.

The word 'unless' highlights some of the issues surrounding inclusive and exclusive disjunction. A simple use of it, as in

28)   We will go for a walk unless it rains

may suggest exclusive disjunction: we will go for a walk if it doesn't rain, but if it does we won't. However the second part of this is only a suggestion. 28) does not definitely imply that we won't go for a walk if it rains. In Grice's terminology, it is an *implicature*. One of the marks of an implicature, something which is suggested by a sentence - as against an implication, something which necessarily follows from it - is that an implicature is *cancellable*. The suggestion that we won't walk in the rain can be cancelled, as with

29)   We will go for a walk unless it rains - in which case, we'll see (we may still go for a walk, or we may not).

So the suggestion of exclusivity is only an implicature - if it were bound up with the meaning of 'unless', it would be an implication, and could not be cancelled. So inclusive disjunction will do for 'unless'.

2.3.3 Necessary and sufficient conditions

In explaining conditionals, it was natural to appeal to the terminology of necessity and sufficiency. I want to consider necessary and sufficient conditions in more detail, starting with an example from chess. (Don't worry if you are not very familiar with chess. The rules of a game provide nicely self-contained illustrations of conditions; you should be able to reformulate the examples in terms of a game with which you are familiar, if you wish.) A condition may be sufficient for something, but not necessary, or conversely: necessary while failing to be sufficient. *Castling* in chess will provide an illustration of the latter. This is the move in which the king is moved next to a castle (rook), and the castle is moved to the other side of the king, for example:

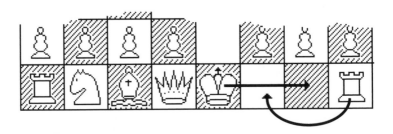

This is a special move in chess, and the rules of chess state that it can only be performed when certain conditions are satisfied - in other words, the rules lay down a number of necessary conditions which must be fulfilled if castling is permissible. One of them is that the squares between king and castle are vacant:

30)   You may castle only if the intervening squares are vacant.

A second is that neither of the pieces concerned has already been moved:

31)   You may castle only if not(the king has moved or the rook has moved).

A third condition is that you can't use castling to get out of check:

32)   You may castle only if not(the king is in check).

(There is a further condition which for brevity I shall omit; it could of course be added to what follows.)   Each of these conditions is *individually necessary* - *only if* each of the three conditions are satisfied may one castle. Since all of the conditions must be satisfied, none of them is individually sufficient - satisfaction of just one of the conditions without the others does not suffice for permission to castle.
        However, barring the simplification just noted, satisfaction of the three conditions together does enable one to castle - the conditions are *jointly sufficient*:

33)   If [the intervening squares are vacant and not(the king has moved or the rook has moved) and not(the king is in check)], then you may castle.

Since 30), 31) and 32) together amount to the converse conditional to this, we can combine them with 33) into a biconditional - the combined conditions are necessary and sufficient. Inserting logical symbols to make the logical structure clear we get:

34)   You may castle ↔ [the intervening squares are vacant & ¬(the king has moved v the rook has moved) & ¬(the king is in check)].

        Let us now consider the other possibility: a condition which is individually sufficient but not necessary. Imagine people betting on the throw of an ordinary six-sided die. The following is certainly true:

35)   If you throw a six, you throw an even number.

It suffices to obtain an even number that one throw a six. Unlike the previous example, this has nothing to do with the rules of a particular game - this sufficiency arises from the nature of numbers. 35) is true because six is an even number. But it is not the only way to obtain an even number using an ordinary die - it would be false to claim that you throw an even number *only if* you throw a six. We also have:

36)   If you throw a two, you throw an even number.
37)   If you throw a four, you throw an even number.

What 35) to 37) tell us is that if you get either a two or a four or a six, you get an even number; we can put them together into this conditional:

38)   (You throw a two v you throw a four v you throw a six) →
You throw an even.

Each of the conditions (throwing a two, etc.) is individually sufficient
for obtaining an even number. Although none is individually necessary,
taken together they do exhaust all the possible ways of obtaining an
even number with an ordinary die. The disjunction of all three does
provide the necessary condition:

39)   You throw an even number only if you throw a two or a four or a
six.

So again it turns out that we can form a biconditional - by combining 38)
with 39):

40)   You throw an even number ↔
                (you throw a two v you throw a four v you throw a six).

        To say that B is a necessary condition for A is to say that A
wouldn't or couldn't occur without B. We could say:

41)   B is a necessary condition for A: it's not possible that (A & ¬B).

The 'not possible' here may be a conceptual or logical impossibility. Or
it may be a physical 'cannot', as for example when the claim is that
the presence of oxygen is a necessary condition for animal life. Animal
life without oxygen is not a conceptual impossibility, it's a physical or
biological one. The discussion of functions (section 2.2.3) demonstrated
that notions of necessity and impossibility cannot be expressed within
our simple truth functional language. If we omit the notion of
possibility from 41), we get our truth functional approximation:

42)   B is a necessary condition for A: ¬ (A & ¬B).

To avoid confusion, we might speak of B being *materially* necessary for
A, meaning just that it's not that A and not B, rather than it's not
possible that A and not B.
        To say that A is a sufficient condition for B is to say that the
occurrence or realization of A suffices for that of B. You can't have A
without also having, or having had, B. If A occurs, B must occur (or
must have already occurred). We thus have the following
equivalence:

43)   B is a necessary condition for A iff A is a sufficient condition for B.

It may be that when we say the former, we put the emphasis on B, and with the latter, on A - but from a logical point of view, we treat them on a par. And the par is, simply: you can't have A without B. (Recall 16 to 19.) To take one more example: consistency is a necessary condition of truth. A theory couldn't be true if it isn't consistent. That is, if a theory is true, it must be consistent, so truth is sufficient for consistency. But to say that B is necessary for A is not to say that B suffices for A. Consistency doesn't *suffice* for truth - so, anyway, goes the traditional complaint against coherence theories of truth. (A coherence theory of truth is one which in some way equates truth with coherence or consistency.) A set of sentences, e.g. those of a novel, may be perfectly consistent, yet not be true.

Exercise 3

A.   Give wffs of LPF which reveal to the fullest extent the logical forms of the following English sentences:

1)   If it's not true that Mary isn't a vegetarian, then it won't be lamb for dinner.
2)   If you don't write the letter you will be in trouble, but if you write the letter, you won't be in trouble.
3)   The question is not genuine if, but only if, the answer does not exist.
4)   You will get cancer if you smoke heavily, but it's not true that you will get cancer only if you smoke heavily.
5)   If the pavements are wet only if it's been raining, then it's been raining.

B.   The *opposite* of a conditional has the same antecedent but contradictory consequent - for example, 5) and 6) are opposites:

6)   If John won, Bill lost.
7)   If John won, Bill did not lose.

Is a conditional consistent with its opposite, or contrary to it? Or contradictory? Show by constructing a truth table for 6) and 7).

C. It's important to be clear that if a condition A is sufficient for something C, this doesn't preclude something else B also being sufficient for C. We can have (A → C) and (B → C). A and B would be alternative routes to C; it would be that if either A or B, then C. Show this, by demonstrating that this equivalence is necessary:

8) ((A → C) & (B → C)) ↔ ((A v B) → C).

Construct the truth table for the complete biconditional. Show also that this is logically necessary:

9) (A ↔ B) ↔ (¬(A & ¬B) & ¬(B & ¬A)).

D. Show by truth table that, understood as a material conditional, 10) is necessarily true:

10) It's either the case that it rains if the gods are angry or that it rains only if the gods are angry.

Use 't' to symbolize 'It is true that'. Give its truth table definition, then formalize the two sentences:

11) It is true that snow is white iff snow is white.
12) It is true that snow is white iff grass is green.

On the basis of the truth tables for 11 and 12, say what their respective statuses are.

2.4 Names and predicates

So far we have looked at the structure of sentences compounded out of simpler sentences, but we have not looked at the internal structure of the basic sentences. In propositional logic, atomic sentences are treated as unstructured units A, B, ... etc. A natural place to start looking at the structure of atomic sentences is with the intuitive idea that the simplest sentences are built up out of a noun and a verb. For example,

1) Mary swims

consists of a noun, 'Mary', followed by a verb, 'swims'. In fact, since nouns and verbs can consist of several words, it is better to talk of noun or verb *phrases*. So we have the following grammatical or linguistic principle:

2)   Atomic sentence = Noun phrase + Verb phrase.

Sentences which are compounded out of the following elements exemplify the pattern:

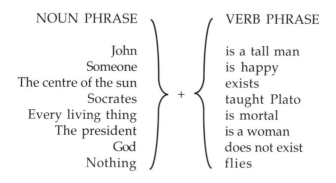

NOUN PHRASE   VERB PHRASE

John   is a tall man
Someone   is happy
The centre of the sun   exists
Socrates   +   taught Plato
Every living thing   is mortal
The president   is a woman
God   does not exist
Nothing   flies

The question we have to address is whether this natural distinction at the level of grammar, the surface level, reflects the underlying logical or semantic structure of such sentences. In other words, grammar provides an account of how atomic sentences are compounded out of the elements of noun, verb, etc. - the question is whether this classification coincides with the correct account of the way they are constructed out of logical components. The answer which modern logical theory provides is that although there is an important distinction which agrees to some extent with the grammatical one, surface grammatical form is often not a true guide to the underlying logical form.

I shall discuss the logical distinction in terms of **names** and **predicates**. This can be thought of as a classification based on function. The function of a name is referential - to pick out a particular, an object; the function of a predicate is descriptive - to express a property of or relation between objects. The distinction thus runs parallel to the traditional metaphysical distinction between particulars (things, individuals, entities) and universals (properties, qualities). An expression counts as a name if it refers to a particular, and counts as a predicate if it expresses a property. Thus in the case of sentence 1), the grammatical distinction between noun and verb agrees with that between name and predicate: 'Mary' stands for an individual, and 'swims' ascribes a property to her. This is why I said there is a degree of overlap between the logical and grammatical distinctions. But, as we shall see, the category of Noun Phrase hides important differences of logical role: not all the expressions in the above list of noun phrases count as names (and not all the verb phrases count as predicates).

Paradigmatic of names in the logical sense are proper names, e.g. 'Germany', '1984', 'Bertrand Russell', 'Mary', etc. These are all liable to exhibit a degree of contextual sensitivity - that is, what they refer to may vary from one context of use to another. '1984', for example, may in one context stand for a number, in another context, a year, and in another, a book. The point is that their function, *within* a given context, is to refer to a particular. So we can also count as names demonstrative expressions like 'this', 'that', 'I', 'you', and so on. An approximate way of characterizing predicates is to say that a predicate is a sentence with one or more names removed. So from 1) we get the predicate 'swims'; from 'Germany is a country' we get 'is a country'; from

3)   Socrates taught Plato

we obtain three predicates: 'taught Plato', 'Socrates taught', and 'taught'. These basically correspond to the properties of teaching Plato, of being taught by Socrates, and the relational property of teaching. This last is a relation which holds between many *pairs* of individuals - Socrates and Plato, Plato and Aristotle, etc.

A predicate will have a certain number of **argument places**. 'taught Plato', for example, has one argument place. It is a one place predicate - it requires one name (e.g. 'Socrates') to turn it into a sentence (e.g. 3). Correspondingly, it is a predicate true or false of individuals (e.g. Socrates) taken one at a time. 'taught' is a two place predicate.

As with propositional logic, we can distinguish two levels of logical formalization. At the first stage, translation into LQE, English words are retained but ordered in a way which corresponds to their logical structure; at the second stage, translation into LPF, all is form - ordinary words are coded into letters. Predicates are the main thing to consider, since we have to take account of their argument places. Various conventions are possible; the most uniform is the **prefix** convention, which puts the predicate before all its arguments. Thus at the first level of formalization, 1) becomes

4)   swims(mary),

the predicate 'swims( )' prefixed to its one argument, in this case 'mary'. Likewise, 3) becomes

5)   taught(socrates, plato),

which says that the relation of teaching holds between the individuals Socrates and Plato, taken in that order.

The important point, in formalizing all these atomic sentences, is to separate out the property- or relation-expressing phrase, and to prefix it to the object-naming expressions which are its arguments (enclosing them in brackets and separating them by commas). Saying that a predicate is what you get by removing one or more names from a sentence won't always go all the way to separating these elements out into the underlying form. Consider

6)   John and Mary are married.

This is genuinely ambiguous. In a discussion of who is single and who is married, it might be used simply to say that John and Mary fall into the latter category. If so, it can be taken to have the form of a conjunction of single predications:

7)   married(john) & married(mary).

Or it might mean that John and Mary are married to each other, an irreducibly relational fact, requiring a two place predicate:

8)   married-to(john, mary).

        Now consider

9)   Reading is between London and Bristol.

You may know that this is true because Bristol is west of Reading and Reading is west of London, a conjunction of facts each relating two things. But you may not - such information is not imparted by 9) nor required for understanding it. So as far as 9) goes, we must treat it as involving an irreducibly three place relation, betweenness, a relation which holds between threesomes, taken in a particular order:

10)   between(reading, london, bristol).

Typically, a predicate with n argument places will be true of n objects when considered in a certain order, but not necessarily when they are considered in another order. This simply generalizes the fact that, say, Reading is between London and Bristol, but Bristol is not between London and Reading.

In principle, there can be predicates with any number of argument places. An example of a four place relation can be found in:

11)   London is further from Montreal than it is from Washington.

This involves a four place predicate, 'further-than(, , ,)', although only three objects are actually mentioned in it. Due to the occurrence of the pronoun 'it', which refers back to the first name in the sentence, London is made to figure twice in the relation. When formalizing such an occurrence of a pronoun, we simply repeat the name in the appropriate place. 11) has the prefix form

12)   further-than(london, montreal, london, washington).

At the second stage of formalization, we abstract away from expressions of the natural language. A common convention to distinguish predicates and names within LPF is to use capital letters to symbolize predicates, and lowercase letters for names. Officially, we use P, Q, R, ..., for predicates; a, b, c, ... for names. Unofficially, more mnemonic letters can be used - B for between-ness, s for Socrates, and so on. Thus 4), 5), 7), 10) and 12) could become:

4´)   S(m).
5´)   T(s, p).
7´)   M(j) & M(m).
10´)   B(a, b, c).
12´)   F(l, m, l, w).

The conventions themselves aren't important; what matters is that, having adopted them, we stick to them: prefix ordering, and uppercase for predicates, lowercase for names.

A different convention is what is called *infix* form, which puts the symbol in between its arguments. It is the convention we have adopted for binary sentence connectives, e.g. to put the conjunction between its conjuncts, A & B. *Polish* notation adopts the prefix convention for sentence connectives, so a conjunction would take the form K(A, B) (K for Konjunction). Prefix form is less natural for sentence connectives. We have adopted it for predicates because it extends naturally to predicates with three or more argument places, whereas infix does not.

I have lingered over the distinction between referential and predicative expressions because it is fundamental to modern logic, and vital to understanding the division between those noun phrases which logic does count as names, and those it assigns another role - the *quantifiers*. Before proceeding any further, you may like to test out your intuitions on which of the noun phrases listed in the diagram above seem to you to be names, that is, which simply refer to a particular.

Consider this sentence:

13)   Some volcano is active.

In order for such a sentence to be true, there must exist a particular thing - e.g. Mount Etna - which is a volcano and active. But the 'e.g.' in 'e.g. Mount Etna' is very significant - there is nothing in sentence 13) which specifically refers to that volcano. It doesn't mention any particular volcano. So although there has to be an active volcano if it is to be true, there is no volcano in particular which it concerns. The sentence would still be true if Mount Etna had never existed, so long as there was some entity - e.g. Popocatepetl - which is both a volcano and active. This fact is fundamental to understanding the logical role of the phrase 'some volcano', and the way it relates to the objects which make true any sentence, such as 13), in which it figures.

We have to get away from the perhaps intuitively appealing idea that a phrase like 'some volcano' *refers* to a volcano. Even if the speaker is thinking of Etna when uttering 13), even if the hearer is thinking of Etna when it is pronounced, even if Etna is the only volcano in the whole wide world, still the expression 'some volcano' does not refer to Etna. Reference is the wrong relation. One can fully grasp - and know - the truth that some volcano is active without knowing, of any object, that it is a volcano and active. By contrast, someone who asserts

14)   Etna is an active volcano,

genuinely refers to Etna, and is thus committed to a much more specific statement. To grasp this fact, one must know what thing Etna is. (But notice that 13)'s not being specific does not mean that it is vague. It has a perfectly definite truth value.)

Some quantified sentences can even be true when there are no entities which, in any intuitive sense, they concern. An example adapted from Bradley, cited by Russell, is

15)   All trespassers will be prosecuted.

This sentence can be perfectly true, even if there never exist any trespassers (on the piece of land in question). It can be true because of a firm intention on the part of the land owners to prosecute anyone, if they were to trespass. This is one major divergence from classical Aristotelian logic; modern logic does not require the existence of As in order for a claim about all As to be true. The important point which emerges from these considerations is that the meaning, and logical role, of expressions like 'some volcano' and 'all trespassers' is wholly independent of particulars. You can understand 15), and know that it is true, without knowing of any particular thing, that it is a trespasser - for, as just mentioned, there might never be any such particulars.

There are some logical tests which corroborate the distinction between referring and quantifying. Consider

16)   Etna is active and Etna is large.

It is perfectly acceptable to re-arrange this to

17)   Etna is active and large.

The move from 16) to 17) is a valid inference; no matter what pair of predicates P, Q you take, if the sentence 'Etna is P and Etna is Q' is true, then so is the sentence 'Etna is P and Q'. But compare this with

18)   Some volcano is active and some volcano is dormant.

This does not entail

19)   Some volcano is active and dormant.

No volcano can have those contrary properties. So although 18) is true, 19) is not. This is clear evidence of a scope interaction between 'some volcano' and 'and'; 18) and 19) are not equivalent, and we should expect this fact to be reflected in their logical forms, when we consider quantifiers in the next two sections. But 16) and 17) are essentially equivalent; there is no difference in their underlying form:

20)   active(etna) & large(etna).

There are similar interactions between other quantifier expressions and propositional connectives which are not exhibited by genuine names. Look at the following pairs of sentences, and consider whether the second is always equivalent in content to the first.

21i)   Nothing is both round and square.
21ii)   Nothing is round and nothing is square.
22i)   John is either resting or asleep.
22ii)   Either John is resting, or John is asleep.
23i)   Everyone is either male or female.
23ii)   Either everyone is male, or everyone is female.
24i)   London is not small.
24ii)   It is not true that London is small.
25i)   At least one man is not bald.
25ii)   It is not true that at least one man is bald.

Like 16) and 17), 22i) and 22ii) are equivalent, as are the pair 24). Again, we find no scope interactions between these proper names and the propositional connectives. Thus with 24), there is only one way to assemble the pieces '¬', 'small( )' and 'London' into a well-formed whole. In LQE:

26)   ¬ small(london)

We could say that it doesn't matter whether the verb phrase is negated, as in 24i), so that the property of *not being small* is attributed to London, or whether negation attaches to the whole sentence, as in 24ii), so that the fact of *London's being small* is denied. And so in LPF:

26′)   ¬ S(l)

The same cannot be said in the case of 21), 23) and 25) - roughly speaking, in each of these pairs, the first sentence is true and the second false. 'everything' and 'nothing' quantify over objects, they don't refer. There is no particular thing, *everyone*, so there's no particular for the word 'everyone' to refer to. And 21) is not made true by a particular thing, *nothing*, it's made true by every thing - by everything not being both round and square. We shall consider the logic of quantifiers in the next section; for now, it is enough to have separated these noun phrases off from the genuine names.

Exercise 4

A.   Some complex nouns can be analysed into a conjunction of predicates. For example,

1)   John is a sixty year old musician,

can be taken to ascribe two properties to John, *being sixty* and *being a musician*, and so be given the form

sixty(john) & musician(john).

This is because if 1) is true then John is, simply, sixty. So if John is also a doctor, then he's a sixty year old doctor. In contrast,

2)   John is an awful musician,

doesn't mean that John is awful, and a musician, it means that as a musician, he is awful, and it wouldn't follow that he's also an awful doctor. So we must treat this as a single predication, of *being an awful musician*, A(j). Adjectival phrases of the former kind are called *predicative*, because they function as separate predicates, whereas adjectives of the latter sort are termed *attributive*.
       Bear this distinction in mind when formalizing the following sentences. Give the formalization both into quasi-English, and into Pure Form.

3)   Chagall was Russian.
4)   Picasso was born in Spain.
5)   Fido is a fast eater but a slow hunter.
6)   Fido is either a labrador or a retriever.
7)   Fido is a carnivorous, quadrupedal mammal.
8)   Othello loved Desdemona, if she loved him.
9)   Cordelia was a sister of Regan and of Goneril.

(Hint: a consequence of 9) is e.g. that Cordelia was a sister of Regan; does your formalization have this consequence?)

10)   Hamlet and Laertes kill each other.
11)   Romeo and Juliet both kill themselves.

B.   Provide a truth table definition of a three place sentence connective if_then_else, i.e. a connective which can join any three wffs X, Y, Z into a single wff if_then_else(X, Y, Z), and which means:
>   Y if X, otherwise Z.

C.   Definite descriptions are those noun phrases which begin with 'the', like 'the president of America', 'the president of England', etc. How should we classify them *logically* - do they function more like names, or like quantifier phrases? Illustrate your answer by providing a couple of pairs, similar to 21) to 25) above, which reveal their logical behaviour.

D.   According to the classical analysis of knowledge, a person x can be said to know a fact A under the following conditions:

>   x knows that A   if and only if i)   A   (i.e. it is true that A),
>   ii) x believes that A,
>   iii) x is justified in believing A.

The task is to give the essential logical structure of this analysis (i.e. leave a phrase like 'x believes that A' as it is, but replace 'ii)' etc. by the appropriate logical connectives). In particular, formulate two LQE sentences which state what this analysis takes to be:

12)   the sufficient conditions for knowledge,
13)   the necessary conditions for knowledge.

In a famous three-page article Edmund Gettier produced a number of counter-examples to this analysis. The kind of story in a Gettier counter-example goes as follows. Smith has worked in a university department for 20 years, and knows his colleagues well. For many years Smith has known that one of them, Jones, has owned a Ford. But unbeknownst to Smith, two things have happened: Jones secretly sold his Ford a week ago, though is renting a similar one, and co-incidentally, another member of the department bought a Ford a month ago (but he's kept it at home so far). So consider the proposition

14)   Someone in the department owns a Ford.

Smith believes this, we may assume, and he has as good a justification for believing it as any of us have for most empirical matters, and it's true - but we wouldn't say he knows it. Does this challenge 12) or 13) above, or both? State your reasons. If we accept that this is a counter-example to the classical analysis, does it show that a condition should be removed, or that one should be added?

2.5 Quantifier and variable

2.5.1 Universality

Suppose that, in an argument over legal responsibility, someone asserts:

1)   If one person borrows a car from another, and runs over someone, the former should pay for the injuries to the latter.

Expressions like 'the former' are rather cumbersome devices in ordinary language for cross-reference. 'the former' refers us back to the first person considered, the one who borrows the car. It's much simpler to use *variables*:

2)   If x borrows a car from y and runs over z, x should pay for z's injuries.

We sometimes say things like this in ordinary discourse, and they're quite intelligible - often more intelligible than the 'former'/'latter' type formulations, because the variables x, y, z, ... make it quite clear what is supposed to be linked to what. When some students are introduced to variables, they get a bit worried, because variables look rather mathematical. Of course, mathematicians do use variables in equations, but as we see from an example like 2), there's nothing specially mathematical about them - we can all use and understand variables.

One thing we intuitively understand about 2) is that a variable like z establishes a cross-reference - it links the predication of being run over with that concerning compensation. The same person, whoever it might be, who gets run over, should be compensated. This "whoever it might be" signals the other thing we intuitively grasp about variables - they don't refer to anyone in particular. Instead, variables can be said to *range over* many objects. We understand the variables in 2) as ranging over the set of people. Variables don't refer to particular objects, but they can take them as *values*. Since the variables in 2) range over people, any person could be a value of its variables. To say that anyone could be the value of z in 2), for instance, is just to say that anyone could be the person who gets run over.

Claims like 2), therefore, are intended as general claims: for *any* people x, y and z ... . In Prolog, as in 2), the quantifier 'any' is not explicitly represented, but is nevertheless understood to be there, tacitly governing the variables. But in predicate logic, it is customary to represent the quantifier explicitly. We use:

The Universal Quantifier, ∀, which expresses the concept of generality, of everything being ... Read the symbol as: for every ...

We combine a quantifier with a variable, as in 'for any (thing) x', 'for every (thing) y', and so on. So to make the universality of 2) explicit, we write:

3)   (∀x) (∀y) (∀z) [(x borrows a car from y & x runs over z)
$$\to \text{x should pay for z's injuries }].$$

In other words, 3) begins: for any x, any y, and any z, if x borrows ... etc.

Now for a second example (21i from the last section):

4)   Nothing is round and square,

This can be re-expressed in terms of universality as:

5)   For every thing x, it is not the case that x is round and x is square,

or more formally:

6)   (∀x) ¬ (x is round & x is square).

Here we understand the variable x as ranging over all objects whatsoever. The ∀ makes the concept of generality explicit - take *any* object x - and the variable links together the predications to be jointly denied - it can't be that x is both round and square. Putting the predicates in prefix form gives:

7)   (∀x) ¬ (round(x) & square(x)).

As this makes clear, variables occupy the same place in logical syntax as names (viz. the argument places of predicates). This is still faithful to the sense of the original sentence 4), but has one crucial advantage over it. Whereas on the surface 4) looks the same as a sentence composed of name and predicate (noun phrase plus verb phrase), the form of 7) accurately reflects its logical structure. Finally, abstracting to pure form we get:

8) $(\forall x) \neg (R(x) \& S(x))$.

Let's look at another example of an English sentence and its underlying quantifier plus variable structure:

9)   Everything Midas touches turns to gold.

How does this say that the predicates 'Midas touches x' and 'x turns to gold' are related? One thing this does NOT say is that Midas touches everything, and everything turns to gold. Rather, it's like saying: *if* Midas touches this, it will turn to gold, and *if* he touches that, it will turn to gold, and ... etc. (for each object in turn). As mentioned in the previous section (the 'trespassers' example, 15), universal generalizations usually have a hypothetical, conditional component. We give 9) the form:

$(\forall x)(\text{touches(midas, x)} \rightarrow \text{turns-gold(x)})$,

for any object, if Midas touches it, it will turn to gold. Similarly with

10)   Every human is mortal.

This does not say that everything in the whole universe is both human and mortal, which is wildly false - conjunction is wholly inappropriate in these cases. 10) states a sober (and sobering) truth, that everything which is human is mortal - or, bending this a little to our logical vocabulary, it says that of every thing that, *if* it's human, it is mortal. It links the two predicates 'human' and 'mortal' with a conditional: anything is, if human, mortal. Or, speaking quasi English,

For any x, if x is human, x is mortal.

More formally, then:

11) $(\forall x) (\text{human(x)} \rightarrow \text{mortal(x)})$.

It is helpful to define what counts, logically, an *instance* or *instantiation* of a generalization. When Thurber went in for collecting generalizations, he classified this specimen as "fascinating but undemonstrable" (*What a Lovely Generalization!*):

12)   People who break into houses don't drink wine.

We can put it into LQE as:

13)   ($\forall$x)(house-breaker(x) $\rightarrow$ $\neg$ wine-drinker(x)).

An instance of a generalization is obtained by wiping out the dominant (outermost) quantifier, ('($\forall$x)', in this case), and replacing the occurrences of the variable connected to it (two occurrences of 'x', here) by a name. Thus an instance of 13) is:

14)   house-breaker(mary) $\rightarrow$ $\neg$ wine-drinker(mary).

So, while 12) and 13) state a certain conditional relation for all things - everything is such that: if it breaks into houses, it doesn't drink wine - 14) states it for a specific instance: if Mary is a house breaker, she doesn't drink wine. It is important to realize that, if 12) is a true generalization about house breakers, every instance of it is true, irrespectively of whether the thing mentioned is a house breaker or not. The generalization says that all those things which do break into houses do not drink wine; if Jim is no house breaker, the corresponding instance, being conditional, is still true:

15)   house-breaker(jim) $\rightarrow$ $\neg$ wine-drinker(jim).

2.5.2 Existence

Returning to example 4), 'Nothing is round and square', we can equally well understand this as the denial of the existence of something both round and square,

16)   It is not the case that there is some thing x which is round and square.

This uses the concept of existence rather than universality, and can be formalized using the corresponding quantifier:
The Existential Quantifier, $\exists$, expressing the concept of existence, of there existing at least one thing which ...   Read the symbol as: for some ...

So 16) can be given this form:

17)   ¬ (∃x) (x is round & x is square).

(This is logically equivalent to the wff 7) above.)
         Let's consider another example from English,

18)   Some human is mortal.

How does this say that the predicates 'human' and 'mortal' are
related? It says that there is something which satisfies both of them.
So in this case we do need conjunction - we need the existential
quantifier, a variable to link the two predicates, and &:

19)   (∃x)(human(x) & mortal(x)).

This would also do as a formalization of

         A human is mortal,
         At least one human is mortal,
         There are (some) human mortals,
         Human mortals exist,

and so on - any English sentence (however unstylish) which gets across
the idea that there is at least one thing which satisfies one *and* the
other predicate. Incidentally, the last of these sentences illustrates a
point hinted at in the previous section - that the grammatical category
of verb phrase does not quite coincide with the logical category of
predicate. The verb 'exists' is treated in terms of ∃, not as a predicate.
         In formalizing sentences at this level, for instance

20)   There are no monsters in Loch Ness.

it is worth trying to keep in mind a checklist of four questions.
i)   What expressions, if any, are functioning as proper names? A
proper name is a word or phrase that refers to some specific entity. A
sentence may contain no such reference to a particular - 4) and 18) do
not. But 20) here does contain a name - 'Loch Ness'. It is important to
formalize a name as a name, and not as a predicate - it is *not* correct to
have something like '(∃x) loch_ness(x) ... '. That would be to ascribe to
'loch_ness' the logical role of an expression which is true of many
different things.

ii)   What expressions are functioning as predicates, i.e. to express properties or relations? By contrast with names, predicates express universals, general features many things can share.   In this case, 'monster' is a one place predicate, and 'in' a predicate which relates two things. It is important to formalize a predicate as a predicate, with the right number of argument places, and not as a name. It is *not* correct to have something like 'in(monster, loch_ness)'. That would be to treat 'monster' as a name of a specific individual.

iii)   What expressions, if any, are functioning as quantifiers, and what quantifiers are they - do they express universality, or existence? In the case of 19), 'There are no ...' looks like an idiom of quantification. As we have seen, this kind of quantification can be thought of either in terms of universality, 'Everything isn't ...', or in terms of existence, 'It is not the case that there exists ...'

iv)   What propositional connectives are needed to connect together the various bits? We have already noted that it is wrong to formalize 'All humans are mortal' using &. The correlative of this mistake is that it is usually wrong to combine ∃ with →. To illustrate this, consider

21)   Some pigs fly.

This is false; but consider what happens if we formalize it using →:

   (∃x)(pig(x) → flies(x)).

This says that something has this property: if it's a pig, it flies. Given the equivalence of A → B with ¬A v B, it is equivalent to this:

   (∃x)(¬ pig(x) v flies(x)),

i.e. something has this property: either it's not a pig, or it flies. But this is true - many things have that disjunctive property. So the point is that formalizing 20) using a conditional produces something too weak - it has converted something false into something true. What is needed here is conjunction - 20) says, falsely, that something is both a pig and flies:

22)   (∃x)(pig(x) & flies(x)).

Returning now to sentence 20), we can formalize it as:

23)   ¬ (∃x)(monster(x) & in(x, loch_ness)).

Let us look at one more example, involving more than one quantifier - another from Thurber's collection of the "Broad Generalization, or Sweeping Statement":

24)   Cops off duty always shoot someone.

We could take 'always' as generalizing over times, but it will be simpler if we take it as an idiomatic way of generalizing over off-duty cops. The quantifier which combines with 'off-duty cop' is universal: *any* cop who is off-duty ... . 'Someone' means 'some person', i.e. the quantifier in this phrase is existential. So we have a universal followed by an existential quantifier - a combination which might be semi-formally expressed as:
        For any off-duty cop x,
                        there is some person y, such that x shoots y.
Again, in going to full logical form, we have to take care to insert the right propositional connectives:

25)   (∀x)((cop(x) & off-duty(x)) →
                        (∃y)(person(y) & shoots(x, y))).

This can be read: take any x, if that x is both a cop and off duty, then there is something y, such that y is a person and x shoots y. This may seem long-winded in comparison with 23), but it has the advantage of making clear its logical structure.

2.5.3   Open and closed sentences

Names and variables have the same logical syntax, and are classified together in the more inclusive category of **term**. Their difference is semantic: a name refers, by itself, to a particular object; a variable does not. Filling the argument places of an n place predicate with n terms produces a wff. If all the terms are names, we have a *closed* wff (like examples 4′) to 12′) of the last section) - it represents a complete sentence, something either true or false. If one or more of the terms is a variable, we have an *open* sentence, such as the complex open wff

        (human(x) → mortal(x)).

This is incomplete, it is not an expression capable of truth or falsity on its own. To get a closed wff from this, we need to *bind* the variables in it with an appropriate quantifier, as in 11).

Basically, an occurrence of a variable is bound by a quantifier if i) it lies within the scope of the quantifier, and ii) that quantifier is immediately prefixed to a letter which is the same as the variable. Otherwise the occurrence of the variable is *free*. To take the second of these points first, contrast the closed wff 11) with

$$(\forall y) (\text{ human}(x) \rightarrow \text{mortal}(x)),$$

where both occurrences of x are free, even though they lie within the scope of a quantifier, because it is combined with a different variable. The nearest equivalent of this in ordinary language would be something like:

Consider any woman whatsoever: if he is human, he is mortal. Here, 'he' is not of the right gender to be bound by the quantifying phrase - the point of the analogy, then, is that the quantifier 'any woman' doesn't really bind the pronouns which follow it, even though they lie within its scope. To illustrate the first point about binding, consider what happens if we change the brackets in 11) to

$$(\forall x)(\text{ human}(x)) \rightarrow \text{mortal}(x).$$

The scope of an expression is, as before, the smallest well formed formula which contains it, so the scope of '$(\forall x)$' here is only '$(\forall x)($ human(x))'. The last occurrence of 'x' lies outside the scope of '$(\forall x)$', and so is not bound by it. An approximate analogy for this would be something like:

She is mortal. Any woman is human.

Although the pronoun 'She' agrees in gender with the quantifying phrase 'Any woman', it's in the wrong place to be bound by it - that occurrence of 'She' is not within the scope of that occurrence of 'Any woman'.

Exercise 5

A.   Give the essential logical structure of the following sentences. (11 is also from Thurber's *What A Lovely Generalization!*).

1)   Every cat washes itself.
2)   If all dogs are mortal, then Fido is mortal.
3)   Not every scorpion is lethal.
4)   Every scorpion is non lethal.
5)   Prometheus likes all men.
6)   No man likes Pandora.
7)   At least one satellite orbits Mars.
8)   There is a planet larger than Neptune but cooler than it.
9)   Every village has at least one church.
10)   Every hamlet has no church.
11)   There are no pianos in Japan.
12)   There are pianos, but not in Japan.

B.   The following English sentences describe the situation at a certain hotel. They can be translated into Prolog to provide a database from which we can obtain information about that hotel - see exercise 3.1 A. The task here is to reveal their logical forms, i.e. to translate them into LQE.

    Brian owns Seaview. Seaview is a hotel. Brian is married to Mary. Brian employs Jane, and he employs Manuel. Employees are staff, and hotel owners are staff. Jones and Smith are guests. All staff serve all guests.

If you use different predicates to formalize the (two place) verb 'employs' and the (one place) noun 'employee', formulate as an LQE generalization the logical relationship between them.

C.   In order to pose what he termed 'the new riddle of induction', Goodman devised the pair of predicates 'grue' and 'bleen', where a possible definition of the former would be:

13)   Anything is grue iff it is either examined before a and green, or not examined before a and blue.

'a' is to be understood as referring to some definite date in the future (e.g. the year 2000). 'bleen' is defined similarly (with 'blue' and 'green' switched). The problem for induction is that all evidence so far obtained for 'All emeralds are green' is equally evidence for 'All emeralds are grue', and thus their being blue when examined after a.
    Formalize this definition, using the wffs 'grue(x)', 'examined-before(x, y)', etc. Note that the definition of 'grue' makes essential

reference to time. Show that, at least in this respect, the position is symmetrical for speakers of the grue/bleen language, by giving the corresponding form of the definition of green in terms of grue and bleen.

D.   There are many ways you can *order* objects, i.e. arrange them by an ordering relation <. In alphabetical order by name, Jones will come before Smith; ordered by height, Jones may come later than Smith. Different ordering relations have different logical properties, so it is important to symbolize these clearly. Let 'a < b' mean: a comes before b, in the ordering <. We can say, for example,

14)   No object is before itself

by either of two forms:

$$\neg(\exists x)\ x < x, \quad \text{equivalently:} \quad (\forall x)\neg(x < x).$$

Such a relation < would be termed *irreflexive*.
        Given an ordering of objects <, we can express the notion of betweenness in terms of it. Express

15)   b comes between a and c

using <. (There will be two possibilities.) Then express the following possible properties of an order <:

16)   Every object is later than itself.
17)   Take any two objects: if one is before the other, then the latter is not before the former.
18)   Given any three objects, if the first is before the second, and the second before the third, then the first is before the third.

        To give another example, the proposition

19)   Every object has one later than it in the ordering,

would be formalized by:

$$(\forall x)\ (\exists y)\ x < y.$$

For any x, there is some y which comes after it. Express the following incompatible pairs of properties of <:

20.i)   Every object has a predecessor.

20.ii)   There is a first object in the ordering.

21.i)   Every object has an *immediate* successor, i.e. given any object, there will be another after it such that no object comes between them.

21.ii) Given any two objects in the ordering, there is always another between them.

       Finally, consider moments of time as the objects being ordered. You can use 't_1', 't_2', 't_3', ... as variables over moments of time. That is, we understand the 't' variables to be restricted to times. Instead of always having to say $(\forall x)(\text{ time}(x) \rightarrow ... x ...)$, we just abbreviate this to: $(\forall t)(... t ...)$. '$t_1 < t_2$' means: time t_2 is later than time t_1, and so on. So for instance

22)   There is a last moment of time

could be formalized:

$$(\exists t_1) \neg (\exists t_2)\ t_1 < t_2$$

There is a time t_1 such that no time t_2 comes after it (which is the contradictory of 19, for moments of time.) Suppose time was *circular* in structure (i.e. if you wait long enough, you'll come back to the very same time - a form of eternal recurrence.) State and formalize three principles (e.g. from the above) which would be true of this ordering, giving your reasons in each case.

Chapter 3
Prolog: analysis in action

3.1 Beginning Prolog

Like a natural language that is spoken in many countries, a computer language that becomes widely adopted develops many dialects and variations. Some variations will be minor, such as the syntactic conventions employed to distinguish variables. In some implementations of Prolog, a variable must be one of 'x', 'y' or 'z', or one of these letters prefixed to a number. In many versions of Prolog syntax, any word beginning with an underscore counts as a variable. Likewise, the logical connectives may take different forms. In some versions, the conditional is expressed by the word 'if'; in Edinburgh syntax, it is the combination ':-'. Other variations may be more significant. Some versions of Prolog may contain pre-defined or primitive expressions which are absent from others. A prompt-based version, for instance, will require expressions which have no place in a multi-windows environment. Still, these are matters of detail. What makes a language Prolog is its logical core; it enables one to program a computer in a version of first order logic, and has a basis in a particular procedure for drawing inferences from those programs. This chapter is mainly concerned with the programming principles which are common to all versions of Prolog. But it does mean that to program a particular machine, you will also need a guide to the details of the implementation you are using.

I shall adopt the convention of displaying all Prolog code in boldface. In this book, I shall adopt *Edinburgh* Syntax, with the following conventions for basic expressions.
Variables: any sequence of letters or numerals, beginning with a capital letter or underscore - e.g.

X, Y, Z, X1, Person, _123, ListSoFar, New_2 .

Variables: any sequence of letters or numerals, beginning with a capital letter or underscore - e.g.

X, Y, Z, X1, Person, _123, ListSoFar, New_2 .

Predicates: any sequence of letters, provided the first one is lowercase. Names: same as predicates. (Note: if you wish a name to begin with a capital letter, enclose it in single quotes. Whereas **London** is a variable in Edinburgh Prolog, **'London'** is not.)

Any version of Prolog needs to be able to create its own variables whilst solving queries, and so will have some means of generating symbols to act as variables. How these appear may depend on the implementation. One way to ensure an inexhaustible supply of variables is to use numerals prefixed with the underscore.

I will illustrate the basic forms of Prolog sentence by developing a program which records some basic facts about our solar system. We shall use **mercury, venus,** ... as names of the planets. We want these to act as constants - to refer to specific planets - so they must, in Edinburgh syntax, begin in lowercase. To assert that

1)   Venus is a planet,

we can write:

planet(venus) .

This states a particular fact of astronomy - that a certain particular entity, the thing referred to by the name **venus**, is of the general type expressed by the predicate **planet**. To name our own planet, we can use **the_earth**. So we will also have

planet(the_earth) .

Note that we could not write the name as **the earth**; if two expressions are separated by a space Prolog will treat them as distinct words. So if you feel that a name, predicate or variable would be most clearly expressed using what in English would be two or more words, use an underscore to fuse them into a single unit. So if we want to record that

2)   The sun is a star,

we can add:

star(the_sun) .

In a prompt-based environment, one needs to tell Prolog that one is adding each fact to the knowledge base - for instance, by embedding it within a command, such as **assert( )**. In a windows-based environment, one may be able to type the sentence directly into a program window.

The simplest structured assertions in Prolog are, like these, the combination of a one place predicate with a name. Note that **the_earth** and **planet** are not distinguished as name and predicate on the basis of their lettering - they are distinguished as such by the way they combine within the sentence. What makes **planet** and **star** predicates is the fact that they come first in the sentence, and enclose their arguments in round brackets. We want them to be one place predicates, because the properties we intend them to express, *being a planet* and *being a star*, are attributes which a single thing either has or does not have. By contrast, *orbiting* is essentially a relation between a pair of things - one thing orbits around another - and so if we want to record information about what orbits what, we will need a two place predicate. To say that

3)   The Moon orbits around the Earth,

we can write:

orbits(the_moon, the_earth) .

When a predicate has more than one argument, we separate each argument from the next with a comma. If you are typing the program in as text, you will also need to end each complete sentence with a full stop, so that Prolog can tell where one sentence ends and the next begins. Every complete Prolog sentence, whether atomic or complex, needs to be terminated with a full stop. Full stops should not occur *within* a sentence.

The exact spelling or formulation of each name and predicate is a matter of choice. It's up to the programmer to choose the words and their spelling - provided they don't clash with anything already chosen for the predefined vocabulary of Prolog. It's advisable to use words which are as close as possible to the ordinary English. The content of your programs should be accessible to others, and also to yourself at a later date, so it's as well to phrase them as clearly as possible. The important thing is that once a particular wording has been chosen as the predicate to record a certain sort of fact, it is used uniformly. Using a predicate uniformly means: you always use the same word, with exactly the same spelling, to express a given property, and you always use it with the same number of arguments, in the same order. Thus if you preferred **revolves_around** to **orbits**, you could write:

revolves_around(the_moon, the_earth) .

But then you must use **revolves_around** to record all facts about orbiting (you don't have half of them with **orbits**, say), you must not use **revolves_around** for any other sort of information, and the predicate must always have two arguments: the first, for the body which orbits, and the second, for the body which is orbited.

So far, our program will be a modest inventory of, say, four facts:

star(the_sun) .
planet(venus) .
planet(the_earth) .
orbits(the_moon, the_earth) .

Even so, we can put it to work by posing it questions. For example, we can ask it

4)   Does the moon orbit the earth?

The logical content of this question is essentially the same as the previous statement 3), and so has the same Prolog form:

orbits(the_moon, the_earth)

And, just as in ordinary speech we need to make it clear that we are asking whether something is the case, rather than asserting it as fact, so now we must make it clear to Prolog that we are asking this as a query, not asserting it. In a prompt-based environment, a context like **is( )** or the query prompt **?-** makes it clear that the sentence involved is being put forward interrogatively, not assertorically. In a windows-based environment, a question might be posed simply by typing the sentence into a special window for queries, rather than in a window for the program. I shall indicate queries by means of the query prompt. Informally, we should understand this question not so much as 4) but as

4´)   Do you know whether the Moon orbits the Earth?

All questions to a Prolog database should be understood as tacitly prefixed by "Do you know whether ...". Computers aren't omniscient - they can only answer on the basis of what is explicitly in their database, or from what can be inferred from that database. The answer **YES** means that it does follow from the information it has. Likewise, if we were to query this database with

?-   **orbits(the_earth, the_sun)**

the answer **NO** it will respond with should be understood as "I don't know", i.e. it cannot be proved from the database of facts in the program - not "No, it is definitely not so".

    We can also put questions which contain variables, for example:

?-   **planet(X)**

This should be understood as "Do you know of anything X which is a planet?" Prolog may allow the user to specify whether he or she wants one solution to this query, or all the things X which it can prove to be so, e.g. in a prompt based system, by the query contexts **one( )** or **all( )**. In this case, asking for one solution will result in Prolog answering with the first thing it can prove to be a planet. Since **planet(venus)** is the first sentence about planets in the program, **X = venus** will be the solution returned. If all solutions are requested, **X = venus** will be followed by **X = the_earth**. When no further solutions to a query can be derived, Prolog will end its series of solutions with a message that that is all - something like **No (more) solutions**. Similarly, we can ask:

?-   **orbits(X, the_earth)**

do you know of any X which orbits the earth, or:

?-   **orbits(the_moon, Y)**

do you know if the Moon orbits anything Y, and

?-   **orbits(X, Y)**

do you know any pair of things such that one orbits the other?

If you are new to Prolog, the value of going through even these simple manoeuvres on a real machine cannot be over-emphasized. Add the sentences, ask the queries, try things out to see what happens. Assuming you have done so, let's consider expanding the knowledge base of our program with a slightly more complex sort of sentence. In pre-Copernican times, everyone believed in a *geocentric* view of the universe: the Earth was the centre of the universe, and everything - most importantly, the Sun - revolved around it. It is true to say that

5)   The solar system is geocentric *if* the Sun orbits the earth.

To describe this we need a conditional linking two atomic sentences. In Edinburgh syntax, 'if' is written with a colon immediately followed by a hyphen:

geocentric(the_solar_system) :- orbits(the_sun, the_earth) .

The combination **:-** vaguely resembles a reversed conditional arrow, ←. All dialects of Prolog write the conditional in the opposite direction to the way familiar to logicians. That is, this Prolog conditional corresponds to the logical form:

6)   orbits(the_sun, the_earth) → geocentric(the_solar_system).

The difference in order between Prolog and logic is not important; the same underlying conditional is involved in both (recall the discussion of examples 6 and 8 in section 2.3.1). Whereas Prolog prefers the order given by 5), traditional logic prefers to put it this way round:

7)   If the Sun orbits the Earth, then the solar system is geocentric.

In logic programming, the antecedent of a conditional, the 'if' part - **orbits(the_sun, the_earth)**, in this case - is referred to as the *body* of the conditional. The part which describes what follows from that, the consequent, is its *head*.

If we want to do justice to the rival hypothesis which Copernicus introduced, of a *heliocentric* (i.e. sun-centred) solar system, we can say:

heliocentric(the_solar_system) :- orbits(the_earth, the_sun) .

Any conditional can be given either a declarative or a procedural reading. We have so far considered the declarative reading, taking the conditional to declare or describe a conditional relation between two atomic facts - in this case,

8)   The solar system is heliocentric if the earth orbits around the Sun.

But we can also understand it as specifying a computational *procedure*. In this case, it is a very simple procedure for proving something:

9)   To prove that the solar system is heliocentric, prove that the Earth orbits the Sun.

The declarative and procedural readings are alternative ways of looking at a program. The first takes it as describing a number of facts and relations, the second way sees it as a procedure for proving various facts. If we now ask the question:

?-   **heliocentric(the_solar_system)**

we set Prolog a certain *goal* - prove (if you can) that the solar system is heliocentric. This last conditional shows Prolog a way to prove this - it must prove that Earth orbits the Sun. Since it has no way to prove that from the current program, and no other way of showing that the solar system is heliocentric, it will answer **No**. This does not mean the program is committed to a pre-Copernican view of the universe - it will equally respond **No** to the question: is the solar system geocentric? It simply doesn't know enough astronomical facts to settle these questions at the moment.

The next step up in complexity is to introduce variables into conditionals. Such conditionals are not tied to particular things, and so express generalizations. For example, to capture the generalization that

10)   Every planet orbits the sun,

we say

11)   X orbits the sun if X is a planet,

which goes into Prolog as:

orbits(X, the_sun) :- planet(X) .

This is to be understood as: *for every x*, if x is a planet, then x orbits the Sun. The convention is that any Prolog sentence containing variables is to be understood as a *universal* generalization. A logician would speak of the **universal closure** of the sentence: any variable is to be understood as governed by a tacit 'for every'. There are no free variables in Prolog. Thus, to translate a Prolog sentence into standard logical form, re-order consequent and antecedent using the standard conditional, and bind any variables with universal quantifiers having wide scope over the entire conditional:

$$(\forall x)(\ planet(x) \rightarrow orbits(x, the\_sun) \ ) \ .$$

In Prolog, universal generalizations are often referred to as *rules*. We can indeed understand this conditional as a rule, to the effect: if you come across any instance of **planet(X)**, you may infer the corresponding instance of **orbits(X, the_sun)**. From a procedural point of view, it is natural to consider this conditional as being about the **orbits** relation (not the **planet** predicate), because it provides a way for proving facts about what orbits what. More generally, then, a conditional is *about* the predicate in its consequent. It is important that when we make additions to a program, the sentences which are about a particular predicate, whether conditional or unconditional, must all occur together. If the sentences are being added through a prompt, Prolog will take care of this automatically. But if the sentences are being added to a program window, as a piece of text, the programmer must make sure to group all the **planet** facts together, all the **orbits** facts together, and so on. So far we have the seven sentences

star(the_sun) .
planet(venus) .
planet(the_earth) .
orbits(the_moon, the_earth) .
orbits(X, the_sun) :- planet(X) .
geocentric(the_solar_system) :- orbits(the_sun, the_earth) .
heliocentric(the_solar_system) :- orbits(the_earth, the_sun) .

Consider what happens if we now re-run the question: is the solar system heliocentric? As before, the last conditional sets up the sub-goal: prove that the Earth orbits the sun. Again, Prolog looks to see what it knows about the **orbits** relation. The first **orbits** fact it comes to, as before, is of no help. But now there is a second sentence about **orbits**, the rule: to prove that X orbits the sun, prove that it is a planet. So this sets Prolog a further sub-goal: prove that the Earth is a planet. Now it must consult what it knows about the **planet** predicate, and this time it finds a definite, unconditional fact: **planet(the_earth)**. Since it can prove that Earth is a planet, it can prove **orbits(the_earth, the_sun)**, and so it can prove **heliocentric (the_solar_system)**. So this time the question is answered **YES**. This provides a modest illustration of the fact that a genuine inferencing mechanism is involved here.   The fact that the solar system is heliocentric is not explicitly recorded in the program - Prolog had to work it out.

The next step up in complexity is to compound the clauses in the body of a conditional. Suppose we want to define a predicate **moon**. Many planets have moons - as the first to make serious use of the telescope to observe the night sky, Galileo discovered four of the moons of Jupiter. (This was one important piece of evidence against the geocentric view of the universe, since it showed that not everything orbits the Earth.) Note the difference between the predicate **moon**, which is true of many things, and the singular term **the_moon**, which we use to refer to just one object, our Moon. To keep the definition simple, we shall say that a moon is anything which orbits a planet. In other words,

12)   X is a moon if X orbits Y *and* Y is a planet.

In Edinburgh Prolog, the conjunction of clauses is expressed with a comma:

moon(X) :- orbits(X, Y), planet(Y).

Since this contains two variables **X** and **Y**, a direct application of the convention that all variables are bound by universal quantifiers yields the following reading:

13)   For any x and for any y, if x orbits y and y is a planet, then x is a moon.

But notice how natural it is to reformulate this as: X is a moon as long as there is *some* planet Y which it orbits:

14)   For any x, if there is some y such that x orbits y and y is a planet, then x is a moon.

Indeed these are logically equivalent. (For those at home with ∀ and ∃: if a variable occurs only in the antecedent of a conditional, we can think of it as bound by an existential quantifier whose scope is restricted to that antecedent. The logical forms corresponding to 13) and 14) are equivalent:

13′) $(\forall x)(\forall y)[$ (orbits(x, y) & planet(y)) → moon(x)] .
14′) $(\forall x)(\exists y)[$orbits(x, y) & planet(y)] → moon(x)) .

For further discussion, and proof, see section 4.5.2.)
        Any number of atomic wffs can be conjoined in the antecedent of a conditional. The dictionary definition of a satellite, as any heavenly body which orbits around another, becomes:

satellite(X) :-   heavenly_body(X), heavenly_body(Y), orbits(X, Y).

In other words, X is a satellite if X is a heavenly body, Y is a heavenly body, and X orbits Y. As in predicate logic, when a variable is used what matters is not the particular letter chosen, but the pattern of its occurrences within a sentence. Since a variable is any expression starting with an uppercase, we could have written, say

satellite(Lesser) :- heavenly_body(Lesser),
                        heavenly_body(Greater),
                        orbits(Lesser, Greater).

The pattern of occurrences of variables is exactly the same, so the two conditionals are wholly equivalent. This point applies equally to queries. We can ask conjunctive queries, such as:

?-   orbits(X, Y), orbits(Y, the_sun)

as if to ask: "Do you know of anything which orbits something which orbits the sun?", i.e. is there an X which orbits a Y which orbits the sun? The particular letters chosen as variables are unimportant - what matters is the pattern. So, for example:

?-   orbits(A, B), orbits(B, the_sun)

is exactly the same question. (What values, if any, will **A** and **B** receive if we put this question to our program?)

Note that the point about patterns of variables does not apply to the program as a whole, but to each separate sentence. The fact that **X** may occur in more than one rule is not significant - what matters is the pattern *within* each rule. If the same word is used as a variable in distinct Prolog sentences, it counts as a distinct variable. Variables in Prolog are *local* - they are bound by quantifiers whose scope extends no further than the sentence they occur in. (In other words, whereas you must use predicates and names uniformly throughout a program, there is no connection between a variable used in one complete sentence and another.) Another point about the whole program is that we understand it as having the combined force of all of its component sentences - as the *conjunction* of each sentence with the next.

But looked at in a slightly different way, all the rules pertaining to a particular predicate can be taken disjunctively. Suppose **heavenly_body** is defined by two rules:

heavenly_body(X) :- star(X) .
heavenly_body(X) :- planet(X) .

Taking this as the conjunction of the two rules, we are saying that anything is a heavenly body if it is a star, AND anything is a heavenly body if it is a planet. But this is just the same as saying that anything is a heavenly body if it is a star OR a planet. These two rules amount to a single rule with a disjunctive body. In Edinburgh Prolog a semi-colon expresses disjunction:

heavenly_body(X) :- star(X); planet(X) .

Reading this as a procedure:

To prove that something is a heavenly body:
    Prove that it is a star, OR: Prove that it is a planet.

From a procedural point of view, the two separate rules and the single disjunctive rule are just equivalent procedures for proving that something is a heavenly body. From a declarative point of view, what underlies this equivalence is essentially the propositional equivalence between a conjunction of conditionals, $(A \rightarrow C)$ & $(B \rightarrow C)$, and a conditional with a disjunctive antecedent, $(A \lor B) \rightarrow C$.

Notice another important feature of all these conditionals: there is no scope ambiguity between the conditional and the other connectives. The conditional always takes widest scope. The general form of a Prolog conditional is

atomic head *followed by* **:-** *followed by* possibly complex body.

The consequent cannot be complex; it must contain exactly one clause. The antecedent, by contrast, can contain any number of conjunctions and disjunctions. For example, we can change the definition of a heavenly body to include moons as well:

heavenly_body(X) :- star(X) ;
planet(X) ;
moon(X) .

Anything is a heavenly body IF it is EITHER a star OR a planet OR a moon. Likewise, conjunctions and disjunctions can be combined in the antecedent in any way we need. Suppose we wanted to be able to draw conclusions from our database about where in the solar system life could occur. If it included information about the relative temperatures of bodies - a rough guide would be **hot(mercury)**, **warm(the_earth)**, etc. - and which planets had atmospheres, then a possible definition would be:

Life is possible on X if X is either a planet or a moon,
and X is warm, and has an atmosphere.

Since there is a possible ambiguity between the 'or's and the 'and's, we need to use brackets to make clear their relative scopes:

life_possible_on(X) :- (planet(X); moon(X)),
warm(X), atmospheric(X) .

The new line is not obligatory, but rules with a complex body such as this are made far more legible if the components are separated out onto different lines.

To sum up so far, we might now have a program with at least the following ten sentences:

```
star(the_sun) .
planet(venus) .
planet(the_earth)  .
orbits(the_moon, the_earth) .
orbits(X, the_sun) :- planet(X) .
moon(X) :- orbits(X, Y),  planet(Y).
satellite(X) :- heavenly_body(X),
                heavenly_body(Y),
                orbits(X, Y).
heavenly_body(X)  :-  star(X);
                      planet(X);
                      moon(X) .
geocentric(the_solar_system) :- orbits(the_sun, the_earth) .
heliocentric(the_solar_system) :- orbits(the_earth, the_sun) .
```

These few examples illustrate the basic forms of Prolog assertions. They are either unconditional atomic sentences, or conditional. Conditionals can only be built up in certain ways. The consequent of a conditional must be atomic. (When Prolog draws an inference from a conditional, it cannot cope with a complex conclusion; it can only draw one conclusion at a time, so it needs conditionals to have simple consequents.) The antecedent can be compounded in certain ways - e.g. by conjunction or disjunction. It cannot itself be conditional in form. So Prolog is written in a restricted version of LQE, constrained by the particular mechanical way of drawing inferences which underlies it.

Exercise 1

In designing a program to answer an exercise, make full use of the query facility of Prolog. Ask as many varied queries as you can, and use the solutions you obtain to improve the program. Make frequent saves of each new version. (Keep a copy of the final version of your program, as it may be modified in a future exercise.) When you are satisfied that your program is correct, print out a paper copy. All answers to Prolog exercises should be in the form of printout; they should not be handwritten.

A.   Write a program in Prolog which encodes the facts about Seaview given in exercise 2.5 B. Test the correctness and efficiency of your program as follows. i) When you have defined the predicate **staff**, query all solutions to **staff(X)**. Does your program generate exactly the three solutions it should, namely **X = manuel**, **X = jane**, and

X = brian? ii) How would you ask the question: Who serves Jones?
Does your program generate the correct solutions to this query?

B.   Below is a small part of the family tree of the royal family of
Mycenae. Describe these relationships in a program, using one place
predicates **male** and **female**, and two place predicates **parent** and
married. (Atreus, Agamemnon, Menelaus and Orestes are the men. If
you have difficulty typing these Greek names, abbreviate each to, say,
the first three letters.)

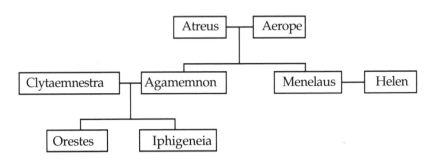

Then provide general definitions of the one place predicates
grandmother, wife, father, and two place predicates **father_of,
daughter_of, brother_of**. Your program should thus entail such facts as
these: **grandmother(aerope), wife(helen), father(agamemnon),
father_of(atreus, menelaus), daughter_of(iphigeneia, clytaemnestra),
brother_of(orestes, iphigeneia)**. Do *not* state these as particular facts,
but define the predicates in terms of the basic vocabulary of **male,
female, parent** and **married**, so that the facts will be entailed.
        Add the information that Agamemnon killed Iphigeneia,
Clytaemnestra killed Agamemnon, and Orestes killed Clytaemnestra.
How would you ask in Prolog: i) Was anyone killed by his or her
parent?   ii) Did any son kill his mother? Check that your program
answers these questions correctly.

3.2   Backtracking; negation; errors

3.2.1   Backtracking: searching for alternative solutions

When writing programs in Prolog, you must always bear in mind that
the sentences you produce are to be read by a machine. There is more to
programming with logic than just producing a correct logical analysis of

the problem. A Prolog program is put to work by setting the goal of proving some sentence. A machine cannot take in the whole program 'at once', and just see whether the sentence follows or not. Nor can it peruse those sentences like a human, with its eye wandering over them, picking out the parts it finds salient. It must scan a program *mechanically*. We might think of it in terms of an entirely stupid Prolog homunculus, sitting inside the machine, which sets about trying to prove a goal by systematically reading through the program text. Set to prove a goal A, if it encounters a sentence of the type: A if B and C, the Prolog homunculus will set up two new sub-goals, B and C, and attempt to prove them. But equally, if it encountered something of the form A if A, the Prolog homunculus would set up the goal: prove A. A person would see that although a sentence of the form A if A is bound to be true, as a line of enquiry (to prove A, prove A) it leads in a circle. A person would not consider it further, but the Prolog homunculus would; if the program sends it into a loop, it will mechanically go round and round.   If a machine manifests a degree of intelligence, it is nevertheless due to the Prolog homunculus obediently and stupidly following where the program leads it. In short, if a logical analysis is to perform as a program, not only must it be correct, it must also guide the Prolog homunculus in the right way.

It is instructive to consider how the Prolog homunculus sets about proving something from a program. Consider our solar system program (p. 85). It is true to say that the Moon is a moon, i.e. that the particular heavenly body which we call **the_moon** falls under the general category of being a moon.   The program will entail the corresponding Prolog sentence:

moon(the_moon)

A moon we defined simply as anything which orbits a planet:

moon(X) :- orbits(X, Y), planet(Y) .

Instantiating the name **the_moon** for the variable **X** in this rule, two goals are set up: first find some Y such that **orbits(the_moon, Y)**, and then prove, for this value of Y, that **planet(Y)**. The proof of this is straightforward, because the first fact about orbiting in the program is **orbits(the_moon, the_earth)**, so the first value for **Y** Prolog finds is **the_earth**, and it can prove **planet(the_earth)**.

Compare what happens if we re-order the conjuncts in the antecedent of the rule:

moon(X) :- planet(Y), orbits(X, Y).

This says that X is a moon if you can find some planet which it orbits, and this has exactly the same logical content as the previous version. But procedurally it can make a difference, since it sets Prolog the tasks in a different order: first find a Y such that **planet(Y)**, and then prove **orbits(X, Y)**. In this case it will come to the same conclusion, but via a different path. Since the first **planet** sentence in the program is **planet(venus)**, **venus** is the first value it gets for **Y**, and so it will first try to prove **orbits(the_moon, venus)**. Since it cannot prove this, it tracks back and tries to find another Y such that **planet(Y)**. It is on this second attempt, when it successfully re-solves **planet(Y)** with **Y = the_earth**, that it has a value of Y with which it can prove **orbits(the_moon, Y)**.

　　　In order to comprehend and produce properly structured programs in Prolog, then, one needs to know how the Prolog homunculus reads a program in attempting to prove some fact. A program may contain one or more solutions to a query, but be so arranged that the homunculus will fail to find a solution immediately. Rather than give up straight away, it needs to check back and look for an alternative way of finding a solution. A rough analogy for this situation would be when you are lost in a maze. The maze may have several exits. Any exit constitutes a solution - to the problem of how to get out. A typical approach is to wander the maze at random, a strategy which is not guaranteed to succeed.   A better approach is to search the maze systematically. For instance: at each point at which you face a new choice, take the path on the left. If you come to a dead end (fail to find a solution), track back to the last point at which you faced a choice. If there is an unexplored path at that point, go down it, again keeping to the policy of choosing the leftmost path at any new choice. If there remains no unexplored path when you backtrack to an intersection, track further back until you do come to an intersection with an alternative you haven't explored - then go forwards again down that path. By searching the maze systematically, you are bound to find the exits (if it has any!)

　　　To program successfully in Prolog, one needs to understand how the Prolog homunculus tracks back and forth in just this way, in reading a program. You may like to try working through other examples with the solar system program, e.g. all solutions to the query: **heavenly_body(X)**. Consider what answers you think can be derived from the program, and how you scanned the program to arrive at them. Then consider it from the point of view of Prolog, undertaking a brute, mechanical search of the database. Finally, run the query on a machine, to see if Prolog generates solutions in the same order.

To make the procedure of **backtracking** as clear as possible, I want to work through an example which is relatively simple and symmetrical. Consider a program which will generate pairs of truth values. We need to tell it what the two truth values are, and that a pair is any combination of the two:

tv(t).
tv(f).
pair(X, Y) :- tv(X), tv(Y).

There are four ways of combining **t** and **f**, corresponding to the lines of a four line truth table. Set to find all solutions to the query **pair(X, Y)**, the program will generate all four combinations. Given this goal, the definition of **pair** sets up two sub-goals. Firstly: find an **X** such that **tv(X)**. Since **tv(t)** is the first **tv** fact in this program, **t** is the first value for **X**. Having found a solution to this goal, Prolog moves on to the second: find a **Y** such that **tv(Y)**. This is a separate goal, and Prolog once again finds **tv(t)** providing the first solution. With **X** and **Y** both assigned **t**, **pair(t, t)** is the first solution to the query.

Prolog will now start to backtrack, in the attempt to find alternative solutions to the main goal. The important point is that Prolog is indeed tracking *back*, i.e. it is reconsulting goals in reverse order. The last one to have been solved becomes the first one reconsidered. If we depict the path to the first solution like this:

$$Y = t \longrightarrow pair(t,\ t)$$

$$X = t \longrightarrow tv(Y)$$

$$pair(X, Y) \longrightarrow tv(X)$$

then Prolog tracks back to the last goal it solved, **tv(Y)**, and resolves it with the second **tv** fact, **tv(f)**:

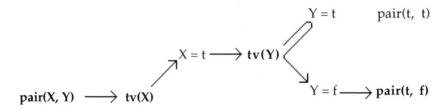

Y is assigned **f**, providing the second solution to the main goal: **pair(t, f)**. Having found this solution, Prolog backtracks again and tries to re-solve **tv(Y)**. Since there are no more facts about **tv** - i.e. no more truth values - this goal cannot be re-solved, so Prolog tracks back one further step and tries the goal before that, **tv(X)**. This of course can be re-solved, with **X = f**, so Prolog can move forwards and try **tv(Y)** again:

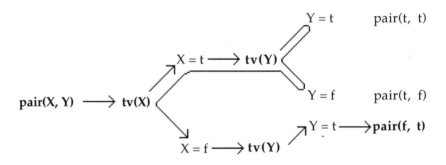

This is how backtracking proceeds. If Prolog fails to prove a goal, it tracks back to the preceding goal, if any. If it can prove a goal, it moves forward to the next one, if any. After producing the fourth solution, Prolog tries to re-solve **tv(Y)**, fails, and so tracks back and tries to resolve **tv(X)**. This too fails, so it tracks back to the goal **pair(X, Y)**:

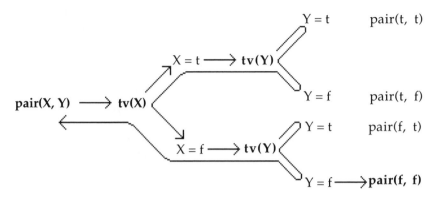

Since there are no further clauses to the definition of **pair**, there are no further ways of finding values for **X** and **Y,** so the query terminates at this point.

If we want to see more than just the solution printed out when Prolog has found it - if we want to see the way Prolog mechanically finds its way to a solution - we can use **spy** to examine the calls made to different predicates. We don't have to reconstruct 'by hand' all the inferential steps which Prolog goes through, we can get the machine to print them out as it goes along. Most implementations of computer languages provide some such facility for looking at the machine going through its steps. This is very useful in *debugging* a program - in trying to find out why it won't work. When a *spy point* is put on a predicate, every time Prolog calls up that predicate in attempting to answer a query, that call will be displayed. We can set as a query **spy(tv)**, to put a spy point on the **tv** predicate, and then ask the main query about pairs. The primitive **nospy** complements **spy**, allowing a spy point to be switched off.

In the execution of a Prolog program, there are four states relevant to the invocation of a particular goal. These four states are usually given the names: call, exit, fail and redo. These states or modes are displayed when a predicate is spied on. When a clause is initially invoked as a goal to be proved, it is *call*ed. If a solution for it can be found, Prolog *exits* from that goal, with any previously unassigned variables given values by that solution. If a solution for it cannot be found, the call *fails*; that particular path in the search for a solution has come to a dead end, and Prolog must re-trace its steps and look for a successful path. When Prolog backtracks and re-consults a clause for an alternative solution, the clause is in the *redo* mode. Type in this simple program, and observe the sequence of calls, exits, etc. by spying on both the predicates **pair** and **tv**.

3.2.2   Negation by failure

To know whether one person may safely receive a blood transfusion from another, it is necessary to determine whether their blood types are compatible. In 1900 Landsteiner discovered four main blood groups, which he termed A, B, AB and O.   Blood from one group may agglutinate - clump together - red blood cells in blood from another group. This table summarizes how the groups affect each other:

Blood from group	agglutinates	blood from groups	and is agglutinated by	blood from groups
a		b, ab		b, o
b		a, ab		a, o
ab		_		a, b, o
o		a, b, ab		_

Compared with the way these relationships can be described in Prolog, the table contains a certain amount of redundancy. If we capture the basic relationships one way round, e.g.

agglutinates(a, b) .
agglutinates(a, ab) .
agglutinates(b, a) .
agglutinates(b, ab) .
agglutinates(o, a) .
agglutinates(o, b) .
agglutinates(o, ab) .

we don't need to state explicitly all the instances of the other relationship - they can be inferred by a general rule:

is_agglutinated_by(X, Y) :- agglutinates(Y, X) .

In another respect, though, the table is just like Prolog. We tacitly assume about such listings of information that they are rounded off with a clause which says "And that's all".   In other words, anything not recorded about this situation is not true of it. This is sometimes described as the *closed world assumption*; here is a complete description of this (aspect of the) world, and anything not explicitly stated can be assumed not to be so. We read the table as saying that, for instance, group a does not agglutinate group o, by its *failing* to state that a agglutinates o. The closed world assumption enables us to produce a compact and efficient description of a situation. If we have a complete record of all the positive facts, then we don't need a separate listing of the negative facts - we can infer them by their absence. In classical logic, by contrast, if we are to reason validly about something's not being the case, we need an explicit statement of the form ¬S. The viewpoint of classical logic would insist that we clutter up the table with an extra column explicitly listing the blood groups which each group does not agglutinate. (Train timetables provide another example. You want to catch a train at 10 a.m. The timetable states that there are trains at 9 a.m. and 11 a.m. So, assuming the timetable is comprehensive (the closed world assumption), you infer there is no train at 10. A timetable which listed every minute (second? millisecond?) that a train does not depart would not be very practical.)

In Prolog, negation works by failure, in two ways. Firstly, you can use the negation sign **not** in queries and in the antecedents of conditionals to check if something is not the case. A test of the form **not** S will succeed when Prolog *fails* to prove the embedded goal S. If we set the negative query:

?-   **not agglutinates(a, o)**

i.e. "Does blood group a not agglutinate group o?", Prolog correctly responds affirmatively, because it fails to prove **agglutinates(a, o)** from the program. In other words, it answers this query **YES** for the very same reason that it answers the plain query

?-   **agglutinates(a, o)**

in the negative, because the latter can't be proved from the program. The second respect in which negation works by failure is that you cannot use **not** to state positively or prove in a program that something is not so. For example, you cannot assert that **not agglutinates(a, o)** in a program even if you wanted to. To secure the effect of **not** S, you must rely on failure to state S - in this instance, you must rely on the omission of **agglutinates(a, o)**. Similarly, you cannot have a rule with a consequent of the form **not** S - which again, would enable you to prove positively that something is not so.

In any blood transfusion, the quantity of blood from the donor will be far less than the quantity already in the recipient. Because of this, what matters is not the agglutination of the recipient's blood by the donor's - the dilution makes this effect negligible - but the possibility of the donated blood being agglutinated by the recipient's blood. This means that we can draw up another table:

Persons of blood type	can donate to	Persons of blood types
a		a, ab
b		b, ab
ab		ab
o		a, b, ab, o

As with **is_agglutinated_by**, we don't need to state these as separate facts in the program, we can state a general rule which will entail them. Suppose we have some medical records which show a patient's blood group:

type(jones, b) .
type(smith, o) .

Then the fundamental rule for blood transfusions is that one person can donate to another if the recipient's blood does not agglutinate the donor's:

can_donate_to(Donor, Recipient) :- type(Donor, X),
                                type(Recipient, Y),
                                not agglutinates(Y, X) .

Here we use negation in the antecedent of the rule, to check that a certain condition does not hold. The program will correctly infer that Jones cannot donate to Smith, but that Smith can donate to Jones.

There is one aspect of negation by failure which requires careful handling: one should generally avoid having unassigned variables within the scope of **not**. That is, it is quite acceptable to have variables within some negated condition in the antecedent of a rule, but one should ensure that those variables will have been assigned values by the time that Prolog comes to evaluate that condition. This is as things are in the above rule: the two **type** goals ensure that the variables **X** and **Y** will be instantiated to blood groups by the time Prolog comes to check whether **not agglutinates(Y, X)**. Let us compare what happens when this constraint is not respected. Suppose that in addition to the predicate **can_donate_to**, which expresses a relation between people, we also want to define a relation **transfusable**, which holds between blood groups. The preceding table summarizes this relationship - group a is transfusable into groups a, ab, etc. But the following rule, although it captures the essential relationship - X is transfusable into Y provided Y does not agglutinate it - will not generate instances of the relation:

transfusable(X, Y) :- not agglutinates(Y, X) .

Consider what happens if we set this predicate the task of generating pairs of suitable blood groups, with the query:

?-   transfusable(X, Y)

The rule sets Prolog to prove the goal **not agglutinates(Y, X)**, and this in turn sets Prolog to check whether the embedded goal fails. Now Prolog is checking whether **agglutinates(Y, X)**, but this goal *succeeds* - it matches with the first **agglutinates** fact, with **Y = a** and **X = b**. If the embedded goal S succeeds, the negated goal **not** S fails - and Prolog will exit the rule wrongly concluding that no blood group is transfusable into another. The general point here is that a condition of the form **not** R(x, y) cannot be used to *generate* examples of x and y which do not stand in the relation R. If R is defined for any cases at all, the goal R(x, y) will match with the first pair of things it can find which do stand in that relationship, and the negation of that goal will fail.

We can still use this rule to *test* whether blood of one group is transfusable into blood of another group. If we supply definite values - if the query is, for example,

?-   transfusable(o, a)

the answer will be affirmative. For now Prolog will try to prove **not agglutinates(a, o)**, which in turn sends it to check **agglutinates(a, o)**. Since it fails to prove the latter, negation-as-failure can now work properly: the **not** goal succeeds, and thus does the query as a whole. This may suggest how the rule can be modified to generate examples - we need to adopt a policy of generate-and-test. If we define all the blood groups, with **group(a)** and the rest, we can use **group** to generate values for the variables, which the **not** condition can then test:

transfusable(X, Y) :- group(X),
                          group(Y),
                          not agglutinates(Y, X) .

Asking for all solutions to **transfusable(X, Y)** will now generate the correct nine pairs. In fact, the pattern of backtracking Prolog will go through in the process will be a generalization of that considered in the previous sub-section. Whereas **tv** generates two values, each **group** goal can generate four solutions, so the number of possible pairs of groups will be $4 \times 4 = 16$. The **not** condition will weed out from these the seven pairs which do agglutinate.

    To summarize negation-by-failure in conclusion. **NO** in Prolog means "No, I can't prove this from the information I have" (and not: "No, I can definitely prove that this is not the case.") On the closed world assumption, this leads to an efficient means of recording what is and is not the case, for it means that we can avoid taking up space by explicitly stating what is not. But it does mean that caution should be exercised to avoid having unassigned variables within the scope of **not**. Consider this in the simplest possible case, a one-line program such as:

loves(john, mary) .

Normally, a goal with unassigned variables in it is existential in force. The goal

1)   ?-   **loves(X, Y)**

can be read as: do there exist X and Y such that X loves Y? If we represent the logical form of a query as the application of an operator '?' ('Do you know whether') to a sentence, then this can be formalized: ? $(\exists x)(\exists y)$ loves(x, y). But

2)   ?-   **not loves(X, Y)**

does not read: are there X and Y which do not stand in that relationship, i.e. ? $(\exists x)(\exists y) \neg$ loves(x, y). The negation-as-failure takes wider scope: ? $\neg (\exists x)(\exists y)$loves(x, y), i.e. are there no x and y which stand in that relationship? To see this we need only trace the steps which Prolog takes. Whereas a positive query like 1) has positive facts to match against, with negation by failure a query such as 2) does not have records of negative facts (e.g. **not loves(mary, john)**) to look up. Instead, to check if 2) succeeds, Prolog checks whether 1) fails, i.e. the 'do there exist' question 1) is asked "within the context" of negation: is it not the case that there exist X and Y such that **loves(X, Y)**? Because Prolog can find instances of **loves**, 1) succeeds and so 2) fails. (If Prolog cannot find any instances of the relation, then from its point of view the predicate is undefined, and it is likely that evaluation of the goal would generate an error message.)

3.2.3 Locating errors

Errors can creep into any program in a variety of ways. Some errors are *syntactic* - caused, for example, by typing an expression in the wrong way. This kind of mistake is relatively easy to track down and rectify, and some common examples are discussed below. Some errors are *semantic* or logical, i.e. they concern the content of the program. If a programmer is simply mistaken about the definition of some predicate P, the definition may wrongly classify some things as P which aren't, or fail to classify some things as P which are. There is nothing specially computational about a semantic error. Anyone can make a mistake about the definition of a word, and there can be no general recipe for identifying them. If the definition is embodied in a program, the error may become apparent as soon as it is run - but it might also lie hidden for a long time.

   Some programming errors are *pragmatic* - a definition may be syntactically and semantically correct, yet the way it is put together may make it worthless as a program. The pragmatic error of negation by failure operating with uninstantiated variables was discussed above. For another example, consider the relation of being married. Suppose the program knows some instances of this relation, say:

married(john, mary) .

Since this is a symmetric relation, it is also true that **married(mary, john)**. It is logically quite correct to capture this symmetry in a generalization:

married(X, Y) :- married(Y, X) .

But procedurally this rule may send the machine into a loop. Prolog might be asked about a couple it doesn't know about, say 'Is Peter married to Jane?'. The rule will set Prolog to prove this by proving **married(jane, peter)**, which in turn will set it to prove **married(peter, jane)**. Since this is exactly the problem it started with, it will continue going round in a loop. One way to avoid this particular pragmatic error is to use two predicates. One records the basic relationships, but is not symmetric, e.g.

wedded(john, mary) .

The other predicate, which we want to be symmetric, is defined in terms of it:

married(X, Y) :- wedded(X, Y) .
married(Y, X) :- wedded(X, Y) .

This avoids the need to state all the particular relationships twice over, **wedded(mary, john)** as well as **wedded(john, mary)**. And it captures the symmetry of the main predicate in a general rule, without generating loops. Generally speaking, the more familiar one becomes with a programming language, and the way its programs are controlled, the easier it becomes to avoid this sort of error.

At the most trivial level, a syntactic error will make the program ungrammatical as far as Prolog is concerned, and it will not be accepted when you try to compile it, e.g. when running a query. Here are a number of simple checks for this kind of error:

i)   Do all the arguments of a predicate (names and variables) follow it, enclosed in round brackets? If a predicate has more than one argument place, is each argument separated from the next by a comma?

ii)   Do all the brackets balance - is every left bracket matched by a right bracket? Is there a full stop after each atomic sentence? Is there a full stop at the end of each conditional sentence (and only at the end)?

iii)   Is there exactly one clause in the head of each conditional, i.e. one clause to the left of the :- connective? If there is more than one clause in the body of a conditional (i.e. to the right of :-), are they separated with either a comma (conjunction) or semi-colon (disjunction)?

If a program is basically correct in its syntax, it can be read into the memory of the computer and you can run queries. But there may still be trivial typing errors which make it incorrect. Here are some common errors of this kind.

iv)   Mis-spelling a predicate or a name. Suppose that a number of facts have been stated using the predicate **planet**; but the rule is mis-typed as

moon(X) :- plant(Y), orbits(X, Y) .

The program will not be able to infer that anything is a moon, since this rule does not connect up with any facts about *planets*. Indeed, if the program knows nothing about **plant** an error message may occur, reporting that that predicate is not defined. Alternatively, the spelling error might occur in one of the particular facts . A symptom of this would be that the rule works in most cases - only the sentence with the error failing to mesh with the other inferences. The same problem would occur if the predicate was mis-spelt in the consequent of a rule.

v)   Mis-spelling a variable. Suppose the expression **list** was written in a rule, where **List** was intended, or x instead of **X**. In other words, a constant was written where a variable should have appeared. Or if the syntax forms variables by prefixing an underscore, a space entered between underscore and word, as e.g. _ **list**, would again mean that no variable appears. A constant appearing in place of a variable will prevent the rule it occurs in from functioning properly as a generalization. Alternatively, if different occurrences of what is intended as the same variable are spelt differently - with, say **List** and **LIst** - this will have the converse effect of making the rule over-general, lacking the appropriate inter-connections. Even though they differ only in that the second 'i' has been made a capital, these will be treated as distinct expressions, and therefore distinct variables.

vi)   The converse of the preceding mistake is to mis-spell a predicate (or a name) by starting it with a capital letter, e.g. **Planet**, thus making it a variable. Since Prolog re-names all variables (e.g. with underscore plus number), if it encountered **Planet(the_earth)** it might come back with an error message reporting **_1148(the_earth)**.

vii)   Not giving a predicate the right number of arguments. Suppose for example that **father** is used as a two place predicate, as in **father(adam, cain)**, and that a certain rule needs to check for individuals X who are fathers. A natural mistake would be to write this as a one place predicate, **father(X)**, which will fail to match with any of the relational facts, rather than as a two place predicate, **father(X, _)**. See also the discussion of **person** in the next section.

To locate these and other errors, we need to take full advantage of the fact that we are *programming* in logic - that we can test out a logical analysis by running it as a program. By posing test queries we can quickly get an idea of whether the program entails the sorts of conclusions we want it to. Sometimes the program will surprise us with a solution which we had not foreseen, and the mistake will be ours, not the program's. More often, though, the source of the discrepancy will be in the program. Once you are sure that the problem lies in the program, use the **spy** relation to zoom in on the predicates which are likely to be at fault. If a predicate does not hold of the cases intended, **spy** on the predicates used to define it - and, if necessary, **spy** on the predicates used in *their* definitions. Spy on the predefined predicates used - it's not that you will discover a mistake in their definition, but you may discover that your program is invoking them in the wrong way. By using spy points, you might locate a fail where there should be success, and by examining the way the goal failed, you should be able to get an idea of where the definition has gone wrong. Alternatively, **spy**ing might reveal that the program is going into a loop, by showing that exactly the same goal is being repeatedly called.

In the previous section we noted that if the syntax of the Prolog you are using allows variables to be more than just **X**s and **Y**s, it can aid the clarity of your program to make them mnemonic - to change **X** to **List**, say. This does *nothing* to the content of the program, its sole purpose is to make the role of that variable clearer to someone reading the program. With simple programs it may seem unnecessary, but in more complex programs, with predicates of several arguments, it can greatly enhance their intelligibility. Another way to enhance the intelligibility of a program, without affecting its logical content, is to add *comments* to it. Comments can be any sequence of expressions, so long as they are enclosed within the appropriate markers, such as /* and */. These act somewhat like quotation marks; they isolate any text they contain from the main program, and so mark the beginning and end of material which is to be ignored by Prolog. Thus I might add after the definition of **moon**, in the solar system program, an explanatory comment such as

/* **X is a moon if it orbits a planet.** */

Each /* must be paired with a */, and Prolog will ignore everything that is in between. So there are no syntactic constraints on what you write between two comment markers. Comments can be inserted at any point in a program.

Exercise 2

Imagine a grid on which objects can be placed. We can suppose that the grid is very large, or even limitless, i.e. stretches beyond the small segment shown here. We can also suppose that different arrangements of objects are to be found on this grid at different times. (These objects could be, for instance, the dots which make up an image on a computer screen - the picture elements, or *pixels*.) Consider this configuration of objects a, b, c, ...

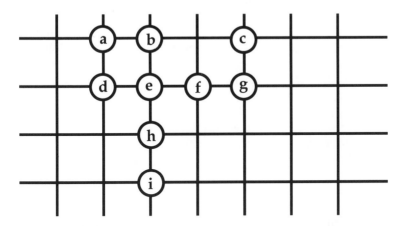

The problem is to convert this spatial representation into a description. At the moment we have a representation in which the spatial relations on the page represent the real spatial relations between the objects on the grid - just as a map represents a particular area of land. We want to convert it into a *description* of those relations - a Prolog program, a database of facts and rules which Prolog can use, to make inferences and answer questions about the objects on the grid. Note that there are essentially two ways to go about this problem. One way is to adopt a system of Cartesian co-ordinates, i.e. to stake out the positions of the objects using a system of numbers. Since we have not yet looked at arithmetic within Prolog, this is *not* the approach to consider at the moment. The way to go about it is to describe the positions of the objects *relative to each other*. No numbers are required.

Naturally, we would like the program to be both efficient and flexible. This means that if, say, a new object is placed on the grid, we can express its position relative to the objects we know about with the minimum effort. If, for example, we know that one object is to the left of another, we don't need a further particular fact that the latter is to the right of the former - we should be able to infer that by a general rule.

Your program must be able to answer the following kinds of questions:

1)   Whether one object is immediately to the left or immediately to the right of another, immediately above or immediately below another.

Take the problem a step at a time, and only go on to part 2) when you have succeeded with this part. First work out on paper what you think an efficient representation of the problem would be - the minimum of particular facts, together with the appropriate generalizations. Then type it in and try it out - does it give all the correct answers, and only correct answers? If it gives more answers than you expected, who is right - you, or the program?

2)   Whether one object is immediately between two others, in either a horizontal or vertical direction. Check the answers to the questions: Is f between e and g? Is f between g and e? Is h between i and e?

Note that your program should be able to answer any of these questions almost instantaneously. If it doesn't, there is probably something wrong with it. Use the key sequence which in your implementation interrupts or breaks the execution of Prolog, then try to locate the error by using **spy**.

3)   Whether one object is directly next to another in a diagonal direction.

Only try this part of the problem after you are satisfied with the program's answers to 1) and 2). Make sure that it gets the answer right both to 'Is a directly diagonal to e?' and to 'Is e directly diagonal to a?'. Can your program tell 'f is directly diagonal to b'? If so, can it tell 'b is directly diagonal to f'?

3.3   Structuring information

3.3.1 Advice on nutrition

A recurrent theme in Artificial Intelligence is the question of finding the optimum framework for representing some domain of knowledge. This section will explore some of these issues, in the course of developing a couple of database programs. A train timetable is an example of a database - a source of information about the domain it concerns, train times, in which that information has been arranged systematically (departures arranged in chronological order, destinations arranged in spatial sequence, etc.) A person who has access to a timetable can perform *intelligent retrieval* from it. Two features in particular mark out the intelligent use of a database. Firstly, the person can perform inferences with the information. That is, not only can they read off the explicitly recorded values - the train which departs at t_1 arrives at d at t_2, and so on - they can also bring general principles to bear to make comparisons and inferences with those values: whether one train takes longer than another, which train one must catch if one wants to be in a certain destination at a certain time, and so on. The second feature is that a person provides a flexible interface to the database. You don't have to access the data in a set format - in ordinary language, you can ask for the same information in many different ways. Both of these features of intelligent retrieval can be provided in Prolog; in this section, we shall be concerned with the former.

The first example is intended to demonstrate how easy it can be to capture an expert's knowledge, in a Prolog program capable of delivering realistic advice. The area of expertise is nutrition. As a basic minimum, a nutritionist needs to know three sorts of facts. i) A description of the medical condition of the people seeking dietary advice. ii) Medical knowledge which relates certain conditions with particular vitamin and mineral needs, for example,

a)   Pregnant women need Folic Acid.
b)   If you have a cold, you should get extra vitamin C.
c)   People who are anaemic need Iron.
d)   Vitamin D is required for the absorption of calcium from the diet.

iii) Nutritional knowledge which tells you in which foods you can find the required vitamins. By encoding this information, the program will be able to infer specific nutritional advice for individual patients.

We can start with the first kind of fact, developing a small database about the condition of some people. Consider the information contained in a simple sentence of English:

1)   Mary is pregnant.

(For brevity, I use first names - a realistic database would have to have the full name.) This would normally be formalized as

2)   **pregnant(mary) .**

It should be emphasized that, modulo conventions of syntax, this is the normal style of representation for 1) within first order logic and Prolog, and should be chosen unless considerations intervene to favour some alternative. Its nearest rival would be something along these lines:

3)   **is(mary, pregnant) .**

This says that the relation **is** holds between Mary and the thing named as **pregnant**. What thing is that? There are two obvious candidates. It might name the class or set of pregnant people, in which case **is** is essentially the relation of set membership, $\in$. Or it might name the property *being pregnant*, or *pregnancy*, in which case **is** is the relation of instantiation or participation. Suppose for the moment that it is the latter. Then 3) construes 1) as the explicit statement that Mary instantiates the attribute *pregnancy*. It treats a property as a named entity of the same order as the individual Mary. As such it involves the philosophically suspect attitude of *reification* of universals. (Here is Mary the individual; where is pregnancy, or having-a-cold-ness, or anaemia?)

    If we are prepared to name a property, as in **pregnant**, it means that we admit such things within our *ontology* - our account of what really exists, our repository of genuine entities. If names are introduced for entities of a certain sort, those names can be replaced by variables - thus making possible quantification over things of that sort. (According to Quine, this is the ultimate test of ontological commitment: to be is to be the value of a variable.) Using variables may be an advantage if we want, for example, a quick way of finding out what properties we know of Mary:

?-   **is(mary, X)**

may return X = **pregnant**, X = **rhesus_negative**, X = **vegetarian**, etc. It also means that we can form higher-order predications of these names, e.g. **vegetarian**:

special_diet(vegetarian) .

(which can be read as saying that the property of being vegetarian has the property of being a special dietary type). This enables the direct formulation of the higher-order question "What special dietary type (if any) is Mary?":

?-   is(mary, X), special_diet(X)

So by treating universal types as particular entities, we may quantify over them, and use variables to link predications about them.

Another advantage of this approach is that it enables the database to be systematized under a single relation, **is**. If one is motivated more by a pragmatic concern with what works best, rather than philosophical scruples about legitimate ontology, one may continue the process of reifying higher orders of properties and relations:

4)   has(mary, special_diet, vegetarian) .
          has(mary, rhesus_factor, rhesus_negative) .

and so on. Notice that in this series of increasing extravagance, 2), 3), 4), we still need a predicate at each stage to bind the elements together into a complete proposition. We could say that 4) treats the fact which 1) concerns as the combination of three elements: the individual Mary, the type **vegetarian**, and the type of types **special_diet**. This scheme reifies properties of properties (or sets of sets).

The value in this increase in complexity of the representation lies primarily in its potential for systematizing the expression of knowledge, by distinguishing property types and particular instances of those types. This kind of categorization can be found in *frame theory*. Frame theory is an approach developed within A.I. for systematically representing the knowledge which is contained within our ordinary concepts. The frame for a given concept consists of a number of *slots*, property types, which will be filled by the appropriate properties. The slots for the concept *patient* might include name, sex, age, blood group, special diet, occupation, medication, and so on. That is to say, a doctor might ordinarily think of any particular patient as exemplifying all these features. Ordinary properties, such as being female, being 30 years old, etc., become values for such slots.

Returning to the task of developing a database for our nutritionist, we can stay with the simplest form of records, such as 2) above. Where we need to note specific instances of a vitamin deficiencies, we need a binary relation, as in

deficient_in(fred, vitamin_A) .

since deficiency is a relation between an individual and a particular kind of vitamin. Turning now to the second sort of fact, the simple medical rules, we need to put them into a common format. Essentially, they all define a relation **needs(Person, Nutrient)**, so what is required is to regiment them into a common, conditional form. For instance, a) can be re-written

a)   A person needs folic acid if that person is pregnant.

and thence into Prolog:

needs(X, folic_acid) :- pregnant(X) .

Rule d) relates one kind of need with another:

needs(X, vitamin_D) :- needs(X, calcium) .

and thus might be called upon when a rule such as this is invoked:

needs(X, calcium) :- has_rickets(X) .

We must also relate need with deficiency:

needs(X, Y) :- deficient_in(X, Y) .

(Strictly, then, **deficient_in** is redundant, but it is included for clarity.)
        We come now to the third body of knowledge - the foods in which you find the different vitamins, minerals and trace elements. Again, this involves what is essentially a binary relation - you can find a certain kind of vitamin in a certain kind of food, e.g.

found_in(vitamin_A, carrots) .

By grouping food types under the taxonomic categories of the nutritionist, such as **oily_fish, pulse, green_leafy_veg**, we can capture significant generalizations, for instance:

found_in(vitamin_A, X) :- oily_fish(X) .

Such generalizations require supplementation by the appropriate classifications oily_fish(mackerel) .

and so on. Thus **mackerel, carrots,** etc. are names of *types* of food, and
oily_fish(X) is a predicate which is true or false of such food types. A
representative listing of the program is given below.

pregnant(mary) .
pregnant(jane) .
has_cold(john) .
anaemic(jo) .
has_rickets(jim) .
deficient_in(fred, vitamin_A) .

found_in(vitamin_A, carrots) .
found_in(vitamin_A, X) :- oily_fish(X) .
found_in(vitamin_A, X) :- green_leafy_veg(X) .
found_in(folic_acid, oranges) .
found_in(folic_acid, X) :- pulse(X) .
found_in(folic_acid, X) :- green_leafy_veg(X) .
found_in(vitamin_C, oranges) .
found_in(vitamin_D, X) :- oily_fish(X) .
found_in(vitamin_D, eggs) .
found_in(vitamin_E, X) :- green_leafy_veg(X) .
found_in(calcium, X) :- pulse(X) .
found_in(iron, spinach) .
green_leafy_veg(lettuce) .
green_leafy_veg(kale) .
green_leafy_veg(parsley) .
pulse(lentils) .
pulse(red_kidney_beans) .
pulse(chick_peas) .
oily_fish(mackerel) .
oily_fish(sardines) .
oily_fish(herring) .

needs(X, folic_acid) :- pregnant(X) .
needs(X, vitamin_C) :- has_cold(X) .
needs(X, iron) :- anaemic(X) .
needs(X, Y) :- deficient_in(X, Y) .
needs(X, calcium) :- has_rickets(X) .
needs(X, vitamin_D) :- needs(X, calcium) .

```
should_eat(Person, Food) :-  needs(Person, Nutrient),
                             found_in(Nutrient, Food) .
```

The program ends with the definition of the main predicate **should_eat**, which connects together the medical and nutritional. It should be noted that there are a number of respects in which the knowledge representation in this program could be improved. Important aspects of nutrition have been ignored - dietary fibre, fat and calorie content. It is non-quantitative - it only lists the best sources of particular nutrients, without stating the quantity contained in a given portion. It ignores such factors as the effect of preparation on loss of vitamins. One possible improvement - to check that the food recommended is not something the person should not eat - is left as an exercise.

3.3.2   The dating database

In this section we shall develop a simplified version of a program which could be used by a dating agency, i.e. to match people who would be suited to each other. Suppose the basic data about each client are to be their sex (m or f), build (large, medium or small), how they regard their personality (shy or extrovert), and age. Since we haven't yet looked at arithmetic in Prolog, we won't record age in years, but simply use three categories - young, mature, and old. How might we record this basic information? As in the previous example, we might record our basic facts using one place predicates - **m(john), young(mary)**, etc. However, in this case it will be convenient to adopt the alternative, relating together all the properties pertaining to each person. In tabular form:

Name	Sex	Build	Character	Age
John	m	large	shy	mature
Mary	f	medium	extrovert	young
:	:	:	:	:

We see the shift in logical grammar described above: a general category such as **young** is now labelled by a name, rather than being expressed through a predicate. To bind five items of information together, we need a five place predicate, as in:

person(john, m, large, shy, mature).

A considerable advantage of this format is that it allows the easy formulation of general rules employing variables over such property types.

   One way for the agency to find out who suits whom would be by asking its clients if they have any preferences about the sort of person they would like to date. So we shall give a general definition of **suits(B, A)**, meaning that B suits A - to be inferred from the preferences of **A**. Note that we shall not make **suits** a symmetrical relation: if B suits A, it will not necessarily follow that A suits B! We will record preferences using a four place predicate **prefers**, which will relate each individual to the sort of person they would like to meet: build, personality and age. An individual with very specific preferences might have a record such as this:

prefers(mary, large, extrovert, young).

Assuming our agency is only concerned with matching people of opposite sex, we do not also need to keep an individual record of each person's preference to meet someone of the opposite sex; this can be built into the general definition of **suits**. (The assumption could be relaxed by adding a fifth argument place to **prefers**. The point is simply that for each dimension of preference along which the agency acknowledges that individuals may vary, **prefers** will need an argument place to record that parameter.)

   We define 'B suits A' to hold when A is a person of sex X, and has such and such preferences, and B is a person not of the same sex as A, who meets these criteria. This definition can be written:

suits(B, A) :- person(A, X, _, _, _),
               prefers(A, Build, Char, Age),
               person(B, Y, Build, Char, Age),
               not(X = Y) .

The important thing is to follow the pattern of variables within this definition. We are concerned to define B's being someone who suits A; that is, we are essentially concerned with B's **person**al details, not A's. The only information from B's **person** record we need is their sex. We don't need to know the last three arguments in it. But this does not mean we can simply write **person(A, X)**. **person** is a five place predicate, and must always figure as such, even when we don't care about some of the arguments. If we tried to write **person**, in the rule, as a predicate with two arguments, it wouldn't match the fact with five arguments in the database, and the rule would be bound to fail. We need to fill out **person** in the rule to five places - the last three places occupied by variables we don't care about. We could just use three variables which don't figure anywhere else in the definition, e.g. **C, D, E**. But Edinburgh Prolog allows another device, the anonymous or 'don't care' variable, which is just an underscore on its own, **_**. The underscore simply acts as a filler. Except for its syntactic role in filling out a predicate to the right number of argument places, the 'don't care' variable is wholly ignored. In particular, two or more occurrences of it in the same sentence are not linked to each other - they do not have to agree on having the same value, as two or more occurrences of a real variable, like **X**, require. This is precisely what is important about the double occurrences of **Build, Char** and **Age**. For example, the first occurrence of **Age** pulls out from B's preferences the sort of age which B prefers, and the second occurrence checks to see whether A is a person of that age.

One of the most important uses of negation is in expressing non-identity. Distinct variables can take the same thing as their value, so if we wish to ensure that they take distinct things as values we have to say so explicitly - by adding a condition such as **not(X = Y)** in the above rule. (That is, whereas using the same variable twice, as in **likes(X, X)**, ensures that the arguments must be the same, using distinct variables does not in itself guarantee that the arguments will be distinct. **likes(john, john)** is an acceptable instance of **likes(X, Y)**.) Distinctness is such an important condition that Edinburgh Prolog approximates the usual drawing of a line through the identity sign, ≠, with the combination **\=**. We can write **X \= Y** in place of **not(X = Y)**. In fact, the use of distinctness in the present context is slightly inefficient. Given that we cannot have an unassigned variable in the scope of negation (for the reasons explained in section 3.2.2), we have to put the condition **not(X = Y)** (or **X \= Y**) after the condition **person(B, Y, Build, Char, Age)**, to ensure that **Y** has been assigned its value from Bs person record, before it is checked that it is not the same as the value of **X**. On this way of doing things, Prolog will have to keep checking through **person** records - many of which will be irrelevant, since they will be for people of the same sex as A. It would be more efficient to generate the opposite of A's sex first, and then only check for Xs of that opposite sex. We need only note that male and female are opposites:

opp(m, f).
opp(f, m).

Since there are only two possible values for **X** and **Y**, these two facts enable us to do what cannot be done with **not(X = Y)** - to take the value of **X**, and generate for **Y** the other value. We can thus organize **suits** to search the database more efficiently:

suits(B, A) :- person(A, X, _, _, _),
**   prefers(A, Build, Char, Age),**
**   opp(X, Y),**
**   person(B, Y, Build, Char, Age) .**

What if someone is indifferent about some of the categories of preference? Suppose John is less discriminating than Mary. He would prefer not to date with an older woman, would prefer her to be small or medium, and has no preference at all about personality. Since he is totally indifferent about character, we can fill that argument place with the anonymous variable. We can accommodate the other preferences - or lack of them - by making his **prefers** record suitably conditional. We specify his indifference to build and age disjunctively:

prefers(john, X, _, Y) :- (X = small; X = medium),
**   (Y = young; Y = mature) .**

(Note that the disjunction **(Y = young; Y = mature)** is used, rather than **Y \= old**, because of the need to generate a value for **Y**. Given the way in which **prefers** is consulted in the **suits** rule, we need to generate a value for **Age**; the condition **Y \= old** again raises the problem of an unassigned variable within the scope of a negation.)

Let us consider another basis for arranging matches. This is to find out each person's tastes and likes, in a number of basic categories of interests and activities - let us say music (classical, jazz, pop), sport (swimming, jogging, tennis) and recreation (cinema, travel, reading). We shall operate on the simple assumption that people with shared tastes will make a good match. A different agency could of course operate on a different principle, e.g. that opposites attract. Our database expands with **likes** information, linking each person with their tastes in the three categories:

likes(john, jazz, swimming, cinema).

What if someone likes more than one item in each category - e.g. if Mary likes both classical music and jazz? One way to handle this would be to record two likes facts in the database:

likes(mary, classical, swimming, travel).
likes(mary, jazz, swimming, travel).

This approach is likely to involve a lot of repetition. If Mary also counts going to the cinema as one of her recreations, we have to reduplicate these two facts with **cinema** replacing **travel**. An alternative is, therefore, to do as we did with **prefers**, and to state her likes as a generalization, using variables where necessary:

likes(mary, X, Y, Z) :- (X = classical; X = jazz),
**   Y = swimming,**
**   (Z = travel; Z = cinema).**

We shall now say that two people **match** if they are of the opposite sex, and share the same likes:

match(A, B) :- person(A, X, _, _, _),
**   likes(A, Music, Sport, Rec),**
**   opp(X, Y),**
**   person(B, Y, _, _, _),**
**   likes(B, Music, Sport, Rec).**

Notice that **match** will succeed provided we can find *some* range of interests on which the two coincide; they do not have to like all the same things in each category. Thus, assuming we have the fact about John and the rule about Mary above, they will match, because they have this range of interests in common: jazz, swimming, cinema. The fact that they do not have exactly the same tastes in e.g. music does not preclude this.

    match, unlike **suits**, is reciprocal: X matches Y if, and only if, Y matches X. We can imagine the agency doing various sorts of trawl through its database, with differing degrees of suitability. The ideal pairing - under the assumptions we have been making - is when two people match, and each suits the other:

ideal(A, B) :- match(A, B),
**   suits(A, B),**
**   suits(B, A).**

Exercise 3

A.   Add to the 'Seaview' program (exercise 3.1 A) the information that Manuel serves all those guests or staff who do not serve themselves. What do you think will happen if you ask: does Manuel serve himself? (Compare exercise 4.5 C.) Before you ask the question, **spy** on the **serves** relation. What happens?

B.   The royal house of Mycenae (exercise 3.1 B): Agamemnon and Clytaemnestra had another daughter, Electra. Add this information, and define the relation **sister_of**. Use negation to ensure that the program does not entail, e.g. **sister_of(electra, electra)**. Add a comment explaining your definition in English. Define the 2 place relation **aunt** (there are two cases to consider).

C.   Extend the nutritional advice program to include a check that the food suggested is not **prohibited** for the person. Examples of prohibitions include: people with allergies to specific foods; for diabetics: sugary foods; and for vegetarians: any fish or meat. Add whatever modifications are necessary to demonstrate that the program does now restrict its advice on food, for the relevant people.

3.4 Lists

3.4.1 A simple grammar

Lists are a fundamental kind of *data structure* in AI programming languages (Prolog, Lisp, Pop, etc.). They provide a very flexible structure in which to hold and manipulate items of data. Lists are quite literally lists of items, like shopping lists, but which are individuated according to strict principles. As far as shopping goes, we would treat the list [bread, wine, fishes] as essentially the same as [wine, bread, fishes]. But as lists in a programming language they are distinct, because they order their items in different ways. For X to be the same list as Y, not only must they mention the same items the same number of times, but they must also list them in the same order. The great advantage of lists is their flexibility - it is easy to change a list by adding something to it, or extracting items from it, chopping it up or appending another to it, and so on.

   An example of their usefulness in Artificial Intelligence is in the processing of human languages. One of the principal objectives of

AI is to produce machines which can process ordinary discourse - for example, to extract semantic information from sentences in English, and to respond to questions with appropriate answers. The processing and generation of sentences requires the program to incorporate an account of the syntax of the language - to pick out all and only the grammatically well-formed sentences of the language, and thus to contain what amounts to a definition of a predicate **sentence**. But sentences come in varying sizes - to take two simple examples:

1)   John walks.
2)   Every man loves a woman.

Both these sentences are of the form Noun Phrase ('John', and 'Every man') followed by Verb Phrase ('walks', and 'loves a woman'). Not only are the sentences of different lengths, but the component Noun Phrases and Verb Phrases are too. So the predicate **sentence** - and the corresponding predicates **noun_phrase** and **verb_phrase** - need to be able to accommodate sequences of words of different lengths. These predicates need to be flexible about the number of words in a phrase or sentence, and treating them as *lists* of words provides just this flexibility. Lists can be of any length, so if we define **sentence** as a predicate of lists, we can allow for sentences of any length.

The beginning of a list is marked by [, a left square bracket, and its end by]. Some versions of Prolog also allow round brackets. In the Edinburgh syntax of Prolog, each thing on a list must be separated from the next by a comma. Thus to say that 2) is a sentence we would write:

sentence([every, man, loves, a, woman])

The outer pair of round brackets are those required - as always - to enclose the argument of the predicate. It is important to realize that those brackets enclose a single thing, a list. In other words, we want to define a *one* place predicate **sentence(X)**, and to ensure that the variable **X** will take lists of words as its values.

Two of the most basic operations on lists are to **append** one list to another, and to find the things which are on a list, its **member**s. In many implementations of Prolog these predicates are predefined (or expressions which are equivalent, e.g. **on** rather than **member**.) In this section, I shall treat them as predefined, since one can start to use them without needing to know exactly what their definitions are. (If you need to define them, see section 5.1.1.) **member** can be illustrated by a query such as

?-   member(X, [john, is, a, man])

This will generate all those items X which are members of the list, and so generates four words as its solutions: **X = john, X = is, X = a** and **X = man**. Notice that the second argument of **on** must be a list. **append** is fundamental to the construction of a sentence list out of two shorter lists. For instance, we can construct the list **[john, walks]** by appending to **[john]** the list **[walks]**:

append([john], [walks], [john, walks])

More generally, **append(X, Y, Z)** holds just when Z is the list which results by joining lists X and Y, by adding the contents of Y to the back of X or, what comes to the same thing, adding the contents of X to the front of Y. A special list is the *empty* or *null* list which, as one would expect, is written as a list with nothing in it, **[]**. Adding the empty list to either the front or the back of a list results in just that list, i.e.

append([], [john, walks], [john, walks])
append([john, walks], [], [john, walks])

These three instances of the **append** relation show the three ways in which **[john, walks]** can be constructed by appending two lists together (the first of them being the one of interest from the point of view of grammar.) What amounts to the same thing, the three statements correspond to the three ways of *splitting* **[john, walks]** into two shorter lists. The query **append(X, Y, [john, walks])** asks for ways of splitting that list into two,

and it has the three pairs of solutions which correspond to these three **append** statements.
        We can now formulate our simple grammar as a Prolog program. The basic definition of a sentence is that it results by putting a Noun Phrase in front of a Verb Phrase:

```
sentence(S) :- noun_phrase(N),
                verb_phrase(V),
                append(N, V, S).
```

It is important to keep in mind that the variables **N**, **V** and **S** all range over lists of words. **append** wouldn't work if not; all three arguments of an **append** must be lists. The definition of **noun_phrase** will allow two sorts of noun phrases - both unstructured ones, proper names, and those which are structured like **[every, man]**. Linguists call quantifier words like 'every' and 'the' *determiners*; 'man' is a common noun.

```
noun_phrase(N) :- p_name(N).
noun_phrase(N) :- det(D),
                  c_noun(C),
                  append(D, C, N).
```

We shall assume that all the proper names we are dealing with are grammatically simple, like 'John', 'Mary', 'London', etc. But although they are unstructured, each name must go into the database as a *list* consisting of a single word:

p_name([john]).

and so on. This is one point at which we ensure that the variables of our grammar will only take lists as values. (If we omitted the list brackets and wrote **p_name(john)**, the definition of **sentence** would not be able to put together any sentences containing **john**, for the **append** goal would fail.) The same point applies to all the other basic lexical items such as, for instance, common nouns:

c_noun([man]).

This simple grammar will be completed by an account of verbs and verb phrases. As with noun phrases, we will allow for two sorts, unstructured and structured. A verb phrase can be an intransitive verb:

verb_phrase(V) :- intrans(V).

An intransitive verb combines with a subject but no object; thus **[john, walks]** is a sentence constructed by combining the noun phrase **[john]** with the intransitive verb **[walks]**. Alternatively, a verb phrase can be constructed by combining a transitive verb with its object:

```
verb_phrase(V) :- trans(T),
                  noun_phrase(N),
                  append(T, N, V).
```

Thus **[john, loves, a, woman]** results by forming the verb phrase **[loves, a, woman]**, and then appending it to **[john]**, as in the previous example. A complete version of this grammar is listed below.

```
sentence(List) :- noun_phrase(N),
                  verb_phrase(V),
                  append(N, V, List) .
noun_phrase(X) :- p_name(X) .
noun_phrase(List) :- det(D),
                     c_noun(C),
                     append(D, C, List).
verb_phrase(X) :- intrans(X) .
verb_phrase(List) :- trans(V),
                     noun_phrase(N) ,
                     append(V, N, List) .
det([the]) .
det([every]) .
det([a]) .
c_noun([man]) .
c_noun([woman]) .
c_noun([city]) .
c_noun([country]) .
intrans([walks]) .
intrans([exists]) .
trans([is]) .
trans([loves]) .
p_name([john]) .
p_name([mary]) .
p_name([london]) .
p_name([england]) .
```

We can now use the program to *check* the grammaticality of various lists of words, with queries such as

```
?-      verb_phrase([loves, every, woman])
?-      sentence([john, is, a, man])
```

We can also ask it to *generate* sentences, by just asking **sentence(X)**. The variety of solutions it can generate, and the order in which it does so, will depend on the variety of basic lexical items recorded, and the order in which they are listed. We can also ask, for example, for just the sentences known to the grammar which contain the word 'the' in them somewhere or other. We need to ask for all sentences **S**, on which the item **the** occurs:

?-   sentence(S), member(the, S)

In several ways this program is only a first approximation to a computational grammar for English. I shall briefly note three of its shortcomings. Firstly, the grammar itself is obviously very simplistic - not only in its small lexicon, but also in its structural rules, its rules of composition. You may be able to think of ways to enrich it, e.g. by adding adjectives (this is left as an exercise). Secondly, given a sentence, it only classifies the whole list as a sentence. It doesn't show why it is a sentence - it doesn't display it broken down on the basis of its structure into its constituents. A linguist would reasonably expect to be told not only that 'John loves Mary' is a sentence, but also to have it properly *parsed* - with its grammatical components properly identified as such, e.g by a tree structure or a labelled bracketing such as:

[Sentence [NP John] [VP [Intrans loves] [NP Mary]]]

A third point is that from a list processing point of view, although the use of **append** works, it is in some respects rather inefficient. But rather than explore these points in more detail here, I want to illustrate the use of lists to improve a program from the previous section.

3.4.2 Lists in a database

We shall now consider how lists might improve the database programs of section 3.3, starting with a brief look at the nutrition program. A natural thought is to use lists in specifying which foods contain which nutrients. There is a choice. Should we make a list of all the nutrients which a food contains:

contains(oranges, [folic_acid, vitamin_C]).
contains(X, [calcium, folic_acid, biotin]) :- pulse(X) .

or should we make a list of the foods where a given nutrient can be found - as in

found_in(iron, [lentils, liver, spinach]) .

The question is really the same as that facing a nutritionist drawing up a chart of information - should it be a chart indexed by foods, i.e. showing all the nutrients which each one contains, or should it be a chart of nutrients, listing the foods in which each can be found? The choice is to be answered by the same criterion in each case - which presentation would be more useful? If we want to approach this database with the question 'These are the foods I eat - how nutritional are they?', then the former version will be best. Look up the food, find the list of nutrients it contains. But if the question is 'I need this nutrient - from which foods can it be obtained?', the latter organization will provide the quickest lookup. The definition of **should_eat** works in this latter way. So if we alter all the **found_in** records to lists of foods, **should_eat** should become:

should_eat(Person, Food) :- needs(Person, Nutrient),
**   found_in(Nutrients, FoodList),**
**   member(Food, FoodList) .**

      The dating agency program requires more consideration - for instance, for the way in which the information about each individual's preferences is recorded. The drawback of these records, as they stand, will be particularly evident when the agency needs to update its knowledge base - to allow for modification in people's preferences and interests. Recall that Mary's preferences were recorded in a fact like this

prefers(mary, large, extrovert, young).

Suppose that she relaxes her preference for men of large build to medium or large. This will necessitate a fairly radical revision in the form of this record - from this atomic sentence to a conditional,

prefers(mary, X, extrovert, young) :- X = medium; X = large .

Lists, being data structures of flexible length, provide a format which allows information to be modified very easily. A slight complication in the rules is required, in order to get at the things on each list. But this is preferable in the long run. The rules are the relatively fixed part of the program; it is better that any complexity is built into them at the start, so that the data can be specified in a simple and readily changeable format.

We can consider in turn each of the three kinds of data statement in the program, and the modifications required in changing over to lists. The **person**al facts require no alteration. Since each person is restricted to a single description from each category, lists of items are not needed in this case, and would just be an unnecessary complication. As far as preferences are concerned, we can get by with just one long list of all the features the individual is prepared to tolerate, e.g.

prefers(john, [small, medium, large, young, mature, extrovert, shy]).

(To avoid ambiguity, features from different categories must not be labelled by the same term - we could not have, say, **medium** to describe the mid range both in build and in age.) So in the revised program, **prefers** can be a two place predicate, relating each individual to a list of preferred characteristics. We now define X to suit Y if Y has build C, hair D, and age E, and each of these figures somewhere on Y's list of preferences:

suits(X, Y) :- person(Y, A, _, _, _),
**   prefers(Y, List),**
**   opp(A, B),**
**   person(X, B, C, D, E),**
**   member(C, List), member(D, List), member(E, List).**

The nature of **match** requires a slightly different strategy for **likes**: we need to keep a separate list for each of the categories of interest. **likes** will remain a four place predicate, with lists occupying its last three:

likes(mary, [classical, jazz], [swimming], [travel, cinema]).

Even if someone has just one like from a certain category, uniformity demands that we record it as a list. If we recorded **swimming** as Mary's sport without enclosing it in list brackets, the use of **member** in the definition of **match** would fail. The need for three separate lists is because we wish to know whether two people share interests in common in *each* of the categories. For each category of interest - music, sport and recreation - we want to pull out of the database both Xs and Ys lists, and to check whether some item occurs on both. We could not make this something-in-each check if we simply merged all of a person's interests onto one long list. If we also want to match, e.g. unsporty types, those with an empty list of sports, then we should also check if the lists agree in both being empty. The required notion of agreement between lists can be defined - they either have at least one item **Z** in common, or else are both empty:

agree([ ], [ ]).
agree(X, Y) :- member(Z, X), member(Z, Y).

The revised definition of **match** can now be stated:

match(X, Y) :- person(X, A, _, _, _),
                likes(X, B, C, D),
                opp(A, E),
                person(Y, E, _, _, _),
                likes(Y, F, G, H),
                agree(B, F),
                agree(C, G),
                agree(D, H).

X and Y match if there is agreement in their lists of music **B** and **F**, their sports lists **C** and **G**, and their recreation lists **D** and **H**.

3.4.3 List patterns and identity

Another relation important to lists is the equality relation, =. Used with lists, = can do more than just check for strict equality. This is because lists can be specified using variables. A list which contains variables is really a list *pattern*. [**X, Y, Z**], for instance, is the pattern of all three membered lists. = can test not only whether one list is strictly identical to another, but also, for example, whether a list pattern can be *made* identical, or *unified*, with another. So the query

?-   [a, b, c] = [X, Y, Z]

can be thought of as asking whether the first list is a list of three things. It succeeds, with **X = a, Y = b, and Z = c**. [**a, b, c**] cannot be unified with, say, [**W, X, Y, Z**]; the former is a list of three items, the latter can only be matched with a list of four. We can use list patterns, for instance, to ask our grammar for all sentences composed of exactly four words - or any specific number of words - by placing that many variables within list brackets:

?-   sentence([A, B, C, D])

An important feature of this question is that the variables **A**, **B**, **C** and **D** will each be assigned *words*, not lists of words, as their values. This is because they are picking out the members of a list, and the sentences of our grammar are lists, each member of which is a word. We can think of this query as a more compact version of this:

?-   sentence(List), List = [A, B, C, D]

We can also ask for all four word sentences which, for example, begin with the definite article:

?-   sentence([the, B, C, D]).

        Unification and list patterns greatly extend the power and versatility of lists. Let us consider some more cases. Whereas the query

?-   [a, b, a] = [X, Y, Z]

succeeds, with **X** and **Z** both assigned **a** and **Y** = **b**, the following query will fail:

?-   [a, b, c] = [X, Y, X]

There is no way to unify these two lists; we cannot match a list with three distinct items with a pattern which requires the first and third elements to be the same. As with predicates, putting the same variable **X** in two positions requires that the same thing, whatever it is, occurs in both. Consider the two list patterns [a, X, Z] and [Y, b, Y]. The former has **a** as its first member, and is unconcerned about its second and third items; the latter requires **b** as its middle item, and its first and third to be the same. So they unify to the list [a, b, a]. The list patterns [a, X, Y] and [X, X, Z] unify to the list pattern [a, a, Z].
        Lists can contain other lists as members, and so can list patterns. We can set the query

?-   [X, [Y], Z] = [a, [[b, c]], [d]]

The first argument of the identity is the pattern of any three membered list, the middle item in which is itself a list - of one item. The second is a list of three items. Its first is an atom; its second is a list which contains one list within it; and its third is a list of one item. So this query succeeds with X = a, Y = [b, c], and Z = [d].

Exercise 4

A.   Extend the grammar program by adding to it the ability to recognize as grammatical a sentence such as

The young man loves a happy woman.

Add to the lexicon a new type of basic expression, **adjective**, and a new type of complex expression, common noun *phrases*. A **c_noun_phrase** is either a common noun, or an adjective followed by a common noun. Bear in mind that other parts of the grammar may need to be adjusted to accommodate these new sorts of expressions. Test your program with all solutions to the query:

?-   sentence(X), adjective([Y]), member(Y, X)

B.   Below is a simplified map of part of the Underground in Central London.

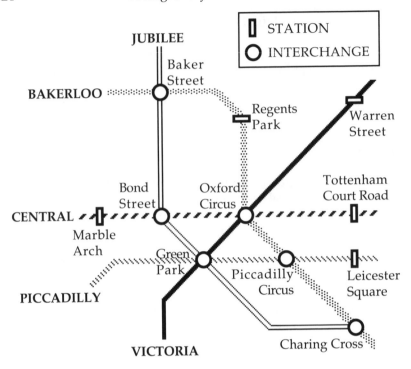

Write a program which encodes this information, by defining a two place predicate which relates each underground line to a list of the stations on it. After recording these particular facts, state general definitions of the following predicates: **interchange**, **direct**, **one_change**. **interchange** is to be a one place predicate, which will enable Prolog to infer which stations lie on more than one line. **direct** is to be a three place relation, which holds between two stations and a line if one can travel from one to the other directly on that line. **one_change** is the corresponding four place predicate, which holds of journeys which require exactly one change (relating two places, and two lines). Ensure your program correctly answers these queries:

```
?-      interchange(green_park)
?-      one_change(baker_st, warren_st, Line1, Line2)
```

and does not affirmatively answer these:

```
?-      interchange(marble_arch)
?-      one_change(marble_arch, oxford_circus, Line1, Line2)
```

We might also want the system to provide informative answers, in that it does not respond affirmatively to these queries:

?-   **one_change(baker_st, green_park, Line1, Line2)**
?-   **one_change(baker_st, baker_st, Line1, Line2)**

Thus, for example, the former is to be ruled out, even though one can make a **one_change** journey from Baker St to Green Park, on the grounds that there is a direct route between them.

3.5 Using numbers

When abroad, we often like to convert prices into our own currency, to get a idea of the amount in terms we find familiar. Consider someone from England on a trip to the United States, looking at a commodity priced at 16 dollars. Suppose the rate of exchange is currently given as $1.615 to the pound. If £1 buys him $1.615 at the bank, then it's going to take him about £10 to buy such an article. The calculation to make is therefore: how many pounds do we need to multiply the rate of exchange by to get the amount of dollars:

1)   price in pounds × rate of exchange = price in dollars

Or, what comes to exactly the same thing, to get the amount in pounds we divide the price in dollars by the rate of exchange:

2)   price in pounds =   price in dollars
                                     rate of exchange

Although Prolog is not intended for very fast or very sophisticated numerical applications, it is well suited to such simple calculations.
        In order to make such calculations in Prolog, we need to look at how the familiar arithmetical operations like multiplication are expressed in it. Standard function symbols are + for addition, - subtraction, * multiplication, and ÷ or / for division. Thus **5 + 7** denotes 12, **(5 + 7) * 2** denotes 24, and so on. **X - 10** denotes the result of subtracting 10 from X. Notice that these combinations are *terms*, not sentences. **5 + 7** doesn't express a proposition - you can't use it to assert something - it denotes a number, just as the numeral **12** does. In order to make use of these expressions, we have to put them into sentences - by

combining them with the numerical evaluator **is**. We can say, for instance,

12 is 5 + 7

This is a sentence - it expresses an identity. Used as a query, it will receive the answer **YES**. Similarly, the query

?-   X is 5 + 7

will receive the answer **X = 12**. Notice that in evaluating an addition (or a multiplication, etc.), what we have is essentially a relation between three numbers: **X is Y + Z** holds iff X is the result of adding Y and Z.

Let us suppose our price translation program will contain a database of rates for different currencies:

rate(fr, 9.22).
rate($,   1.615).

and so on. If we want the program to convert from the foreign currency to the home currency, the essential operation will be division: to divide a price, e.g. given in dollars by the current rate of exchange for dollars, giving the value in pounds:

convert(Price, Currency, Pounds) :- rate(Currency, N),
**   Pounds is Price / N.**

So **convert** can take a given price and currency; **rate** will pull the rate of exchange from the database, and / will make the required calculation. Although I could have used Xs and Ys as variables, I have chosen to use mnemonic variables, such as **Price**, simply because they make clearer to us which parameters the different argument places concern.

We can also dress up the output of this program, by defining a relation **show** to print out a statement of the conversion. We might naturally require that prices which convert to less than one pound be displayed in pence, rather than as fractions of a pound. In order to do this, we need to know about the *less than* relation, and something about getting Prolog to print out messages. The inequality relation may be expressed by the infix predicates < and >:

X < Y, or Y > X, holds iff X is a smaller number than Y.

Note that **2 < 3** is a sentence (unlike **2 + 3**). As well as strict inequality, an implementation of Prolog is likely to contain a relation of less than or equal to, **=<**.

In Edinburgh Prolog, **write** enables messages to be output to the screen. It is primitive both in the sense that it is predefined, and in the sense that more elaborate printing predicates can be defined in terms of it. **write** is a command, primarily - we understand it as an instruction rather than a description. But since it is possible to regard commands as having truth conditions - an order is true iff it is obeyed - we can also give it a declarative reading:

> **write(X)** is true iff X is printed on the screen.

(The difference between this and a normal condition is that Prolog *makes* this true, whenever it encounters it.) If the argument of **write** is or contains a variable, and that variable has received a value when Prolog comes to execute the **write**, then the value will be displayed in place of the variable.

If our predicate **show** is to distinguish between amounts less than one pound and larger amounts, its definition will have two parts. Firstly, it will check whether the value which **convert** supplies is less than 1. If it is, that value must be multiplied by 100, to get the number of pence (£0.7, for instance, is 70 pence). It will then need to display a message that the price is this many pence:

show(Price, Currency) :- convert(Price, Currency, X),
                                X < 1,
                                N is X * 100,
                                write([Price, Currency, is, N, pence]) .

The argument of **write** here is a list containing three variables, which will be instantiated to specific numerical values. A query such as **show(1, $)** will result in the display of a message

[1, $, is, 61.9, pence].

The display is rather inelegant, since **write** just prints the list as a unit; a better version must await a more detailed treatment of lists. Any amount not strictly less than £1, i.e. which is equal to or greater than £1, will cause the < check to fail, and so Prolog will automatically pass on to the second part of the definition of **show**:

**show(Price, Currency) :- convert(Price, Currency, X),
                            write([Price, Currency, is, £, X]).**

In principle, the arithmetical predicates are defined for infinitely many numbers. Numbers can be classified into different *number systems*. The most basic systems of numbers are as follows. Firstly, there are the *natural numbers* - whole numbers, from 0 onwards. Then there are the *integers* - whole numbers, both negative and positive. There are the *rational numbers* - those which can be expressed as ratios, as fractions. And there are the *reals*, which can be expressed using a decimal point. All natural numbers are integers, all integers rationals, and all rationals are real numbers. From a mathematical point of view, a computer should be able to handle any of these numbers, no matter how minute or massive. A mathematically ideal computer can be allowed an unlimited memory, but a physically real computer will only have a finite number of memory cells - so there are bound to be numbers which are, for example, too large for it to represent accurately, digit for digit. In practice, a real computer must approximate some of these numbers. A standard form of approximation is provided by *floating point* notation. In a floating point expression such as '3.147e2', the 'e2' means 'shift the decimal point two places to the right'. So it is what we would standardly represent with the (fixed point) numeral '314.7'. This numeral is short enough not to need approximation. But if the expression was '3.147e200', it would abbreviate, and so approximate, a numeral requiring over 200 digits in the usual notation (i.e. '3.147×10^{200}' written out in full). The same goes for very small numbers; 'e-200' means 'shift the decimal point 200 places to the left'.

Since there are infinitely many numbers, any variable in an arithmetical context has a potential infinity of different possible values. A consequence of this is that there are certain constraints on the use of variables as the arguments of arithmetical predicates. We cannot simply ask, for instance:

?-   **X < 3.147**

as if to ask "Give me a number less than 3.147". The question is too unspecific; we might as well ask "Give me a number." (We can of course define functions to produce answers to such a question. One function might enumerate the natural numbers, another might pull numbers out of a hat, at random - but such functions are essentially nothing to do with <.) The role of < is to check whether one number is less than another; its purpose is not to generate numbers at random.

Similar remarks apply to addition and the other numerical functions. We cannot properly ask the question:

?-   X is Y + Z

as if to say "Give me three numbers, such that one is the sum of the other two." There are too many answers, and no systematic way of generating them. The question is underspecified. Nor - unlike **append** - can we ask + to work with just one argument specified. We cannot ask, for example, "Give me two numbers, such that one is 5 more than the other". Both this and the preceding question do not pose well-defined problems. Only if two or more numbers have been specified is an addition well-defined. Notice that this is not a prohibition on the number of variables per se, but on the number of *unassigned* variables in the goal. Although the question **Y is X + 5** on its own is too unspecific, in the context of the query

?-   X is 4 + 3, Y is X + 5

it is not. Here, the first addition assigns **X** the value 7, which is then carried to the second - which therefore reads "What is the sum of 7 and 5?", which is quite determinate. So the prohibition is this: when Prolog comes to evaluate an addition, no more than one variable can be unassigned.

The same prohibitions apply to the use of <, +, *, etc. in programs. A program can contain the sentence **X < 3.147** provided that it is so placed that whenever Prolog encounters it, the variable **X** has been assigned a value. The above definition of **show** contains just such an occurrence. Or consider addition. It is sometimes important to keep track of the number of times a certain operation has been performed in the execution of a program. Each time the operation is called, we need to add 1 to a number which records the total number of calls so far made. We can use **M is N+1**, provided **N** has received a value. (Note that, unlike in many programming languages, you cannot update the value of a variable in Prolog, with, for instance, **N is N+1**. To Prolog such a goal is bound to be false - it's like saying 2 = 2+1.)

In looking at this feature of the operations, we look beyond their literal meanings to their pragmatics, their control behaviour - the way they can actually be used as procedures. Another control aspect of an operation is whether it is *invertible*. If, for instance, + is invertible, it can be used for both addition and subtraction. Most obviously, + can be used to find the result of adding two numbers, e.g.: what **Z** is such that **Z is 5 + 7**? We can depict this using the diagrams introduced in section 2.1.4.

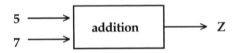

But if it is invertible, we can also ask for the **X** such that **7 is X + 5.** That is: what number X do you have to add to 5 to get 7?

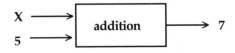

If we make the output of the addition function one of the inputs, the effect is to turn it into subtraction. The answer, X = 2, is the result of *subtracting* 5 from 7. In short,

Y is X + 5

gives us addition by 5 if we supply a value for **X** and use **Y** (for **Y** is 5 more than **X**); it gives us subtraction of 5 if we supply **Y** and use **X** (for **X** is 5 less than **Y**).

It may well be that, in the interest of efficiency (speed), the numerical operations are not implemented to be invertible. If + is not invertible, it can only be used for addition: the numbers to be added must be supplied. In **Z is X + Y**, the values of at least **X** and **Y** must be given. If we require invertible operations, we can define them in terms of the non-invertible ones. We can define three place relations **sum** and **times**, so that, for example, **times(2, 2, 4)** expresses the same complete fact as **2*2 is 4**. If

times(Pounds, Rate, Price)

is invertible, it may be used either for multiplicaticn or division, depending on which two values are supplied. As well as multiplication of the number of **Pounds** by the **Rate** of exchange to get the price in dollars - 1) above - it will also divide the **Price** in dollars by the **Rate** of exchange to find the number of pounds - 2) above. To define an invertible multiplication relation **times(X, Y, Z)**, we need to check which variable, if any, is uninstantiated. Prolog has a type predicate, **var**, which can be used to check if its argument is a variable which as yet has no value assigned to it. Using **var**, we can check which value is to be calculated, and make a division or multiplication accordingly:

times(X, Y, Z)	:-	var(X), X is Z/Y .
times(X, Y, Z)	:-	var(Y), Y is Z/X .
times(X, Y, Z)	:-	Z is X*Y .

The third clause covers both the case where **Z** is uninstantiated, and the case where all three variables are instantiated. With invertible **times**, we can now adapt **convert** to two-way translation:

convert(Price, Currency, Pounds) :- rate(Currency, N),
times(Pounds, N, Price).

      In one respect a person's calculations are like those of a Prolog machine. We have certain arithmetical operations as primitive - addition, multiplication, etc. - the ones we were taught at school. In order to perform some arithmetical tasks, we have work out what sequence of our basic operations will solve it, and then apply them in the appropriate order to the case in hand. Let us briefly consider an example of this. In restaurants, it is common for prices to be cited without the service charge included. In business, it is a common convention to quote prices without tax being included. In both of these cases, in order to know what you will actually be charged, you have to make a minor calculation: take the rate in question (e.g. 10 per cent service charge; 15% Tax), work out that percentage of the price quoted, and then add it to the price.
      There may be more than one way of putting together a sequence of operations to make some calculation. In this case, there is more than one way to achieve the calculation:

actual price = given price + (given price × rate ÷ 100)

In the terminology of section 2.1.3, there is a syntactic ambiguity in the equation which does not correspond to a genuine, semantic ambiguity. To find the amount to be added, we can, for example, divide the rate by 100 and then multiply by the given price, or we can multiply the given price by the rate and then divide by 100. If we adopt the former sequence, the Prolog definition of the **charge** relation between given and actual prices will be as follows:

rate(15).
charge(Given, Actual) :- rate(R),
**   N is R/100,**
**   Extra is Given*N,**
**   Actual is Given+Extra .**

The order of conjuncts in the definition corresponds to the order in which the basic operations are performed. To find out the actual price charged, express the percentage rate as a fraction **N**, use that to find the proportion of the given price which is the **Extra** to be charged, then add that extra on to the given price. We can condense this sequence into a single formula. **is** can evaluate complex numerical terms, so a variable like **N**, which is only used to hold the value of an intermediate calculation, can be replaced by its equivalent, **R/100**. Similarly, **Extra** can be replaced by **Given*N**, i.e. **Given*(R/100)**, producing:

charge(Given, Actual) :- rate(R),
**   Actual is Given+(Given*(R/100)) .**

The brackets, by determining the relative scopes of the arithmetical operations, ensure that they are applied in the correct order - starting with the innermost expression, **R/100**, and working outwards.

I close this section with one final example of the use of elementary arithmetic in Prolog. A farmer lives in a house near a river - or maybe a canal - and keeps some fowl in a shed nearby. The farmer wants to go down to the river with her bucket each morning, and fetch some water for the birds. Naturally, she wants to take the shortest route from house to river to shed. Many routes are possible; some are depicted below:

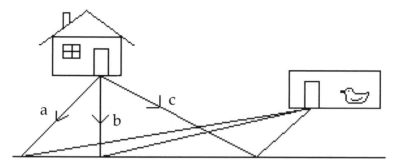

Route a looks pretty inefficient, since it's heading away from the chicken shack. Route b, going straight down from the house, looks more promising. But some path like c looks to be the optimal one. But which one? To make the problem definite, let's suppose that the distances are like this:

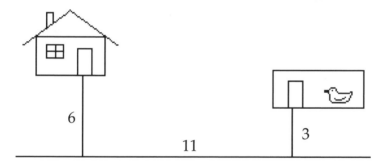

The farmer's house is 6 units - metres, say - from the river, and so on. Then we can put the question: what is the length of the shortest path from door to door, via the river? The solution should be cast as a general procedure, one which could compute the answer for any three distances such as those given. I invite you to pause and think a little about the problem before reading on.

The procedure of writing a program that will tell us the shortest path really requires two stages: i) informal problem solving; ii) encoding the solution into Prolog. Stage i) is the hard part. There is a very simple and elegant solution to this problem, but there is no reason to expect that someone not practised in this sort of problem, familiar with the relevant parts of geometry or physics, would be able to find it. Here we see one of the limitations of pure reason. It is a general feature of problem solving: the more specific knowledge you have of the domain you are working in, the easier it will be for you to represent and solve problems in it.

Familiarity with the domain in question can guide problem solving by suggesting fruitful ways of redescribing the problem. Redescription may take the form of a model - an analogous case which abstracts from irrelevant details, and which preserves its essential features in a form in which familiar rules and strategies can be applied. Here's a suggestion for modelling this problem: think of the river bank as a mirror, and recall that light always takes the shortest path. If you didn't see before how to solve it, does this now give you a hint? Another form of redescription is to change the problem slightly, to transform it into a related problem. In this case, imagine another farmer on the other side of the river with an exactly symmetrical set-up. His problem would be identical. Moreover, the distances they would have to walk would remain the same if they swapped tasks: she goes to the river and fills her bucket, then crosses over and waters his chickens; he does likewise for her ducks. But seeing the task this way makes the shortest path obvious: it is a straight line from the house to the opposite shed. And this remains the essential route of the shortest path if we revert to the original task: if instead of crossing over to the mirror image shed on the other side, the farmer is 'reflected' back and walks to her own shed. We can picture it thus:

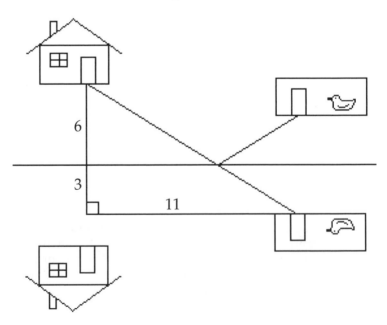

The problem is now in a form amenable to a little elementary geometry - in particular, Pythagoras' Theorem: the square on the hypotenuse (the longest side of a right-angled triangle) is equal to the sum of the squares of the other two sides. The general solution is:

> Take the distance of the house from the river (e.g. 6 metres); take the distance from the shed to the river (e.g. 3 metres), add them together - this is the length of the vertical side of the triangle. Square this number. Take the horizontal distance between house and shed doors (e.g. 11 metres), and square this. Add these two squares together and you have the square of the hypotenuse. So the solution, the shortest path, is the square root of that sum.

We now have a sequence of basic arithmetical operations; the programming task is the relatively easy one of stringing them together in the right order.

It will make things a little more perspicuous if we define the **square** operation; M is the square of N if it is N multiplied by itself:

square(N, M) :- M is N*N.

Note that this operation is not invertible. We can use it to calculate squares, i.e. by supplying N and taking the result M, but we cannot use it to calculate square roots, by supplying M and asking for N. If we ask for the square root of 100 we are asking for the number which multiplied by itself gives 100, **N*N is 100**, and this has too many variables. To calculate square roots, we need a predefined predicate:

$$\textbf{sqrt(M, N)} \quad \text{holds iff } M = N^2, \text{ i.e. N is the square root of M.}$$

Suppose we have the particular values stored in the database:

house(6).
shed(3).
horizontal(11).

All that remains is to get Prolog to carry out the sequence of calculations in the right order:

```
path(A) :- house(B),
          shed(C),
          D is B + C,
          square(D, E),
          horizontal(F),
          square(F, G),
          H is E + G,
          sqrt(H, A).
```

Exercise 5

Note: these exercises have been deliberately designed not to require any advanced knowledge of mathematics. They presuppose only everyday arithmetic, and the ability to use the familiar operations with numbers to help represent and solve a variety of problems.

A.   Define a relation **discount(X, Y)**, where **Y** gives the discounted price of **X**. The program should use a predicate **rate** to hold the current rate of discount (20%, say). Note: if you have difficulty with this (or another of these exercises), tackle it in stages. Work on a particular example, and then generalize. i) Imagine someone offering you something worth £300 at a 20% discount - work out on a piece of paper what it would cost. ii) Look at the sequence of calculations you made, and generalize it - replacing specific amounts by variables. iii) Code your general formulation into Prolog. iv) Try out the program on various test cases, e.g. the specific example you started with.

B.   This exercise models the use of computers in preventative medicine. It is a practical impossibility for a medical centre with a card filing system to keep checking through its several thousand records for patients whom they could advise to come in for a check up. The task is ideally suited to a computer. Let us consider one example: breast cancer. Suppose that childless women aged 40 or older should be advised for a screening if they have not been screened in the last five years. Women with one or more children should be advised for screening from age 45 onwards.

        Define a predicate **advise**, which will pick out the right names from the database. The database will have a record for each woman, relating her surname, her year of birth, the number of children, and the last year when she was screened. The program needs to know the age of a patient, but if each person's current age in years is recorded, the whole database will require continual updating. Better, then, to have just one record which needs updating, the current year, and to let **advise** compute a person's age by comparing her year of birth with the current year. Invent a database with a few fictional records - a woman under 40, a childless woman over 40 who has not been screened in the last five years, a woman with two children who has been screened in the last five years, etc. - and check that **advise** picks out the right ones. You can stipulate a year (e.g. 1900) as a default for those who have never been checked.

(Note: the criteria here are only illustrative. The point is that a screening programme will look for the positive incidence of risk factors. Other factors may actually be more significant for breast cancer: a family history of the disease, for instance. Since the question "Has anyone in the patient's family had this type of cancer?" essentially admits of a Yes/No answer, an extra argument could be added to the personal records, hold a *boolean* value - i.e. a truth value **t** or **f**, or **yes** or **no** - which records the presence or absence of this factor.)

C.   The question of what is required for one theory (e.g. biology) to be *reduced* to another (e.g. physics) is a matter of philosophical dispute. Some paradigms of theory reduction are provided in mathematics - where for example Descartes' system of co-ordinates enables geometry to be reduced to arithmetic. A point on a two-dimensional plane is represented by a pair of numbers, each number giving the distance of the point, in one of the dimensions, from some point fixed as the 'centre', or origin - the zero/zero point.

Start a new program to represent the Grid (exercise 3.2) by a system of Cartesian co-ordinates. Fix on the location of one of the objects as the origin, and define a three place predicate which relates each object to the two co-ordinates of its position in the Grid. (The usual convention is that the first co-ordinate gives the location of the point in a horizontal direction, the second its position in the vertical dimension.) Define predicates for the following relations: i) X being directly to the left of Y; ii) **online(X, Y)**: X is on the same line as Y (whether horizontal or vertical); iii) X is anywhere to the left of Y; iv) X is anywhere above Y. Check that your program generates the right solutions to these queries:

?-   online(b, X)
?-   online(X, g)

3.6   Introducing recursion

3.6.1   Recursive search of a graph

Below is a rather inaccurate map of the Cyclades, and possible connections from the mainland port of Piraeus and various islands:

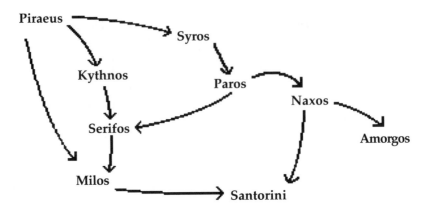

For the moment we shall only be concerned with travel in one direction, the direction of the arrows.   The map displays eleven direct connections between places, which we can encode as eleven basic links:

link(piraeus, syros).
link(piraeus, kythnos).

etc.   (A set of entities with a relation defined on them like this is known as a *graph*. The entities in a graph are its *nodes*, and the arrows between them *arcs*. If there is an arc from node X to node Y, X is said to be a *parent* of Y. More precisely, this map is a *directed acyclic graph* or DAG - directed, because there is a direction to the relationship (as indicated by the arrows), and acyclic, because there are no cycles leading from a node, via a succession of links, back to itself. Trees (see below) are also DAGs - in which, moreover, every node has at most one parent, and there is a node with no parents - the *root* of the tree.)

   Looking at the map, we can see that we can get by boat from Piraeus to Naxos. How can we get Prolog to infer such a fact from the basic database? Clearly, you can get from A to B if there is a direct connection between them. So we can make a start with:

get_to(A, B) :- link(A, B).

This clause will enable Prolog to infer that one can **get_to**, for example, Syros from Piraeus, and to Paros from Syros. But it cannot put these two facts together to infer the fact that **get_to(piraeus, paros)**, that Paros is accessible from Piraeus. For these two places are not directly connected by a **link**. To make this connection, it looks as if we should add that one can **get_to** C from A if A is linked to some intermediate place B, which in turn is linked to C:

get_to(A, C) :- link(A, B), link(B, C).

This will enable Prolog to infer that one can **get_to** Paros from Piraeus. This brings us closer to Naxos, but still Prolog cannot infer **get_to(piraeus, naxos)**. To obtain this, we could add that one can **get_to** D from A if they are linked by *two* intermediate stops:

get_to(A, D) :- link(A, B), link(B, C), link(C, D).

This approach is along the right lines, and yet there is something very inefficient about it. We have to keep adding new statements, one generalization for each possible number of intervening links. We would need to add a further rule to capture the fact that **get_to(piraeus, amorgos)**, and if the database were to expand at a later date to include islands linked to Amorgos, yet more rules for connections involving five or more intervening **link**s. It would be much better if we could compress this possibly never-ending series of rules into one, which was flexible about the number of intermediate steps. We would like to be able to say: you can **get_to** Z from A if A is linked to B, and B is linked to C, and ... and Y (the penultimate link in the chain) is linked to Z - as if we could say this

get_to(A, Z) :- link(A, B), link(B, C),   ...   link(Y, Z).

But this is not a proper sentence of Prolog. The dots make it schematic: a way of showing that we want to leave open how many intervening links there are. The way to get this flexibility is to use **get_to** in its own definition:

get_to(A, Z) :- link(A, B),
**   get_to(B, Z).**

Prolog can use this rule with the **link** facts to prove, for example, that **get_to(piraeus, amorgos)**, because it can prove this:

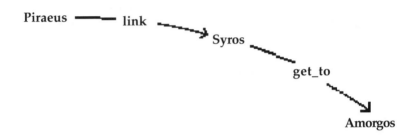

The **link** fact is stated explicitly in the program, and the **get_to** fact is proved by using the rule a second time:

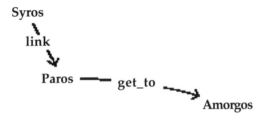

Again, the **link** follows immediately, and the **get_to** fact follows by a further application of the rule:

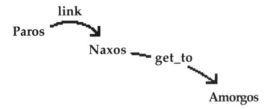

In this final case, we need to say that **get_to(naxos, amorgos)** because there is a direct **link** between them. That is, we also need the first of the candidate rules considered above. In sum, our definition of **get_to** will have these two parts:

get_to(X, Y) :- link(X, Y).

get_to(X, Y) :- link(X, A),
                        get_to(A, Y).

The important point is to see how the definition embodies the flexibility we wanted. Instead of trying, impossibly, to pack an indefinite number of **link** statements into the definition, we leave it open for the definition of **get_to** to *call itself* an indefinite number of times. The rule can loop round on itself, **get**ting ever closer **to** its destination, until it eventually hits a direct **link**, and no longer needs to call itself. Such definition is called *recursive*.

      Ordinarily, when a definition defines something in terms of itself, as this does, it would be deemed circular.

> Lepidus: What manner o' thing is your crocodile?
> Antony: It is shaped, sir, like itself, and it is as broad as it has breadth. It is just so high as it is, and moves with its own organs. It lives by that which nourisheth it, and the elements once out of it, it transmigrates.
> Lepidus: What colour is it of?
> Antony: Of its own colour too.
> Lepidus: 'Tis a strange serpent.
> Antony: 'Tis so; and the tears of it are wet.
> Caesar: Will this definition satisfy him? (*Antony and Cleopatra*, II, vii.)

What makes a definition genuinely circular is that it gives no independent characterization of the predicate in question; one can never escape the circle. What makes our recursive definition of **get_to** non-circular is that although the second clause helps itself to that very notion, the first does not. The first part states outright what the basic case of **get_to** is: a direct **link**. What is characteristic of a recursive definition is that it contains both a 'circular' part - the recursive or inductive clause(s) - and a non-circular part, the basis clause(s). Provided these are put together in the right way, so that even if we pass round the recursive part many times, we always eventually hit the basis part, the definition will be non-circular.

      The notion of recursion is fundamental to computing. A widely accepted thesis is Church's Thesis: All and only recursive functions are computable. The notion of a computable or effectively calculable function is an informal one - it is the intuitive idea of a function which could be applied in a purely mechanical way. A machine could be given a set of instructions so that, for any arguments the function is applied to, after a finite period of time the machine can work out what the value of the function is. The notion of a recursive function, by contrast, is a mathematically precise one (although we need not consider its precise definition here). Church's thesis is not susceptible to mathematical proof, precisely because it links an informal notion with a formal one. But it has been well-confirmed; several other notions have been proposed as the formal correlates of computability, and they have all proved equivalent. It could be refuted, if someone found a function which was intuitively computable, but non-recursive; all attempts to do so have failed.

3.6.2 Recursion in ordinary language

In one sense, you are already very familiar with recursive notions. Some figured centrally in chapter 2. The definition of the wffs of propositional logic (section 2.1.2) contains both a basis part (the atomic wffs) and a recursive part - a complex expression is a wff if it is built up in the right way out of parts which themselves are *wffs*. In this respect the grammar for our artificial language mirrors that for any natural language. In English, a sentence like 'John believes that Mary is happy' contains a sentence, 'Mary is happy', as a part. So the definition of 'sentence of English' would, in such cases, call upon itself. It needs to allow that something of the form 'John believes that X' is a sentence, if X is a sentence. Truth tables also embody a recursion; they tell us how the truth value of a complex wff is determined by the truth values of its parts.

In this section we shall examine one way in which the grammar of English allows complex *noun phrases* to be built up, in part, out of components which are in turn smaller *noun phrases*. Consider the examples in this sentence:

1)   The sister of the father of John knows the king of some country.

The important point is that there is no principled limit to the number of such embeddings of terms within terms. As the noun phrase lengthens it may become very unwieldy, and difficult to keep track of its reference - 'The sister of the father of the mother of the author of the appendix to the report of the committee of the inquiry into the killing of the president'. But this is syntactically acceptable, and it can still have a definite semantic value. Wherever a language permits such unrestricted embedding of expressions of some category within expressions of that category, the grammar rules for that language will need to embody a correspondingly general recursion.

Let us now review the rules of the simple grammar of section 3.4.1. We had, for example,

```
sentence(List) :- noun_phrase(N),
                  verb_phrase(V),
                  append(N, V, List) .
```

Consider this from a procedural point of view. It reads: *first* find a noun phrase, then find a verb phrase, then join them together. This is an acceptable procedure for generating examples of sentences, but it is extremely inefficient as a means of *testing* whether a given list is of that category. For given a list to test, that procedure may generate many noun phrases and verb phrases which have nothing to do with that particular example, before coming upon the right combination. It only worked in section 3.4.1 because the grammar was very simple: it had only a very small number of noun and verb phrases to run through. Now that there are literally infinitely many noun phrases, it becomes not just inefficient but wholly unworkable. For testing whether a given list is a sentence, it is better to split it into two lists *first*, and then test whether the resulting lists are a noun phrase and verb phrase. Natural language processing programs are needed both for testing the grammaticality of input, and for generating grammatical output - but we should not necessarily expect the same procedures to do both tasks. The emphasis here will be on testing, so we should re-position the **append** in this

```
sentence(List) :- append(N, V, List),
                  noun_phrase(N),
                  verb_phrase(V) .
```

and all the other rules.

This discussion of placing **append** illustrates that the grammatical question of how sentences are put together is a separate matter from how a set of grammar rules should be implemented within a program. So it can only serve clarity to distinguish what so far we have not separated - the syntactical rules from their implementation. A convenient formalism is that of *Definite Clause Grammars* (D.C.G.s), which writes a syntactic rule like this:

sentence --> noun phrase, verb phrase.

Read '-->' as 'can be', and the comma as 'followed by'. In other words, this rule says that a sentence can be of the form: a noun phrase followed by a verb phrase. Continuing for the fragment of English which includes sentence 1):

> noun phrase --> proper name.
> noun phrase --> determiner, common noun phrase.
> common noun phrase --> common noun.
> common noun phrase --> common noun, prep phrase.
> verb phrase --> intrans.
> verb phrase --> trans, noun phrase.
> prep phrase --> prep, noun phrase.
> prep --> 'of'.
> determiner --> 'the'.
> determiner --> 'some'.
> determiner --> 'every'.

And so on, for all the other basic lexical items. Basic expressions (those here quoted) are sometimes called *terminal symbols*, and the names of categories *non-terminals*.

To understand such a grammar, it is important to follow through the way it puts together phrases. A prepositional phrase comes by taking any noun phrase, for instance 'France', and appending it to a preposition - thus 'of France'. This can then combine with a common noun to form a common noun phrase, e.g. 'king of France'. To see things built thus is to see the prepositional phrase as restricting or qualifying the description supplied by the common noun. Combining the complex description 'king of France' with a determiner produces a noun phrase, for instance the definite description 'the king of France'. By the recursive nature of this grammar, this term can be fed in to make a more complex term by the same process, e.g. 'the brother of the king of France'.

It is now a straightforward matter to convert these D.C.G. rules to Prolog code. The most relevant parts of the program are these:

```
noun_phrase(List) :- append(D, C, List),
                     det(D),
                     c_noun_phrase(C).
c_noun_phrase(C) :- append(A, B, C),
                    c_noun(A),
                    prep_phrase(B) .
```

```
prep_phrase(P) :- append(A, B, P),
                  prep(A),
                  noun_phrase(B) .
prep([of]) .
```

3.6.3 The Towers of Hanoi

The Towers of Hanoi has become something of a classic within computer science - the problem is easy to grasp, and admits of a simple recursive solution. I want to discuss it from the point of view of attempting to discover and formulate a recursion. The story can be embellished in various ways, but it comes down to this. There are three rods, on one of which a number of discs are stacked, forming a small pyramid. I have illustrated the arrangement with eight discs, but the pyramid can be formed with as many or as few discs as we like. The important thing is that the discs are stacked in order of size, with the largest at the bottom:

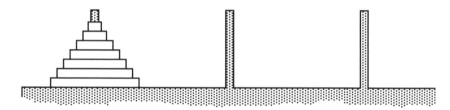

The task is to transfer the pyramid to the rod on the right. What makes it into a non-trivial problem is that three constraints must always be obeyed:

i)   The discs can only be moved one at a time.

If it wasn't for this constraint, the problem would admit of an immediate solution: simply move the pile *en bloc* from left to right.

ii)   A disc can only be moved to another rod.

Again, this prevents a trivial solution - just lay the discs out on the floor, then stack them up on the right rod. The second constraint requires us to make use of the middle rod, as a place where we can temporarily store discs.

iii)   A larger disc can never be placed on top of a smaller disc.

If it wasn't for this constraint, the problem would again be easy to solve. Do you see what the solution would be?

        If you haven't encountered The Towers of Hanoi before, get a feel for the problem by working through a few simple cases before reading beyond this paragraph. You can model the problem with a few coins of different sizes and three positions marked out on a piece of paper. Try the problem with a pyramid of just three coins. When you succeed in transferring the stack from the left position to the right, without violating any of the constraints, make sure you can repeat the operation. Then try it with a stack of four coins. When you have worked that out, try to describe your procedure systematically - describe how the main task of transferring a stack of four coins breaks down into various sub-tasks. Finally, look at the procedures for each of the different cases of one, two, three and four coins, and try to find a common pattern among them.

The basic computational problem which the Towers of Hanoi presents is to write a program which will tell us, for any number of discs n, the operations to perform in transferring a stack of n discs from the left rod to right one. If you have worked through a few cases in the way suggested, you may have got an idea of the recursive structure of the solution. Faced with a pile of discs, the first thought one tends to have is: what do I do with the top disc? That is, the question which naturally occurs is: where do we go from here - the mid pole or the right pole:

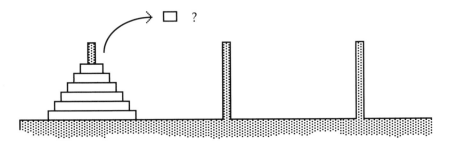

Trial and error with a few coins should have convinced you that this is not a fruitful way to tackle the problem. It may suggest the way to go if the stack has just a couple of coins in it - but try it with a stack of eight, for example. The reason it is not fruitful is because it is the wrong way to approach a recursive problem. The way to think about a recursion is always to break it into two questions:

1)   What is the basis case? The simplest case of the Towers problem would seem to be for a pyramid of just one disc. The simplest case is often so straightforward it's easy to overlook, but it's crucial to the success of any recursion. Here, the question is essentially this: How does one transfer a stack of 1 disc from the left pole, via the mid (if

need be), to the right? The answer is straightforward: just to move the disc from the left pole to the right.

We may not know at this stage precisely how to formalize this answer. Because the basis case is the simplest, it may not be clear what factors have to be taken into consideration, and so what arguments the predicates require.   But it carefully maintains a distinction which is crucial to the solution - between transferring a *stack* of discs, and moving a *single* disc. Let us continue to reserve **transfer** for stacks, and **move** for discs. The overall task is about *transferring* a pyramid of n discs from one rod to another, making use of a third rod as a temporary store. But constraint i) ensures that its solution must involve *moving* single discs from one place to another. Moving a single disc has only two parameters that count: the pole the disc is on, and the pole it's going to.

2)   What's the recursive case?   To think about the problem recursively is to think how we might use **transfer** to help in its own definition - to think how the problem of transferring n discs can be reduced to a simpler case of transferring. The trick is to look at the task in very general terms, to abstract from the particular moves and look at the overall strategy for transferring n discs. In order to get to the point where we can start building up the pyramid on the right pole, we have to have the largest disc sitting at the bottom of it. So there is one step on which the whole operation turns: we have to get the largest disc, the nth disc, from the left rod to the right rod. In order to achieve this, the right rod must have no discs on it - it must be ready to receive the nth disc - and there must be nothing on top of the nth disc, so that it is free to be moved. In other words, all the other discs must be on middle rod. Since they must obey constraint iii), they must be stacked up to form a pyramid. This suggests the first stage of the recursion: in order to transfer n discs from x to z via the storage rod y, we first have to transfer n-1 discs from x to y. The first stage can be depicted thus:

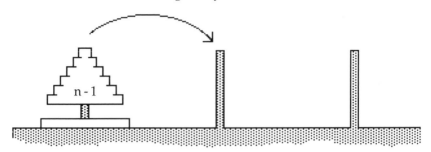

Figure **3.1**

Notice there is no suggestion of just *moving* the pile of discs - constraint
i) prohibits that. This is why it is a recursion: the problem of
transferring a pile of n disks is reduced, at this first stage, to the
problem of transferring a pile of n-1 discs. Notice also that for this
transfer z is spare - so we will need it to act as the storage rod. And now
comes the pivotal step: having prepared things for the last disc, we
can now move it across:

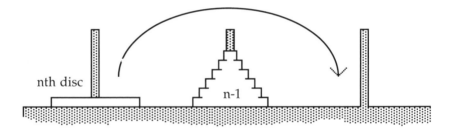

Figure **3.2**

The third stage of our recursion requires that we rebuild the remainder
of the pyramid on the right rod. That is, we need to transfer n-1 discs
from y to the target rod z. During this stage, x will act as the
temporary store.

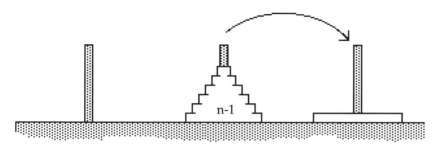

Figure **3.3**

One thing this solution requires is the distinction between each particular rod and the role it is playing at any stage in the operation. Starting with n discs, the left rod is the source of the pile, the right rod is the target and the middle rod is the store. When this is reduced to the task of transferring n-1 discs, the middle rod becomes the target, and the right rod the store. What is required is a predicate which keeps track of four parameters, the number of discs, and each of the three roles:

> **transfer(N, X, Y, Z)** - transfer a pile of N discs from source X,
> via store Y, to target Z.

The basis clause of our definition of **transfer**, for a stack containing only one disc, just requires the disc to be moved from source to target:

transfer(1, X, Y, Z) :- move_disc(X, Z).

We can worry about how to define **move_disc** in a moment. Firstly, we should complete the recursion - it's just a question of translating into words the sequence of operations depicted above:

transfer(N, X, Y, Z) :- M is (N - 1),
                        transfer(M, X, Z, Y),   /* **fig. 3.1** */
                        move_disc(X, Z),   /* **fig. 3.2** */
                        transfer(M, Y, X, Z).   /* **fig. 3.3** */

In fact, there is a simpler alternative for the basis of the definition: the problem of **transfer**ring 0 discs. The solution to this problem is immediate: do nothing! So we can replace the preceding basis clause by

transfer(0, X, Y, Z) .

Having formulated the recursive clause, we can now see that the case
we had previously taken as the basis, the one disc transfer, is really a
special case of the recursion - **move_disc(X, Z)** between two vacuous
transfers of 0 discs.

How should **move_disc** be defined? If we wanted the program
to operate directly on a real stack of discs, we would need to connect the
computer to a robot arm, and define the complex sequence of motor
controls the process requires. However we define **move_disc**, this will
be a technical problem, not the essential algorithm, which is provided
by the definition of **transfer**. So we might as well compromise at this
point, and get the program to tell *us* what to do - to print a series of
messages describing the moves to be made. We need something like
this:

move_disc(Here, There) :- write([move, disc, from, Here, to, There]).

Finally, we can set the program to work by posing it a query such as
transfer(8, left, mid, right).

3.6.4   Trees: a simple spatial recursion

Several implementations of Prolog now provide a graphics facility - a
set of predefined procedures which enable a program to produce
diagrams within a graphical display area, and perhaps also to
respond to input in the form of a user's manipulations of images. This
section introduces the idea of graphics in Prolog, by introducing a
simple spatial or visual recursion, that involved in the production of
tree structures. The recursion involved in producing a tree is essentially
this: to *grow a tree*, extend some branches and then *grow a tree* at the
ends of those branches. If we conceive of a recursion in this way, as an
instruction, the basis of the recursion is a termination condition, a
condition which tells you how to stop. The termination condition for
growing a tree is: produce a leaf!

This description of trees is quite unspecific; there is room for it
to be realized in many different ways. The following questions raise
some of the issues that need to be addressed. How many branches
should grow at any given point? At what angle, or with what degree
of separation, should the branches grow? To what depth is the
recursion to be performed - how many recursive calls should be made
before applying the basis condition? These questions suggest different

parameters for controlling the shape of a tree. The growth of a real tree is determined by its genetic code. Genes are not a blueprint giving every detail of every branch and twig - they provide a formula for growing, which sets some of these parameters in a way which will typically result in a tree with the characteristic shape for its species. We could mimic this in a program by setting some of the parameters arithmetically (e.g. number of branches = 2), perhaps incorporating a randomizing function to introduce asymmetry and variation in the trees. But the kind of trees we shall consider here will be fully detailed in advance, by a complete blueprint. To put it another way, we shall use trees as a means of graphically presenting fully formed structures. In particular, the structures which will act as blueprints for trees are the labelled bracketings produced by Linguistic analysis (cf. the end of section 3.4.1. A parsing program which generates these structures from English sentences is described in section 5.5.1.)

The graphics area will be mapped out by Cartesian co-ordinates (cf. exercise 3.5 C), where each location will be a point on the display which can be filled by black or white (or perhaps some colour). A graphics package for Prolog must supply a number of predefined predicates for addressing this display area - for instance, a predicate to draw a straight line between any two points within it. A straight line is defined by four numbers: the X and Y co-ordinates of its two ends. I shall assume that there is available a predefined relation which I shall call **line**, so that a call to a goal of the form **line(X, Y, X1, Y1)** will be made true by the drawing of a line from <X, Y> to <X1, Y1>.

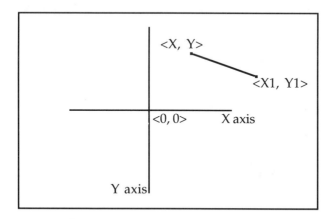

Figure **3.4**   A line in the graphics display area

A node of a tree is a point at which it can grow one or more branches, or a leaf. A node is here defined by the co-ordinates of its location within the graphics area. The procedure for producing a tree must be relativized to nodes - it must take into account the point which the tree construction has currently reached. At the start, we need to specify the point from which the tree will grow, the location of the root. This could be the origin, <0, 0>. The recursion, then, is to *grow a tree* at a node:

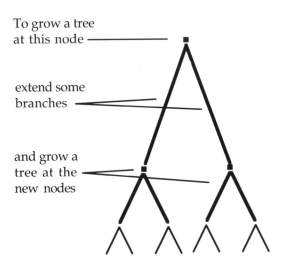

To grow a tree at this node ———————

extend some branches ———

and grow a tree at the new nodes

We shall define a relation **grow_tree(List, X, Y)**, where X and Y are the co-ordinates of the node currently being considered. **List**, the labelled bracketing structure to be displayed as a tree, will usually contain nested lists within it. Here is an example of the kind of goal set to **grow_tree**:

?-   grow_tree([sentence, [noun_phrase, [p_name, john]], [verb_phrase, [transitive, loves], [noun_phrase, [det, a], [c_noun, woman]]]], 0, 0)

and the output required:

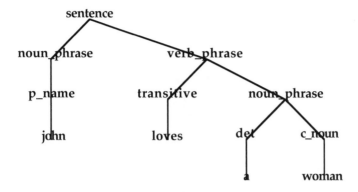

Figure **3.5**   Parse tree for the sentence 'John loves a woman'

The nesting of brackets in the labelled bracketing list corresponds to the order of construction of the sentence out of its constituents, in much the same way that the nesting of brackets in an arithmetical or logical formula reflects its construction (cf. section 2.1.4). Indeed, we can use the program developed here to display formulae of propositional logic, provided they are converted into prefix, Polish form (see p. 56), and represented as lists. Converting the wff (¬P & R) v ¬¬Q into this form we get the nested list **[v, [&, [¬, p], r], [¬, [¬, q]]]**, which can then be handed to **grow_tree** to display its structure:

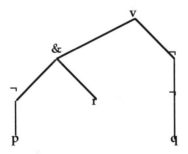

Figure **3.6**   The structure of (¬p & r) v ¬¬q

A definition for **grow_tree** is listed in figure 3.7 below. The cases which it must cover will be determined by the kinds of nesting of lists it will encounter. For the linguistic labelled bracketing structures, there are two different continuations of a tree possible at a node: the straight branch, and the forked branch. A straight branch is encoded by, for example, **[noun_phrase, [p_name, john]]**, where we want this to be displayed as:

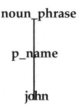

The point is that a straight branch will be encoded by a list of the form **[Word, Rest]**, where **Word** will be the label of a syntactic category, and **Rest** may be either a nested list, or a leaf - an English word like **john**. What this requires of **grow_tree** is for it to display the **Word**, draw a straight line down, then recursively apply to the **Rest**. A straight branch requires no change in the X co-ordinate, but requires some addition to the Y co-ordinate. The values involved will depend on the particular system - its level of resolution, as well as the size at which the tree is to be presented. Here we have picked a value of 30: the new Y co-ordinate, Y1, is Y+30. So the line is drawn is straight down from <X, Y> to <X, Y1>, **line(X, Y, X, Y1)**.

    grow_tree encounters a forked branch when it encounters a list structure such as **[verb_phrase,** Left, Right]. Here Left and Right will be lists, which may represent further forked branches, or straight branches. **grow_tree** will have done its work in this case if it displays the label **verb_phrase**, draws an appropriate fork below it, and then recursively applies, in turn, to the Left and Right:

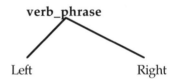

The complication is that perhaps the Left branch contains no further branching below it, whereas the other branch contains a large sub-tree below it. If the display is not to get into a tangle, the Right branch must be pushed over further, proportionally to the amount of further branching under it. There are various ways to accommodate this. The solution adopted here is to provide a relatively unsophisticated measure based on the extent of branching which a given list contains - the greater the number of branches, the larger this **branching** measure, and consequently the further over that branch will be pushed. **branching** recursively counts the number of branches below - a recursion called within the main recursion of **grow_tree**.

```
grow_tree(Leaf, X, Y) :- atom(Leaf),
                         put_text(Leaf, X, Y) .
grow_tree([Word, Rest], X, Y) :- put_text(Word, X, Y),
                         Y1 is Y+30,
                         line(X, Y, X, Y1),
                         grow_tree(Rest, X, Y1) .
grow_tree([Word, Left, Right], X, Y) :- put_text(Word, X, Y),
                         Y1 is Y+30,
                         branching(Left, LB),
                         X1 is X-LB,
                         line(X, Y, X1, Y1),
                         grow_tree(Left, X1, Y1),
                         branching(Right, RB),
                         X2 is X+RB,
                         line(X, Y, X2, Y1),
                         grow_tree(Right, X2, Y1) .
put_text(Word, X, Y) :- text_length(Word, L),
                         N is X-(L/2),
                         text(Word, X1, Y) .
branching(Leaf, 30) :- atom(Leaf) .
branching([_, Rest], N) :- branching(Rest, N) .
branching([_, Left, Right], N) :- branching(Left, L),
                         branching(Right, R),
                         N is L+R .
```

Figure **3.7**   A program to draw tree structures

The basis condition for **grow_tree** handles the leaves of the tree - displaying the individual English words of the sentence being parsed. It checks to see that the argument is an atom, not a list, and then calls on **put_text** to display that word. **put_text** is also used by the other clauses in **grow_tree**, to display the syntactic category labels, such as **noun_phrase**. We assume a predefined procedure **text(A, X, Y)**, which places a text string A within the graphics area, <X, Y> being the point from which A starts - the co-ordinates of its bottom left corner. But for good display, text should be centred at the node where it is to appear. To centre a piece of text at a node <X, Y> means that half of it appears to the left of X, and half to the right. We assume another predefined predicate **text_length**, to measure the length L of a string in terms of its dimensions in the graphics area - its length in pixels. The text is shifted over by half its length - by L/2. That is, **text** is to start displaying it at X-(L/2).

Exercise 6

A.   So far the first version of the Grid program (exercise 3.2) can determine whether one object is *directly* to the left of another, but not whether an object is *anywhere* to the left of another. Recursively define a predicate **left**, using the relation of being directly to the left of. Break it into two cases. Firstly, what is the basic case of being anywhere to the left of? Secondly, think of two objects separated by an arbitrary number of objects along one of the Grid's lines. How can you define **left** in terms of itself, which reduces the question of whether one thing is to the left of another to a case which is one step simpler? Check that your program proves **left(d, e)**, **left(d, f)**, and **left(d, g)**.

B.   Add to the family tree program a recursively defined relation **descendant**, so that Prolog can infer that, for example, Agamemnon is a descendant of Aerope, and that Orestes is a descendant of Aerope, and any descendant of Orestes would also be.

C.   Modify the grammar program so that the **append**s are correctly positioned for sentence recognition rather than generation. Then extend it so that it can recognize the iteration of propositional attitude constructions, as exemplified by:
      John knows that Mary says that every man believes that some dog talks.
The extension should recognize a new category of attitude verbs, such as 'knows', 'says', 'believes', and employ them in a new rule for verb phrases.

D   If you have access to Prolog with graphics, revise the definition of **grow_tree** so that it can be fed wffs of propositional logic, and arithmetical formulae, in their usual infix form. So it should be able to display (P v ¬Q) & (¬¬¬R v R) and ((9*3)/6)-2, given the lists [[p, v, [¬, q]], &, [[¬, [¬, [¬, r]]], v, r]] and [[[9, *, 3], /, 6], -, 2].

Chapter 4
Logic: the art of deduction

4.1 Reasoning

4.1.1 Arguments

One sentence or statement X *entails* another Y if it's not possible for X to be true and Y to be false. Consider these two sentences, used with reference to the same object:

1)   This is red.
2)   This is coloured.

1) entails 2), because it's not possible for a thing to be red and not be coloured. Does 2) entail 1)? No - because it is possible for something to be coloured without being red. We can extend the notion of entailment more generally to *arguments*. An argument can be identified by its *premises*, the propositions which it assumes or takes for granted, and its *conclusion*, the proposition which it purports to establish, given those premises. Consider the following piece of reasoning:

3)   If Jones retires, either Brown or Williams will take charge of finance.
4)   If Smith still has influence, then Williams won't take charge of finance.
5)   Jones will retire.
Therefore:
6)   If Brown doesn't take charge of finance, Smith no longer has influence.
We can abstract from this the following LPF form:

$$A \rightarrow (B \lor C). \quad D \rightarrow \neg C. \quad A. \quad \text{Therefore:} \quad \neg B \rightarrow \neg D.$$

We can abstract from this the following LPF form:

$$A \rightarrow (B \vee C). \quad D \rightarrow \neg C. \quad A. \quad \text{Therefore:} \quad \neg B \rightarrow \neg D.$$

Premises of an argument can be either simple or complex sentences; the conclusion can also be either atomic or complex. In this particular case, there are three premises - the sentences 3), 4) and 5). A word such as 'Therefore' or 'So' signals the claim that the conclusion follows from the premises. Given an argument with one or more premises X, Y, Z, ..., and a single conclusion W, we say that

> X, Y, Z, ... entail W iff in no possible state of affairs are
> X, Y, Z, ... all true, and W is false.

In other words, the premises entail the conclusion if it's impossible for all the premises to be true and the conclusion false.

If the premises entail the conclusion we also say that the argument is *valid*. A deductively valid argument is ***truth-preserving***, i.e. under no possible circumstances could it lead from true premises to a false conclusion. The conclusion is true in every situation in which the premises are true. (A limiting case of an argument is one whose

A B C D	$A \rightarrow (B \vee C)$.	$D \rightarrow \neg C$.	A.	Therefore: $\neg B \rightarrow \neg D$.
T T T T	T	F	T	T
T T T F	T	T	T	T
T T F T	T	T	T	T
T T F F	T	T	T	T
T F T T	T	F	T	F
T F T F	T	T	T	T
T F F T	F	T	T	F
T F F F	F	T	T	T
F T T T	T	F	F	T
F T T F	T	T	F	T
F T F T	T	T	F	T
F T F F	T	T	F	T
F F T T	T	F	F	F
F F T F	T	T	F	T
F F F T	T	T	F	F
F F F F	T	T	F	T

Figure 4.1

conclusion depends on no premises. If an argument with no premises is valid, the conclusion is true in every situation, i.e. it is a logical truth, something which could not be false, no matter what.) To check for validity or entailment by truth table: is there no line on which all the premises are T, while the conclusion gets F. Consider the table for the argument just given, in figure 4.1. Can we find a line on which all the three premises are true, and the conclusion false? None of the last eight lines will help, because on all of these the third premise, A, is false. If you check the lines on which all of the premises come out T - lines 2, 3, 4 and 6 - you will see that the conclusion also comes out T in each of those cases. So the argument is valid. By contrast, the abductive inference at the beginning of section 2.3 is deductively invalid. It is an example of the fallacy of affirming the consequent, i.e. affirming the consequent of a conditional, and inferring its antecedent:

A B	$A \rightarrow B$.	B.	Therefore:	A.
T T	T	T		T
T F	F	F		T
F T	T	T		F
F F	T	F		F

The third line of the table shows the invalidity of the inference.

In chapter 3 we relied on a mechanical device to carry out deductions for us. A Prolog program forms a set of premises, and querying Prolog with a goal is asking it whether it can derive that conclusion from those premises. We have just formulated a semantic notion of acceptability for inferences, and the truth table method of checking those of propositional form. But we haven't looked at the process of actually *constructing* an argument, the process of starting with some assumptions or premises, and filling in the reasoning which leads one to the conclusion, by a series of inferential steps. (The difference is like that between using the **get_to** program (section 3.6.1) to check that one can reach Y from X, and defining a procedure which constructs a path leading from X to Y - which shows how one can make the journey (cf. section 5.4.3).) Unlike the semantic technique for *checking* validity, constructing an argument - deriving a conclusion from a set of premises - is essentially syntactic. What we need to know is, if we have sentences of such and such forms, we can proceed to a sentence of some other form - e.g. from A and A → B, to B. The inferential step is characterized in terms of the forms of the wffs, rather than their semantic content. The branch of logic which deals with the kinds of syntactic manipulations which are the valid derivation of wffs from other wffs is known as **proof theory**. The particular technique we shall be concerned with in this chapter is often referred to as *natural deduction*.

4.1.2 Rules of inference

To make clear what's going on in natural deduction, it will help to take a particular argument and look at some of the inferential moves that are made in it. We will then see that the abstract rules of inference of natural deduction are just the formalization of such ordinary inferential steps. Good examples are provided by the kind of reasoning we use to solve the problems about the island of knights and knaves. The first problem was this. We come across two of the locals, to whom we referred as a and b, and a says to us 'At least one of us is a knave'. With this information, we can reason about the nature of these two characters - in effect, we construct a proof, the conclusion of which is the solution of the problem. I shall be as tediously explicit about this reasoning as I can - to separate out as many steps in the argument as possible, and number each one, to bring out all the assumptions being used, and make clear exactly when they are appealed to. So here's the argument, with some explanations interpolated.

We assume: 1)   a says: at least one of us is a knave.

This is an *assumption* about how things are - we assume that the information we have been given is correct. To get the argument going, we need to make a further assumption:

Suppose: 2)   a is a knave.

Now, it follows by definition of what it is to be a *knave* that

	3)	If a is a knave, then what he says is false.
So	4)	What a says is false,
i.e.	5)	It's false that at least one of them is a knave.

In other words, neither of them is:

	6)	a is not a knave and b is not a knave.
So	7)	a is not a knave.

This contradicts our supposition 2) - so 2) can't be true:

8)   a is not a knave.
9)   a is either knight or knave.

This is another assumption - that anyone we come across is of one or other type.

So   10)   a is a knight.
            11)   If a is a knight, what he says is true.
So   12)   What a says is true.
i.e.   13)   Either a is a knave or b is a knave.
So   14)   b is a knave.

We may conclude, putting 10) and 14) together,

15)   a is a knight and b is a knave.

Now let's look at some of the inferential moves that are made in this argument. All the rules, except for the first one, are classified according to the kind of logical connective they concern.

Assumption: You can assume any sentence, at any stage in an argument.

At first this may strike one as an exceedingly liberal rule, and certainly more needs to be said about what constrains its use. But for now we need only note that it's the principle we use when we say 'Suppose ...' in an argument, i.e. when we make a supposition or hypothesis about how the world is or might be. In the above argument, the rule of assumption is used at lines 1), 2) and 9). The supposition at line 2) illustrates a typical use of the rule: when we're not sure about how things are, we make an assumption ('for the sake of argument'), and trace out its consequences. That is, we deduce (often with the help of some further assumptions) what would follow if it were the case.

& Elimination: Given any conjunction, you may infer either conjunct.

The rule is intuitively quite straightforward. We may have established a conjunction at a particular stage in an argument, and wish to use only one or other of the conjuncts - as in the transition above from line 6) to line 7). We can formally represent this rule as follows:

$$\frac{X \ \& \ Y}{X}$$

- which should be read: from any wff of the form X & Y, you may infer
X. Since it would be equally correct to infer Y, we should add a second
clause to this schema:

$$\frac{X \ \& \ Y}{Y}$$

    The rule is called an elimination rule because in a certain sense
we 'eliminate' an & - we pass from a formula containing & as its
dominant connective, to one which lacks that &. Each connective
requires two rules, one for its elimination, and one for its introduction.
& Introduction: Given any two wffs in an argument, you may infer their
conjunction.
This is 'and' introduction because it *introduces* a wff with & as its
dominant connective. The rule can be represented:

$$\frac{X, \ Y}{X \ \& \ Y}$$

Given any two wffs, in whatever order, you may conjoin them. This
rule can be found in the final step in the argument above, where lines
10) and 14) are collected up into the conclusion.
→ **Elimination**: Given a conditional, and the antecedent of that
conditional, you may infer its consequent:

$$\frac{X, \ X \rightarrow Y}{Y}$$

As in the formulation of the previous rule, when two wffs are written
above the line, separated by a comma, this means that it doesn't
matter what order they come in. In our argument, the inference is made
a couple of times - in the move from lines 2) and 3) to 4), and again, from
10) and 11) to 12). The traditional Latin name given to this form of
inference is *Modus Ponens* (or *Modus Ponendo Ponens*).
v Elimination: If you have established a disjunction X v Y, and you
also establish that one disjunct is not true, you may infer the other:

$$\frac{X \ v \ Y, \ \neg X}{Y} \qquad\qquad \frac{X \ v \ Y, \ \neg Y}{X}$$

We find this above in the move from 8) and 9) to 10), and also from 8)
and 13) to 14). This is 'or' elimination because we infer something *from*

a disjunction. It might also be said to be an elimination inference in a looser sense, because it can be put like this: if you know that one or other (or both) of two possibilities holds, X or Y, and you can *eliminate* one of them (X, say), you know it must be the other. (The rule is also known as the disjunctive syllogism.)

All these inference rules apply regardless of whether X, Y themselves have structure, or are atomic. For instance, the move

$$(A \& B) v (\neg A v C), \quad \neg (\neg A v C) \quad \text{therefore:} \quad (A \& B)$$

is as valid an instance of the pattern of v Elimination as, say,

$$A v B, \quad \neg B \quad \text{therefore} \quad A.$$

The point is that the rules apply on the basis of the overall structure of the wffs. Both of these instantiates the overall pattern: disjunction, negation of one disjunct, therefore: other disjunct.

v Introduction: To establish a disjunction, it suffices to establish one disjunct:

$$\frac{X}{X v Y} \qquad\qquad\qquad \frac{Y}{X v Y}$$

If X is true, then the weaker judgement X v Y must be true; likewise for Y. This inference is not used in the above argument, and it may not be clear at first why one would ever want to weaken a sentence by disjoining it with another, but here's a small argument where it can be put to use:

If animals have rights or animals have souls, we shouldn't eat them.
Animals have rights.
Therefore: We shouldn't eat animals.

This has the form $(A v B) \to C$, A So: C. We can show that an argument with these premises and conclusion is valid, by producing a formal derivation that corresponds to it. In our derivation, we shall start by assuming the premises and then, using the rules of inference, prove the conclusion.

Each line of the derivation has the form: line number, wff obtained at that stage, and information about how the wff was arrived at. I will first give the derivation, which in this case is very short, and then describe it.

1)	(A v B) → C	ASS.
2)	A	ASS.
3)	A v B	vI, 2.
4)	C	→E, 1, 3.

On the first two lines, the information cited is ASS, i.e. that the rule of assumption is used - we start by assuming the premises. Other forms of information specification typically mention a connective, and I or E, according to whether the rule used is an Introduction or Elimination of that connective, and some line numbers - the lines to which the rule has been applied. Thus the information on line 3) specifies that the wff of that line, A v B, comes by v Introduction from line 2). In the argument we are formalizing, this would correspond to the move

Animals have rights
So: Animals have rights or animals have souls.

We now have both a conditional, (A v B) → C, and exactly the antecedent of that conditional, A v B, so we are in a position to apply → Elimination to those two sentences and infer the consequent, which is the conclusion we are seeking, C. This is essentially what the information on line 4) summarizes: the wff on that line comes by →E applied to the wffs on lines 1 and 3.

→ **Introduction**: Often it is convenient to package a line of reasoning from some assumption X to a conclusion Y into a single, conditional sentence: If X then Y. Imagine you are reasoning about some issue. You don't as yet know whether or not X is the case, but you want to know what would follow if it were the case. So you say: Suppose X. There then follows a chain of reasoning, a number of intermediate sentences, which results in conclusion Y. You have shown that, on the assumption of X - if X is the case - Y follows. So you summarize this line of reasoning with a conditional: *if* X, then Y. This is how to prove a conditional: assume the antecedent, and show that the consequent follows. Schematically,

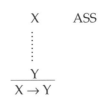

Read this: given a proof of Y, from the assumption of X, you may infer X → Y.

An example of →I in a formal proof is the derivation of A → (B & C) from the premises A → B, A → C.

1)	A → B	ASS.
2)	A → C	ASS.
3)	A	ASS.
4)	B	→E, 1, 3.
5)	C	→E, 2, 3.
6)	B & C	&I, 4, 5.
7)	A → (B & C)	→I, 3, 6.

We start by assuming the two premises. At line three we make the further assumption of the antecedent of the conditional we want to prove. This enables us to derive B and C separately (lines 4 and 5), which can then be conjoined to form the consequent we are aiming for. We have a proof of B & C, on the assumption of A, so at line 7 we conclude that if A then B & C.

4.1.3 Three ways of showing something isn't so

Suppose on waking up one morning that you become suspicious that the electricity in your house is off. Let us consider various ways that might be available to you, without getting up, of establishing that there is no electricity in the house that day. The first method is a *direct refutation* of the proposition that there is electricity in your house. To prove that ¬A, you check directly whether or not A. In this case, let us suppose that there is no light by your bedside, but just an electrical socket, into which you may insert your fingers. The notions of direct verification and refutation may (or may not) be philosophically problematic, but it at least makes intuitive sense to think of putting one's finger in the socket as such a direct procedure.

Whether or not these notions are problematic, they are not our concern here, since they do not involve establishing a proposition by reasoning towards it. There are plenty of ordinary sentences for which a procedure of direct refutation is not available (or perhaps: not desirable!) Indirect means of establishing that A isn't so are also possible - for instance, by showing that ¬A follows directly from other propositions which one accepts. Suppose you remember that the electricity board will cut off the electricity in your area every Tuesday, and that today is Tuesday. If you sincerely believe this, then you will believe that there is no electricity in the house. Schematically, you could be said to believe that B → ¬A (If today is Tuesday, it is not the case that there is electricity) and also B, so you infer ¬A. Showing in this way that ¬A follows directly from your beliefs involves no new rule of inference - this just requires an → Elimination.

The third way is the least direct, but it is the one which most concerns us here: to show that A isn't so, you show that A is inconsistent with some other beliefs you hold. You demonstrate this by showing that the assumption of A, together with those other beliefs, leads to a contradiction. Suppose you believe that if there is electricity, you will hear some gadget humming away, e.g. the motor in your old fridge. But you don't hear any humming. Formally, then, you believe A → B (If there is electricity, a gadget will be audible); on the supposition that A, B follows. But you believe something inconsistent with B, namely: a gadget is not audible, ¬B. So you may reject the assumption A and conclude ¬A. You have established ¬A by showing how to reject A: an absurdity, a contradiction, may be derived from the supposition of A (with the help of some further assumptions which you do not want to reject). We have here an important new rule of inference:

Reductio Ad Absurdum: Roughly, this rule says that if you can derive a contradiction from some sentence, then that sentence can't be true:

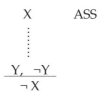

This can be read: if some sentence Y and its negation can be derived, on the assumption of a sentence X, you may infer ¬X. This is just our formal way of saying that if a contradiction follows from a sentence, you may infer that the sentence is false. Note that all three ways of showing that something isn't so can also be used, when appropriate, for showing that something *is* so. In the case of Reductio, we have :

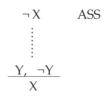

The first version of Reductio is the negation introduction form, and this version is negation elimination: if you assume the negation of X and can derive a contradiction, you may infer X. I have used the Latin name of the rule, because in classical logic it covers both negation introduction and elimination.

   In our original argument, the derivation of line 6), that a is not a knave, is a Reductio Ad Absurdum of the initial assumption, that a is a knave. The inferential situation might be put like this. We start off not knowing whether or not a is a knave. First we *assume* that he is. We derive a contradiction. So that assumption is false - we now *know* that he is not. Notice that this is a special case of Reductio, in that the assumption we make also supplies one half of the contradiction - the assumption itself is contradicted. We might represent it thus:

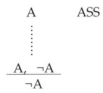

This is a special case of Reductio, where the same sentence plays the role both of assumption, and one half of the contradiction.

   Here is another example of a formal derivation, which involves use of Reductio. The argument is: ¬(A & ¬B), A, So: B.

1)	¬(A & ¬B)	ASS.
2)	A	ASS.
3)	¬B	ASS.
4)	A & ¬B	&I, 2, 3.
5)	B	RAA, 3, 1, 4.

First of all we assume the two premises. But with these two assumptions, we can't immediately derive B. The way to proceed is by Reductio: to show that given these two assumptions, ¬B can't be true. So suppose it were the case that ¬B (line 3) - this leads immediately to something (line 4) which contradicts one of our assumptions. Note this very important feature of RAA, that an explicit contradiction must be produced: a wff, here A & ¬B, and the *exact negation* of that wff, ¬(A & ¬B). We conclude that B, and cite line 3, the assumption shown to be false, and lines 1 and 4, the two wffs which contradict each other.

In each application of a rule, the number of lines cited in the information corresponds to the number of wffs the rule is applied to. ASS is not applied to any line, it is the making of a fresh assumption, so no lines are mentioned. &E and vI are both inferences from a single wff - one line is cited. →I requires the assumption of the antecedent, and the derivation of the consequent; two wffs, so two lines to cite. &I, vE and →E are also two-liners. With RAA, always cite three lines - the assumption reduced to absurdity, and the two sides of the contradiction. (If a wff is both the assumption and half of the contradiction, cite it twice.)

Exercise 1

A.   Formalize these three sentences:

1)   If Hegel is right and Marx is right, contradictions exist in nature.
2)   If Hegel is right or Marx is right, contradictions exist in nature.
3)   If Marx is right, contradictions exist in nature.

3) only validly follows from one of 1) or 2). Use truth tables to demonstrate which of the two inferences (1 therefore 3; or 2 therefore 3) is valid. Then use natural deduction rules to derive 3 from whichever of 1 or 2 it genuinely follows from.

B.   Formalize the following arguments, and show by natural deduction that the conclusion follows from the premises.

4)   Either Mary will leave at four or John will leave at four. Mary is teaching until five and she won't leave at four. If John leaves at four he will arrive before eight. Therefore: John will arrive before eight.
5)   Either we use the large table or we sit Bill next to Mary. If we sit Bill next to Mary, there will be an argument about politics. Therefore: If we don't use the large table, there will be an argument about politics.
6)   If computers can follow rules then computers can understand language. Computers can't understand language. Therefore: Computers can't follow rules.
7)   If there are scorpions or snakes, John won't go. If there are lizards, there are snakes. So: If there are lizards, John won't go.

8)   Jekyll is the same person as Hyde only if they are psychologically continuous. Therefore: If Jekyll is not psychologically continuous with Hyde then they are not the same person.

C.   Prove the following by natural deduction.

9)   A & B   So: B & A.
10)   (B & A) v (B v C),   ¬B   So: C.

4.2 Assumptions and strategy

4.2.1 Making and discharging assumptions

As we have seen, two deductive rules are associated with each logical constant. An elimination rule tells us what we may infer from a wff which has a particular constant as its dominant connective, i.e. what follows *from* it. → Elimination tells us that, given any wff which has the overall structure of a conditional, we can infer the consequent of that conditional, if we also have its antecedent. We move from a wff of form X → Y to Y - we thus 'eliminate' a conditional. An introduction rule tells us when we may infer *to* a wff with a structure dominated by a particular connective. & Introduction tells us that we may introduce a conjunction if we have, in whatever order, the two conjuncts.

Natural deduction involves an element of choice - most apparent in rule of assumption, ASS - which is often puzzling to the beginner. To an important extent, it's up to us to choose what assumptions to make, and what to do with them. (E and I rules are all about what one *may* infer - what inferences are permissible.) But this corresponds to a feature of our natural reasoning. A good problem-solver is someone who can make relevant conjectures about a problem, and who can put them to good use - following out their consequences, holding onto them while consistent, rejecting them when inconsistent. This is not an ability which in general can be reduced to a set of mechanical rules, but it is something for which informal guidance can be given, both on overall strategy and particular tactics. In the case of natural deduction, a number of heuristic rules - informal and fairly common-sense principles - can be given to guide deduction.

Firstly, we can state some general principles concerning overall strategy in constructing a derivation.
1.   Assume the premises of the argument - assume what you're entitled to assume - and see what can be done with them.

2.   If a wff of a certain form occurs as a *premise*, it's likely that if it is to play its part in the argument, at some point an *Elimination* rule will need to be applied to it, to draw out its consequences.

3.   If the *conclusion* has logical structure, it is probable that the *Introduction* rule for a wff of that structure will be required - most likely, the last step in the proof. Even if it's the last step, it may nevertheless influence the overall structure of the proof. If, for example, the conclusion is a conditional, to set things up for an →I you need to assume its antecedent and aim to obtain a proof of its consequent.

4.   If 1 to 3 don't go far enough, assumptions additional to the premises will need to be made. This is just what we do when problem solving, e.g. with the knights and knaves examples, when the information we are given (our premises) doesn't enable us to reach the conclusion directly - we start conjecturing hypotheses about the problem. In a formal proof, it may be that we need to assume the negation of the conclusion, and then proceed by Reductio.

Let's consider this last point in more detail. One of de Morgan's Laws is this: (A v B) is equivalent to ¬(¬A & ¬B). We can demonstrate the equivalence by showing these two wffs to be inter-derivable. We shall consider the derivation of the former from the latter. The proof is rather obscure, so to begin with just try to follow the basic steps. We start off by assuming the premise and the negation of the conclusion, but that doesn't give us anything we can use straight away, so we have to make some further assumptions. The proof takes the form of producing successive Reductios of these additional assumptions, and then the negated conclusion.

1)	¬ (¬A & ¬B)	ASS.
2)	¬ (A v B)	ASS.
3)	¬A	ASS.
4)	¬B	ASS.
5)	¬A & ¬B	&I, 3, 4.
6)	B	RAA, 4, 1, 5.
7)	A v B	vI, 6.
8)	A	RAA, 3, 2, 7.
9)	A v B	vI, 8.
10)	A v B	RAA, 2, 2, 9.

A natural thought to have, on seeing this proof, is: why so many assumptions? To put it at its most provocative: if you can assume anything (as the rule ASS says you can), why not just assume the conclusion straight off? The answer, or at least the beginning of one, is that any assumption made will remain in force in an argument, and ultimately count as one of its premises, *unless* it gets cancelled out en route to the conclusion. Certain rules of inference have the effect of cancelling, or **discharging**, assumptions. If an assumption gets discharged, it no longer counts as one of the propositions relied on to get the conclusion - that is, it will no longer be counted as one of the premises of the argument.

Again, this corresponds to a perfectly natural feature of our reasoning, it's just one we tend not to be very explicit about. Look again at the knights and knaves reasoning analyzed in the previous section. In that argument, the conclusion we reached, that a is a knight and b a knave, rested on certain assumptions, e.g. that a said 'At least one of us is a knave.' In order to get the reasoning going, we made a conjecture about a - that he is a knave. Do we think that the conclusion ultimately rests on that assumption? No - we don't say "We have established that a is a knight and b is a knave, on the assumption that a is a knave". That assumption was rejected. We made a conjecture, and were able to rule it out. The fact that we don't treat it as an assumption upon which the conclusion rests just shows that we implicitly understand it to have been discharged. Reductio has this effect - it discharges an assumption which leads to contradiction.

With the above proof, we start off with assumptions: 1, 2, 3, 4. We get a contradiction (line 1 with line 5). So we know that those four assumptions can't all be true together. This means that at least one of them must be false, and can be eliminated. We choose to discharge 4 - it can be crossed off the list of assumptions we are appealing to. The list is in effect: 1, 2, 3, ~~4~~. We then get another contradiction (lines 2 and 7). So of the remaining three assumptions in force, at least one of those can't be true. We discharge 3, and can strike it off the list: 1, 2, ~~3~~, ~~4~~. Finally, we derive yet another contradiction (lines 2 and 9), so of the remaining two undischarged assumptions, yet another must be false.

We *could* take this as a Reductio of line 1. Discharging 1, and keeping 2 as the premise, would give us a proof of (¬A & ¬B) from ¬(A v B) (another de Morgan Law). But given what we're trying to show, we want to keep 1 as the premise, and discharge 2. We thus infer A v B from ¬(¬A & ¬B), and our final list of what has been assumed is: 1, ~~2~~, ~~3~~, ~~4~~. The only assumption which remains in force at the end is the only one which should remain - the premise of the argument. If any other assumption had remained undischarged it too would have to count as a premise, as something the conclusion rests on. Other things being equal, the more premises you have, the less interesting the proof, because the more you've helped yourself to in getting the conclusion. At the limit (triviality), you could just assume the conclusion straight off.

Most rules of inference have no effect on the total number of assumptions. The result of an &E, say, depends on whatever assumptions the conjunction it came from depends on. An &E neither introduces a fresh assumption, nor discharges an old one. Of the rules of natural deduction we are considering, only RAA and →I discharge an assumption. To illustrate the point in respect of →I, consider this fable from an old edition of Aesop:

> A Country Maid was walking very deliberately with a pail of Milk upon her head, when ſhe fell into the following train of reflections: The money, for which I ſhall ſell this Milk, will enable me to increase my ſtock of eggs to three hundred. Theſe eggs, allowing for what may prove addle, and what may be destroyed by vermin, will produce at leaſt two hundred and fifty chickens. The chickens will be fit to carry to market about Chriſtmas, when poultry always bear a good price; ſo that by May-day I cannot fail of having money enough to purchaſe a new gown.

All of Aesop's fables have a moral. The moral of this tale is that →I discharges an assumption. Condensing the Country Maid's reasoning slightly, we have a series of conditionals: If I sell the milk, I shall obtain 300 eggs, if I obtain 300 eggs, I will sell 250 chickens, if I sell 250 chickens, I will purchase a new gown. The Maid believes all these; since she also believes the antecedent of the first conditional, she infers that she will purchase a new gown:

1)	A	ASS.
2)	A → B	ASS.
3)	B	→E, 1, 2.
4)	B → C	ASS.
5)	C	→E, 3, 4.
6)	C → D	ASS.
7)	D	→E, 5, 6.

Thus represented, her train of thought relies on four assumptions: 1, 2, 4, 6. However, if you know or suspect the denouement of this tale - she gets so lost in her day-dream that she drops the pail - you will not accept her first assumption, that she will sell the milk. We can nevertheless accept all the conditional premises, and consequently we can agree that *if* she sells the milk, she will purchase a new gown. To reach this more cautious conclusion, we need to take one further step in the proof:

8) $A \rightarrow D$ $\rightarrow$I, 1, 7.

(This proves a lengthened version of the Transitivity of the Conditional, the law which says that $A \rightarrow B$, $B \rightarrow C$ entail $A \rightarrow C$.) We can accept the conditional if A then D - because we believe that D follows from A - without being committed to A. Both we and the maid are agreed that if she sells the milk, she will buy the gown; intuitively, the difference between us is just that she also accepts that she *will* sell the milk. From our point of view, the assumption A was made 'for the sake of argument', i.e. to show that D follows from it. Now that we have moved to the more cautious, conditional proposition $A \rightarrow D$, we have discharged our commitment to its antecedent. Instead of saying we have proved D, on the assumption of A (and other assumptions), we can say instead: If A then D. The rule $\rightarrow$I discharges the assumption of A, not by ruling it out (like a Reductio), but by converting it into the antecedent of a conditional. The point of the example is to try to bring out how this accords with our intuitions about what we are committed to in this kind of reasoning.

From now on we will keep track of the assumptions in force in an argument, with a record of What is Assumed (abbreviated to W.i.A.). Record-keeping is basically simple: whenever a fresh assumption is made, list its line number; when an assumption is discharged, cross the number off. An application of RAA discharges the assumption which is reduced to absurdity; an application of $\rightarrow$I discharges the assumption of the antecedent of the conditional. The fourth heuristic can now be revised to:

4.   If this is still insufficient, assumptions additional to the premises will need to be made - assumptions which must therefore be discharged by the time you obtain the conclusion (else they will count as additional premises).

4.2.2 Proof strategy

To illustrate how proof construction is amenable to strategic planning, I will use a very simple problem as an analogy. There are three blocks, and three positions where they may be placed. The task is - moving only one block at a time - to shift all the blocks from their initial configuration to the goal configuration:

From initial state: To goal:

```
┌───┐                                                    ┌───┐
│ 1 │                                                    │ 1 │
├───┤                                                    ├───┤
│ 2 │                                                    │ 2 │
├───┤                                                    ├───┤
│ 3 │                                                    │ 3 │
└───┴──────────────────              ──────────────────┴───┘
  a      b      c                       a      b      c
```

(The task is a little less simple if we place the additional constraint that a higher numbered block cannot sit on a lower numbered block - it is then a version of the Towers of Hanoi problem (cf. section 3.6.3). What is of interest here is not the blocksworld problem itself but the sort of reasoning we employ in solving it. We can distinguish two different strategies:

Forwards Reasoning. This is the approach which would ordinarily predominate in our thinking about this problem. We have an initial configuration and we think: what is the next stage from here, and the next after that ...

From: move block 1:   and then 2:

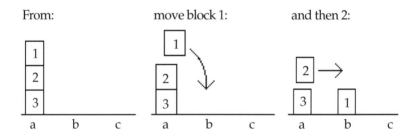

and then move block 3 to position c, and so on. But there is an alternative way of looking at it:

Backwards Reasoning. This approaches the problem from the opposite direction: I am aiming for this goal, so how could I establish it? From what configuration could I make the final step to the main goal, i.e. what could be the penultimate goal? And then: how could I establish that - what position could immediately precede that? And so on, reasoning backwards from the position one is ultimately aiming for:

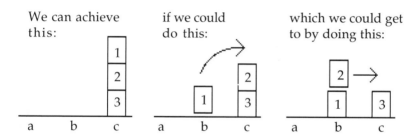

Forwards reasoning requires one to keep in mind a chain of intermediate states which represents a provisional path towards a solution, whereas backwards reasoning requires one to keep track of a chain of states leading back from the goal. The terminology forwards/backwards *chaining* is sometimes preferred.

It makes sense to adopt a forwards reasoning strategy when the number of possible opening moves from the initial state is relatively small, and the number of closing moves to attain the goal state is relatively large. This is characteristic of problem solving examples like the island of knights and knaves. With such problems, there are in fact endlessly many possible moves from the initial information, but we can use our understanding of the problem domain to select a unique relevant opening inference. We are given information that some individual x said something - we have to consider the possibility that x is a knight, and that x is a knave, so we can arbitrarily select one of these cases and make our initial move the assumption that x is a knave, say. This in turn will determine further moves. 'Impure reason' - reasoning which is constrained by knowledge of the problem domain - is thus efficient, because there is heuristic selection of the appropriate inferential step. At the other end of the argument, the conclusion we are aiming for is not fully specified, since it is the solution to the problem. A problem about two islanders will have at least nine possible solutions, since for each of them there are three possibilities: knight, knave or unknown (and a fourth, if we allow for normals). Since there is not a single, determinate goal - we do not know which of these possible conclusions is the solution - a backwards strategy is not really feasible. Conversely, backwards chaining will be efficient when the number of initial moves is large relative to the number of closing moves. This is often the case with standard natural deduction proofs, since the conclusion is specified, and heuristics will usually suggest the most likely single rule for establishing it.

A purely forwards approach would be blind to the goal state - it would look only at the current configuration, and what moves could be made at that point. The goal would play no role in guiding the choice of moves, i.e. helping to select the next move to make. One would look at the current state, make a move, check to see if the new state was the goal, then make a new move, check, and so on, until by chance one hit upon the goal state. Clearly, our approach to a knights and knaves problem is not random like this - we are guided at least by the *form* of the conclusion we are aiming for. Similarly, in a blocksworld problem one would keep in mind the goal of the task, the final state. To this extent, then, we adopt a combined, bidirectional strategy. This is usually the optimal approach - to look at what one has actually got, and reason forwards from there, but also to look at where one is going, and reason backwards from that goal. It is possible that none of these strategies will be especially fruitful. But in general, a combined forwards-backwards approach is likely to be the most efficient - working from both ends of the problem, and hoping to meet in the middle.

The purpose of this discussion is to emphasize the value of a bidirectional strategy in natural deduction. I suspect that one of the reasons why beginners have difficulty in constructing proofs is that they rely too heavily on a forwards approach - they look at what they've got, but not at where they're going. To correct this, we need to emphasize the reverse approach. What conclusion are we asked to prove? If it is structured: what is its dominant connective; by what rule of inference, applied to what wffs, could it be obtained? If it is atomic: in which premise does that atomic wff occur; by what rule of inference could one obtain it from that premise? And if you have answered this question, of how to obtain the main conclusion, does the answer set you a new goal to prove? If so, repeat the process: what is its structure; how can it be proved?

Let's work through an example of reasoning backwards from the conclusion we are aiming to establish. Since $(A \rightarrow B)$ is logically equivalent to $\neg(A \& \neg B)$, the conditional

$$\neg(A \& \neg B) \rightarrow (A \rightarrow B)$$

is a logical truth. Since it's a truth of logic, it depends on no facts about how the world is - it can be derived from no premises at all. At the end of the proof, any assumptions we make must have been discharged. Since no premises are required, heuristics 1 and 2 do not apply, but heuristic 3 advises that, as we're aiming for a conditional, we should assume its antecedent and aim for its consequent:

1)	¬(A & ¬B)	ASS.	W.i.A.
:	:	:	1
n-1)	A → B	?	
n)	¬(A & ¬B) → (A → B)	→I, 1 , n-1.	

On the right, we now have 'W.i.A.', as a record of the assumptions appealed to. We don't know how long the proof is going to be, so at the moment we shall just say that the last line, where we establish this logical truth, is line n, and so the penultimate line, where we establish its consequent, will be line n-1.   We don't as yet know how we will establish that consequent, so I've just put a '?' instead of a definite rule. But since it too is a conditional, it looks as if we should heed the advice of the same heuristic again: within the →I which is the overall proof of the main conditional, there will be an →I which is the proof of its consequent. The proof plan becomes:

1)	¬(A & ¬B)	ASS.	W.i.A.
2)	A	ASS.	1,2
:	:	:	
n-2)	B	?	
n-1)	A → B	→I, 2, n-2.	
n)	¬(A & ¬B) → (A → B)	→I, 1 , n-1.	

So now our task has become to prove B from assumptions ¬(A & ¬B) and A. For if we can do that, we know the final two steps that will take us to the conclusion we are aiming for. Since B is atomic, and doesn't follow directly from those two assumptions, it looks like a Reductio is called for - in fact, it is the Reductio described in the previous section. With this brief reflection on the structure of what is to be proved, the structure of how to prove it has fallen into place. The gap can be filled in, and the complete proof written out:

1)	¬(A & ¬B)	ASS.	W.i.A.
2)	A	ASS.	1̶, 2̶, 3
3)	¬B	ASS.	
4)	A & ¬B	&I, 2, 3.	
5)	B	RAA, 3, 1, 4.	
6)	A → B	→I, 2, 5.	
7)	¬(A & ¬B) → (A → B)	→I, 1, 6.	

The assumptions at lines 1, 2 and 3 were discharged, in reverse order, at lines 5, 6, and 7.

Now that we have looked at how the structure of the premises and conclusion constrain the shape of the proof, tactics for dealing with specific moves in a proof should be fairly self-evident. Here are some suggestions.

1.   Does the conclusion you want follow directly from what you already have? If so, apply the appropriate rule. If not:

2.   Is the conclusion you want atomic? If so, where does it occur within the premises? If an inference with consistent premises and an atomic conclusion is valid, that atomic wff must be contained somewhere within those premises. So: how can you extract that atomic wff from those premises? For instance:

3.   Is the conclusion you want the consequent of a conditional which you already have? (More generally: is the conclusion contained *within*, i.e. a sub-wff of, the consequent of a conditional? If it is, and you established that consequent, could you then go on to extract the wff you want from it?) If so, aim to establish the antecedent of that conditional - you will then be in a position to obtain the consequent by →E. Alternatively:

4.   Is the conclusion one half of a disjunction? (Or again, more generally: is the conclusion contained within one half of a disjunction?) If so, try aiming for the negation of the other disjunct - you can then apply vE.

5.   Does the conclusion you are aiming for have structure? If so, aim to put yourself in a position where you can apply the introduction rule appropriate to something with that structure. For instance, if it is a conjunction, aim to establish each conjunct. If it is a disjunction, aim to establish one or other disjunct. If it is a conditional, try to get into a position where you can apply →I: assume the antecedent, and aim to prove the consequent. That is, add the antecedent to your stock of assumptions, and make the conclusion you are now aiming for the consequent of the conditional.

6.   Is the conclusion you want a negation - something of the form ¬X, whether or not X itself has structure? If so, try aiming for a negation introduction: assume X, and establish two sides of a contradiction.

7.   If the conclusion X you want is not a negation, it may still be that Reductio is appropriate - in its negation elimination form. Assume ¬X, and aim for a contradiction.

4.2.3 Caveat

In one respect the system of tracking assumptions used here involves a simplification. 'What is Assumed' is a global record of the assumptions relied upon in an argument; it does not keep track, as many systems do, of local dependencies - of what each line depends on. So, attending to the letter but not the spirit of the method, one might get a 'proof' like this:

1)	A	ASS.	W.i.A.
2)	A → A	→I, 1, 1.	~~1~~
3)	A	→E, 1, 2.	

If this were correct, we would have a recipe for proving any proposition whatsoever! It looks as if we have a proof of A, any A, from no assumptions at all. The diagnosis is not hard to fathom. At line 2) we have a correct proof of the logical truth that if A, then A. It involves a limiting case of the use of →I - the assumption of A is a trivial proof of A from A. So at line 2) that assumption is discharged. The illicit step is the last one - the assumption 1) is *re*-used, as a premise of the →E, but is not acknowledged as such. It's as if that assumption has been made afresh, without being reported.

When reasoning informally, we are not tempted to make this kind of move. In working through a knights and knaves case, we might break the argument into what are in effect two ***sub-proofs***, one for the possibility that the speaker is a knave, and one for the possibility that he is a knight. In general, a sub-proof lasts from the making of an assumption until the point where it is discharged. In reasoning about the possibility of the speaker's being a knight, say, we don't make use of anything which crucially depends on the assumption that the speaker is a knave. Since the sub-proofs concern different cases, we know intuitively that we shouldn't take something which belongs in one sub-proof and import it into the other. In formal reasoning, the mistake of re-using without acknowledgement a discharged assumption, or something which depends on an assumption after it has been discharged, is occasionally made. (In the above three line proof, A → A at line 2 does not depend on A - it is a logical truth, and depends on nothing. The problem is the re-use of A outside the sub-proof.) But I do not think it is frequent enough to make it worth sacrificing the relative simplicity of this procedure - chalk up an assumption when you make it, cross it off when you finish with it. But, strictly speaking, there should be this qualification: if you re-use a discharged assumption, (or something inferred from it prior to its discharge), it should be acknowledged again as an assumption.

Exercise 2

In these and all subsequent derivations, keep track of any assumptions in force with 'W.i.A'. Use this to check that the assumptions which remain undischarged when you reach the conclusion are no more than the premises permitted.

A.   The positivists wanted to eliminate metaphysics on the basis of their verificationist theory of meaning. Metaphysical statements were adjudged meaningless because unverifiable - whether they were true or false could never show up in anything we might possibly observe. One problem facing the positivists was the formulation of the required notion of verifiability. A.J. Ayer tried to formulate this idea of making a difference to what we might observe, into a notion of weak verifiability, as follows. A statement S is weakly verifiable iff "some experiential propositions [O] can be deduced from it in conjunction with certain other premises [P] without being deducible from those other premises alone". That is,

S is weakly verifiable iff for some P and O: S, P entail O, but not: P entails O.

But this is hopeless: any S will count as weakly verifiable, if we choose an appropriate P. Show that the definition is too liberal, by giving examples in English of S, O and P which provide a counter-example. O should be observational (i.e. it should be possible to determine its truth or falsity by observation alone), S should be unverifiable (i.e. intuitively it should *not* qualify as a verifiable statement), and P should enable O to be derived from S, without entailing O on its own. (Hint: what propositional combination of O with S will fill this role?)

Ayer tried to revise his definition, by placing restrictions on the supplementary premise P: P should either be necessary or weakly verifiable independently of S. But Alonzo Church showed that still, any S would be weakly verifiable. Let O_1, O_2, O_3 be three logically independent observation reports (i.e. none is deducible from any of the others). We choose P as follows. Let P be: $(\neg O_1 \ \& \ O_2) \ v \ (O_3 \ \& \ \neg S)$. Two proofs are required to demonstrate Church's point. Firstly, to show that S together with this P entail one of these observation sentences, and then to show that P is, independently, weakly verifiable - that P together with O_1 entail another observation sentence. Produce one or other of these derivations.

B.   Formalize and prove the following by natural deduction:

1)   If the agriculture ministry is correct, it is safe to eat eggs. If the health ministry is correct, many eggs are infected with salmonella. If many eggs are infected with salmonella, it is not safe to eat eggs. Therefore: it is not the case that the agriculture ministry and the health ministry are both correct.
2)   If naive realism is true, it is not true.   Therefore: Naive realism is not true. (Adapted from Russell).
3)   If the currency is strong, exports will be more expensive. Therefore: If it's the case that if the currency is strong, inflation will rise, then it's the case that if the currency is strong, exports will be more expensive and inflation will rise.

Derive 4) as a logical truth, i.e. discharging all assumptions made:

4) $(A \rightarrow B) \rightarrow ((C \rightarrow D) \rightarrow ((A \, \& \, C) \rightarrow (B \, \& \, D)))$.

C.   There are really two different versions of vE, which correspond to two ways one can reason from a disjunction X v Y. The simplest version, the one we have adopted, can be paraphrased: if you know that either X or Y is true, and you also come to know that one of those is false, you may infer the other. The alternative form of inference is adopted when we are not in a position to rule out one or other of the disjuncts, but can show that a certain conclusion Z follows whichever of the disjuncts is the case. The argument proceeds by taking each case in turn: showing that Z follows from X, and that it follows from Y. So if either X or Y is true (whichever it is), Z must be true. We can formulate the rule like this:

PC $$\frac{X \vee Y, \ X \rightarrow Z, \ Y \rightarrow Z}{Z}$$

The rule is called 'PC', for 'Proof by Cases'. In ordinary reasoning, neither of these forms of 'or' elimination has priority - we use whichever one is appropriate to the case in hand. Formally, either can be derived from the other. Show that PC can be derived from our rule of v Elimination, by assuming A v B, A → C, B → C as premises and using vE to derive C as conclusion.

4.3 Reasoning further

4.3.1 Derived rules

The biconditional is not very distinctive from an inferential point of view - we can and will treat it essentially as a conjunction of conditionals.

$$\leftrightarrow \textbf{Introduction} \qquad \frac{X \rightarrow Y, \; Y \rightarrow X}{X \leftrightarrow Y}$$

$$\leftrightarrow \textbf{Elimination} \qquad \frac{X \leftrightarrow Y}{X \rightarrow Y} \qquad\qquad \frac{X \leftrightarrow Y}{Y \rightarrow X}$$

Various alternatives are possible. We would also be treating it as a conjunction of conditionals if we formulated its elimination rule like →E, but in both directions:

$$\frac{X \leftrightarrow Y, \; X}{Y} \qquad\qquad \frac{X \leftrightarrow Y, \; Y}{X}$$

But rather than take this as the basic rule of inference for ↔, we can show that it follows as a *derived* rule of inference. We have nominated the first version as our rule of ↔ Elimination; taking it as primitive, we can show that the other follows:

1)	A ↔ B	ASS.	W.i.A.
2)	A	ASS.	1, 2
3)	A → B	↔E, 1.	
4)	B	→E, 2, 3.	

(The proof of the right-hand version would obviously be almost identical.)

We can, if we want, give this rule of inference a name, and appeal to it directly in proofs. Once a rule has been derived within a system, we know that any use of it must be acceptable, because that use just telescopes the steps made in its derivation. A more interesting example would be the de Morgan law proved in the last section. We can, in any future proof, appeal to the inference from ¬(¬A & ¬B) to (A v B) directly, citing de Morgan in the information, because we know that that move would just abbreviate the ten steps in our derivation of it - steps which could, if we wanted to write the proof out solely in terms of our basic rules, be inserted at that point.

As exercise 4.2 C shows in connection with vE, which rules of inference are taken as primitive within a system, and which derived, is to some extent a matter of choice. Some proofs may be more natural with one rule of inference rather than another. For instance, it is natural to prove the distributive law

$$(A \& B) \text{ v } C \text{ So: } (A \text{ v } C) \& (B \text{ v } C)$$

using Proof by Cases, because the conclusion can be shown to follow from each disjunct of the premise:

1)	(A & B) v C	ASS	W.i.A.
2)	(A & B)	ASS	1, ~~2, 9~~
3)	A	&E, 2	
4)	A v C	vI, 3	
5)	B	&E, 2	
6)	B v C	vI, 5	
7)	(A v C) & (B v C)	&I, 4, 6	
8)	(A & B) → ((A v C) & (B v C))	→I, 2, 7	
9)	C	ASS	
10)	A v C	vI, 9	
11)	B v C	vI, 9	
12)	(A v C) & (B v C)	&I, 10, 11	
13)	C → ((A v C) & (B v C))	→I, 9, 12	
14)	(A v C) & (B v C)	PC, 1, 8, 14.	

One or two other important derived rules have also been encountered in exercises. For example, *Modus Tollens*:

$$\frac{X \to Y, \ \neg Y}{\neg X}$$

And then, *Contraposition*:

$$\frac{X \to Y}{\neg Y \to \neg X}$$

The rules for double negation introduction and elimination are also derived rules within our system.

DNI $\dfrac{X}{\neg\neg X}$ DNE $\dfrac{\neg\neg X}{X}$

For example, double negation elimination can be derived using the negation elimination form of RAA. Given ¬¬A, the assumption of ¬A can immediately be discharged and its negation inferred:

1)	¬¬A	ASS.	W.i.A.
2)	¬A	ASS.	1,2
3)	A	RAA, 2, 1, 2.	

A special case of a derived rule of inference is the introduction of a theorem or law of logic. Since Excluded Middle is a logical law, any instance of it can be proved from no premises at all:

1)	¬(A v ¬A)	ASS.	W.i.A.
2)	A	ASS.	1,2
3)	A v ¬A	vI, 2.	
4)	¬A	RAA, 2, 1, 3.	
5)	A v ¬A	vI, 4.	
6)	A v ¬A	RAA, 1, 1, 5.	

This means that if we want to introduce an instance of the Law of Excluded Middle into a proof, we can do so without it counting as an extra assumption about how the world is. For its introduction will just abbreviate this six line proof, in which all assumptions have been discharged. The general rule of inference will look like this:

$$\dfrac{}{X \text{ v } \neg X}$$

The Law of Excluded Middle is intimately connected with the semantical principle that every sentence is either true or false. The anti-realist view countenanced in exercise 2.2 D embraced the outright rejection of that principle. A more cautious form of anti-realism involves neither the acceptance nor the rejection of such classical principles. Intuitionist philosophers of mathematics, for example, regard the assertion of A v ¬A for all mathematical statements whatsoever (whether or not we could discover *which* of A or ¬A holds), as invoking an unacceptable metaphysical view: a determinate mathematical reality which renders judgements about it either true or false.   It's not that they think that mathematical reality must be indeterminate (cf. the third truth value for the future) - there is no justification for that - but they regard insistence on Excluded Middle as equally unjustified. So intuitionist logic simply omits certain classical principles. Intuitionist logic is *weaker* than classical logic - you can't prove as much in it. Naturally, if you drop some principles, you must also omit any other principles from which they could be derived.

In intuitionist logic it is definitely wrong to reject Excluded Middle, and this is reflected in the fact that ¬¬(A v ¬A) is a theorem of that system. Since they accept ¬¬(A v ¬A) but not A v ¬A, it is clear that Intuitionists do not allow Double Negation Elimination as acceptable rule of inference, else commitment to the former would inevitably lead to commitment to the latter. Notice that the same form of Reductio is used in the both the derivation of DNE and Excluded Middle - the negation elimination form. We might call this *classical* Reductio, to distinguish it from the intuitionistically acceptable negation introduction form. Another way to achieve double negation elimination is by appeal to this form of contraposition:

$$\frac{\neg X \rightarrow \neg Y}{Y \rightarrow X}$$

For consider this proof:

1)	¬A	ASS	W.i.A.
2)	¬¬¬A	DNI, 1	+
3)	¬A → ¬¬¬A	→I, 1, 2	
4)	¬¬A → A	Contrapos, 3.	

Another intuitionistically unacceptable argument form is **Dilemma**:

$$\frac{(X \rightarrow Y), \ (\neg X \rightarrow Y)}{Y}$$

Dilemma is a specialized form of Proof by Cases. Consider the following example, due to R.C. Moore. There are three blocks in a row, a, b and c; the colours of a and c are shown, but the colour of b is not known:

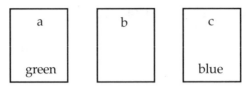

The question we are asked to consider is: 'Is there a green block next to a block which is not green?' Once we recognize that we can reason about b by dilemma, an affirmative answer becomes obvious: If b is green, then since b is next to c, b is a green block next to a block which is not green; but if b is not green, then a is a green block next to a block which is not green. There need be no need for the Intuitionist to object to classical reasoning in such ordinary cases as this; it is only the blanket acceptance, in all cases, which they find objectionable.

4.3.2 Conditionals

The discussion of 'unless' in section 2.3 illustrated how there is bound to be room for dispute over how well a word from ordinary language corresponds to one whose meaning is, by definition, given by a truth table.   Conditionals have provided the greatest source of such controversy, both from the point of view of their semantics, and their rules of inference. Let us briefly consider the semantic angle - how one may doubt that the truth functional material conditional can serve to analyse ordinary conditionals.   One group of conditionals which are difficult to analyse as material conditionals are contrary-to-fact, *counterfactual* conditionals. Counterfactuals are conditionals whose antecedents are false, or are at least assumed to be false by the speaker. Concerning a match m, which was never placed in water, we can say

1)   If m had been placed in water, it would not have dissolved.

The antecedent involves a supposition which is contrary to fact - we may suppose that match m was burnt and destroyed before ever getting near any water.

Construed as a material conditional, sentence 1) is true. The truth table semantics for the material conditional can be summarized like this:

2) $(A \rightarrow B)$ is true iff either A is false or B is true.

This states necessary and sufficient conditions for the truth of a material conditional. Note in particular what suffices: any material conditional with a false antecedent (or true consequent) is bound to be true. So far so good - but then the *opposite* conditional to 1) (same antecedent, denial of consequent), if it can be analysed as a material conditional, must also be true:

3)   If m had been placed in water, it would have dissolved.

So here's the problem. 1) is true, and 3) is false, and for the same reason: matches are not soluble. The fact that a material conditional works in the case of 1) is entirely fortuitous - it doesn't work for 3). The truth of a counterfactual doesn't follow automatically from a fact about the antecedent, it depends on antecedent and consequent being suitably related - in this case, by a dispositional feature of the object described.
      Let's take a different case, where both antecedent and consequent are true:

4)   Tigers exist only if unicorns don't exist.

A natural reaction, when faced with a puzzling sentence, is to try to interpret it charitably - to try to interpret it as true. We try to think of a reason why the existence of tigers should depend upon the non-existence of unicorns. Finding none, we must conclude that 4) is false. As we might put it counterfactually, tigers would exist *even if* unicorns existed. So again, it looks like there is a discrepancy between the ordinary conditional (false) and the material conditional (true). Much more can be said about such examples, and things can be said in defence of the material conditional.
      From the point of view of reasoning with conditionals, one source of difficulty lies in the fact that what we choose to express in a conditional can vary greatly according to what we assume are the normal circumstances of the case. Our picking out some A as a sufficient condition for B can be influenced by what we think of as the background of standard conditions, against which A stands out as the crucial factor. If I say

5)   The car will start if the battery is connected,

I surely don't mean that the battery's being connected suffices on its own - turning the ignition, for example, is usually quite important in getting a car to start. The conditional is likely to be used where the connection of the battery is the crucially varying factor, and which, if everything else is as usual - including the switching of the ignition - will suffice if present.

The point is important to a classically valid inference, Strengthening the Antecedent. Here is a plausible instance of it:

6)   If the breathalyser is positive, you're drunk.   Therefore:
        If the breathalyser is positive *and* you insult the policeman, you're drunk.

To put it differently, if A *suffices* for B, B will still follow if some further condition, C, is satisfied. We derive (A & C) → B from A → B:

1)	A → B	ASS.	W.i.A.
2)	A & C	ASS.	1, 2
3)	A	&E, 2.	
4)	B	→E, 1, 3.	
5)	(A & C) → B	→I, 2, 4.	

But what about this, the standard kind of counter-example to the inference:

7)   If you strike the match, it will light.
        Therefore: If you strike the match and it's wet, it will light.

We take the former conditional to be true - not because we believe that, come what may, striking a match is sufficient for it to light, but because we believe that under the usual conditions, it suffices. 'Usual conditions' covers the presence of certain factors (e.g. dryness) and, what may come to the same thing, the absence of certain others (e.g. wetness). It covers conditions we may know about, such as the presence of oxygen, and conditions which we may not know about - the absence of large quantities of some arcane inert gas, for instance. Clearly, the latter category is potentially limitless. When we strengthen the antecedent with a sentence which takes away a factor contributing to the presumed normal state of affairs, as in 7), there can be no guarantee that the original condition remains sufficient.

Another suspect inference is this: if we assume B, we can derive *any* material conditional with B as its consequent:

1)	A	ASS.	<u>W.i.A.</u>
2)	B	ASS.	~~1~~, 2
3)	A → B	→I, 1, 2.	

This is one of the two *paradoxes of material implication* - 'paradox' in the loose sense of being counter-intuitive (rather than the strict sense of entailing a contradiction). The counter-intuitive feature can be put like this: a true sentence is materially implied by any sentence. The derivation involves a perfectly acceptable application of →I, since →I says that if you have a proof of B, on the assumption of A, you may infer A → B. But in a sense it is a vacuous application, since it wasn't a proof of B *from* A. A itself didn't figure in our proof of B; we just assumed B.

   Some systems of deduction prohibit such vacuous cases of →I - they impose the condition that, for the introduction of A → B, A must have been used in the proof of B. This restriction on the rule →I is adopted in systems of *relevance* logic. Relevance logicians want the antecedent to be relevant to the consequent, if a conditional is to be true, and one way to get relevance is to require that the antecedent is used in obtaining the consequent. But notice this about our more liberal version of →I: it is in perfect accord with the simple semantics we gave for the conditional. The truth table for the material conditional, summarized as 2) above, has the immediate consequence that any material conditional with a true consequent is itself true. Since relevance logicians reject the proof-theoretic manifestation of this principle, they must also provide a different (more complex) semantic account of the conditional.

   The other paradox of material implication is that a false sentence materially implies any sentence - from ¬A we can infer (A → B). Again, the connection with the semantics of the material conditional is straightforward. It is interestingly related to another principle of classical logic: a *logically* false sentence *logically* implies any sentence. From a contradiction, anything follows - from (A & ¬A), B (or *ex falso quodlibet*). One might say: if you're prepared to believe a contradiction, you're prepared to believe anything. The standard derivation, which was known to medieval logicians, goes:

1)	A & ¬A	ASS.	<u>W.i.A.</u>
2)	A	&E, 1.	1
3)	A v B	vI, 2.	
4)	¬A	&E, 1.	
5)	B	vE, 3, 4.	

Relevance logicians also refuse *ex falso quodlibet*. Since this derivation does not involve conditionals, →I is not the only classical rule they are prepared to modify.

4.3.3 |– and |=

We now have both a syntactic and a semantic characterization of valid reasoning. In section 4.2.1 we saw that A v B can be produced from ¬(¬A & ¬B) by the rules of natural deduction. We can write this: ¬(¬A & ¬B) |– A v B. More generally,

$$X, Y, Z, ... \quad |– \quad W$$

means that W is *syntactically derivable* from X, Y, Z, ... - it can be produced by a sequence of inferential steps, relying only on X, Y, Z, ... as (undischarged) assumptions. A limiting case of this is |– W, where W can be produced by the rules of natural deduction from no premises whatsoever. We saw above that |– A v ¬A.

With a truth table we can show that whenever ¬(¬A & ¬B) is true, A v B must also be. This is written: ¬(¬A & ¬B) |= A v B. More generally,

$$X, Y, Z, ... \quad |= \quad W$$

means that W is *semantically entailed* by X, Y, Z, ... - under no possible circumstances can X, Y, Z, ... all be true, and W false. The limiting case, |= W, is when under no possible circumstances can W be false. In introducing truth tables, we saw that |= (A v ¬ A).

Notice how other concepts we have defined semantically have their proof-theoretic counterparts. We can define inconsistency syntactically: a number of wffs X, ..., Z are inconsistent with each other if their conjunction is *refutable*, that is, we can prove its negation: |– ¬(X & ... & Z). The notion of truth functionality can also be characterized inferentially. We defined the truth functionality of a context C (e.g. negation) in terms of what it functions on: the truth value of any sentence embedded in it. If C is a truth function, it will be indifferent to all features of a sentence other than its truth value, so if X and Y are materially equivalent, the truth value of C(X) will be the same as that of C(Y). You can substitute Y for X in C *salva veritate* (preserving truth). In other words, C is a truth functional context iff C(X), X ↔ Y |– C(Y) (or, equivalently, iff X ↔ Y |– C(X) ↔ C(Y)).

What was a principle about semantic equivalence turns up as a principle about inferential substitution.

An important distinction here is that between *object language* and *meta-language*. When we ordinarily use language to talk about the world, this distinction does not apply; but sometimes we use one language to talk about another. We might discuss, in English, the meanings of certain French words - in such a case French, the language under discussion, is the object language, and English, the language in which the discussion takes place, is the meta-language. With natural languages, the distinction is largely relative - for French speakers talking about English, the roles of object and meta- language would be reversed. In logic, an object language is typically one in which certain forms of reasoning have been formally characterized - so it is a language in which one can actually *carry out* certain inferences - just those permitted by the rules of inference for that system. The meta-language is that in which one theorizes *about* such forms of reasoning - in our case, it is English supplemented with logical terminology. Certain concepts may belong to one language but not another. As we saw in section 2.2.3, the concept of necessity, for example, is not one which can be expressed in a simple truth functional language. As far as elementary propositional logic is concerned, it belongs to the meta-language; we can use the concept of necessity to characterize certain sentences in LPF, but we cannot express it within our truth functional LPF. Likewise, '$\vdash$' and '$\models$' belong to the meta-language; a statement of the form $X \models Y$ is a meta-linguistic statement that the relation of entailment holds between sentences X and Y of the object language.

We have seen that the syntactic notion of derivability, $\vdash$, and the semantic notion of entailment, $\models$, coincide in certain specific instances. In fact, they always coincide in the case of propositional and predicate logic. This is not something one can demonstrate working within propositional or predicate logic - it requires a meta-logical proof about the system. There are in fact two things to prove:

Soundness: If $X, Y, Z, \dots \vdash W$, then $X, Y, Z, \dots \models W$.
Completeness: If $X, Y, Z, \dots \models W$, then $X, Y, Z, \dots \vdash W$.

Roughly, soundness shows that our inference rules never lead to trouble - we could never derive a conclusion from some premises which wasn't entailed by them. For instance, from a consistent set of premises, the rules of proof won't generate some sentence A and also $\neg A$. Completeness shows that the rules capture *all* the entailments and truths we want to get. From a logician's point of view, it is desirable that a system is both consistent and complete - it shows that essentially the same notion has been characterized from two different perspectives, in terms of syntactic rules of proof, and semantic rules of interpretation.

A further notion is that of *decidability*. A property P is said to be decidable, for a set S, if we have an effective method for deciding, given any entity x in S, whether P(x) or ¬P(x). An effective method is a set of explicit rules, which could be carried out by a mechanical device, and which will return an answer within a finite time. That is, it is a program which is guaranteed to terminate - it won't run on forever without providing an answer. For instance, take the set of strings of symbols formulated with the vocabulary of propositional logic - such as '& A ¬ B', '¬A & B', 'Bv', etc. The property of being a well formed formula is decidable for that set: given any such string, we can get a mechanical device to recognize whether it is a wff or not, and to come back with the answer within a finite time. You can write a method in Prolog (exercise 5.3 A). When the decidability of a logical system is discussed, the property P at issue is | =, and the set S is the set of wffs of that system. In other words, a system is

Decidable: If we can get a machine that is guaranteed to recognize correctly whether a wff is a theorem of the system or not -
i)   If | = A, there is an effective method that will recognize that | = A, and
ii)   If not | = A, there is an effective method that will recognize that not | = A.

Propositional logic is decidable - a decision procedure is described in detail in section 5.4.2. Predicate logic, although consistent and complete, is not fully decidable - i) holds but not ii) (thus it is sometimes said to be *semi-decidable*.)

Exercise 3

A.   Suppose we can state necessary and sufficient conditions which define the terminology *airship* and *blimp* as follows:

1)   It is an airship iff it is a balloon or a dirigible.
2)   It is a blimp iff it is a balloon and it is small and it is not rigid.

(Assume that some definite object is fixed as the reference of 'it' throughout.) Clearly, the statement

3)   It is an airship

is weaker (easier to be true), less informative, than the statement

4)   It is a blimp.

Formalize 1) and 2), and use them as supplementary premises in producing a proof of 3) from 4).

B.   Prove the following:

5)   A → D, ¬(¬A & D), B ↔ ¬D |− A ↔ ¬B.
6)   (A v B) & C |− (A & C) v (B & C).
7)   ¬(A v B) |− ¬A & ¬B.

C.   This exercise is the converse of 4.2 C. Take Proof by Cases as the primitive rule of 'or' Elimination, and use it to derive A from A v B, ¬B. (Hint: to get in a position where you can use PC, you need to establish the two conditionals: A → A, and B → A.)

D.   Does vagueness pose a problem for classical logic? Take a predicate like 'bald' - this exhibits vagueness, in the sense that the boundary between something being bald and being not bald is not clear cut, but admits of degrees. Consider the plight of the manufacturers of GROW-IT, a hair restorer which, although it can't help people who are definitely bald, works wonders on those who are *balding*, i.e. who are in the borderline area between hairy and bald. The suppliers of the rival PLANT-IT hair transplant process argue as follows:

8)   If you're not bald, GROW-IT is superfluous. (You don't need it.)
        If you're bald, GROW-IT is ineffective. (As its makers admit.)
        So: GROW-IT is either superfluous or ineffective.

i) What principle of classical logic is this argument tacitly relying on?
ii)   Show that for classical logic, it is a valid argument, by reconstructing it in terms of natural deduction. (Ignore the bracketed explanations.)
iii) Given that the makers of GROW-IT will contest the conclusion, should they object to its premises, or the form of reasoning employed?

4.4 Generalizations

4.4.1 Reasoning with ∀

∀ **Elimination**:   The rule here is very similar to the tree rule, but stated in inferential terms: from a universal generalization one may infer any instance. For any variable v, any name n, and any predicate P,

$$\frac{(\forall v)\ P(v)}{P(n)}$$

The name n must replaces all free occurrences of v in P(v). Like all the quantifier rules, this applies for all predicates unrestrictedly, no matter what their complexity. So for instance, the moves

(∀z) finite(z) therefore: finite(socrates),   and
(∀y)(dog(y) → (∃x)(cat(x) & chases(y, x))) therefore:
                dog(fido) → (∃x)(cat(x) & chases(fido, x)

are both valid applications of ∀E. The reason for requiring that all occurrences of the variable bound by the ∀ be replaced by the name is to ensure that what results from the inference is a complete sentence, a closed wff. (If we didn't respect this in the second example, we could obtain 'dog(fido) → (∃x)(cat(x) & chases(y, x)'. This has a free variable ("If Fido is a dog, then y chases some cat"), and as such is incomplete - it is not something which is either true or false.)
        The rule is thus one of instantiation: in eliminating an ∀, one moves from a generalization to an instance of it. For an example of it in use, consider this inference:

        Only those with tickets will be admitted.
        John is without a ticket.
        So: John won't be admitted.

Using 'A(x)' for 'x will be admitted', and 'T(x)' for 'x has a ticket', the formal proof is as follows:

1)	(∀x)(A(x) → T(x))	ASS.	W.i.A.
2)	¬T(j)	ASS.	1, 2
3)	A(j) → T(j)	∀E, 1.	
4)	¬A(j)	MT, 2, 3.	

∀E neither introduces a fresh assumption, nor discharges an old one. Intuitively, an instance depends on whatever the generalization it came from depends on. So ∀E has no effect on the record of What is Assumed.

∀ **Introduction**:   How might one establish a generalization - introduce an 'Every' statement, such as 'Every P is Q'?   There are at least two important methods, which might be termed Enumeration and Induction. With the former, one enumerates all the Ps: a, b, c, ..., n, and then establishes that Q is true of them all: Q(a), Q(b), Q(c), ..., Q(n). This is essentially the method of Prolog's **forall** (see section 5.1.3). It is only feasible when there are a relatively small number of Ps. Otherwise, one must rely on some inductive technique: take a *typical* P, and show that it is Q. This is what lies behind the rule ∀I (also known as Universal Generalization). Since ∀I is more complex than ∀E, let's consider the idea informally some more. Here's what Bishop Berkeley had to say:

> an idea, which considered in itself is particular, becomes general, by being made to represent or stand for all other particular ideas of the same sort. To make this plain by an example, suppose a geometrician is demonstrating the method, of cutting a line into two equal parts. He draws, for instance, a black line of an inch in length, this which is a particular line is nevertheless with regard to its signification general, since as it is there used, it represents all particular lines whatsoever; for that what is demonstrated of it, is demonstrated of all lines ... (*Principles of Human Knowledge*; Introduction, paragraph 12)

Abstracting from some aspects of this peculiar to Berkeley's own views, the basic picture we get is this: if you show something of an individual which is truly representative of its class, you've shown it for all things of that class.

This kind of reasoning often leads to generalization in empirical matters, in science and everyday life. For instance, how would you demonstrate that all humans have a liver? You could make a good start on it by picking one out at random, opening it up, and checking that it's got one. Of course, with an empirical induction one may sometimes be unlucky or incautious in generalizing. This can happen if the case one picks is a freak specimen, one which is not truly representative of its kind. In empirical matters, one tries to preclude this, by choosing the specimen *at random* (and by repeating the test, etc.) By choosing an arbitrary specimen, one hopes that it has no peculiarities - that the demonstration will depend on no facts peculiar to it. If the demonstration *does* depend on no special facts about the particular chosen, it will be truly generalizable. With logical or mathematical induction, we can lay this down as a precondition that this must be satisfied by a universal introduction: if you want to generalize a conclusion about some individual a, that conclusion must not depend on any special assumptions about a. (If any assumptions were made about a, they must have been discharged by the time you come to generalize.)

There are three constraints in all on the rule:

$$\frac{P(n)}{(\forall v)\, P(v)} \qquad \text{Provided: i), ii), iii)}$$

i) There are no assumptions involving n, left undischarged, used to obtain P(n) (n must be an arbitrarily chosen, truly representative example).

ii) Substitution is uniform. For whatever name n and variable v are involved, every occurrence of n in P(n) must be replaced by the variable.

iii) A variable is chosen which doesn't occur in P(n) - variables shouldn't 'clash'. (Remember that the predicate can be of any complexity of structure, and so may contain within it quantifiers and variables.) More precisely: any quantifier in P(n) which has n within its scope must not bind the variable chosen which replaces n.

The first restriction is the one which is most distinctively concerned with generalization, but all three are there to ensure that any application of $\forall$I is valid. For example, suppose we prove on purely general grounds (as we can) that Socrates is identical to himself,

socrates = socrates.

Then if we were prepared to disregard the second constraint, and not replace all occurrences of the name by the variable introduced by the universal quantifier, we could obtain the obviously false conclusion that $(\forall x)(x = \text{socrates})$.

Finally, an example of the formal rule in action, with the syllogism:

All horses are mammals. All mammals are animals.
So: All horses are animals.

1)	$(\forall x)(\ horse(x) \to mammal(x)\ )$	ASS.	W.i.A.
2)	$(\forall x)(\ mammal(x) \to animal(x)\ )$	ASS.	1, 2, 3
3)	$horse(a)$	ASS.	
4)	$horse(a) \to mammal(a)$	$\forall E, 1.$	
5)	$mammal(a)$	$\to E, 3, 4.$	
6)	$mammal(a) \to animal(a)$	$\forall E, 2.$	
7)	$animal(a)$	$\to E, 5, 6.$	
8)	$horse(a) \to animal(a)$	$\to I, 3, 7.$	
9)	$(\forall x)(\ horse(x) \to animal(x)\ )$	$\forall I, 8.$	

We choose an individual at random at line 3), and suppose it's a horse. It might as well be the Eiffel Tower as Bucephalus, for our proof must ultimately depend on no assumptions about that individual, not even that it's a horse. At line 8) we make the $\to$I which discharges that assumption about a - line 8) rests only on the general statements 1) and 2). We thus reach the conditional conclusion, concerning a, which we can generalize.

4.4.2 Some laws of predicate logic

Suppose we have a sentence involving two universal quantifiers, say

1) Each politician visited every house.

We can formalize this as:

2) $(\forall x)(\forall y)[\ (politician(x)\ \&\ house(y)) \to visited(x, y)\ ]$,

(take any x and any y: if x is a politician and y a house, then x visited y.) It is important that the different quantifier phrases are associated with different variables. If we didn't choose a fresh variable for the second quantifier there would be a clash of variables:

3) $(\forall x)(\forall x)(\ (politician(x)\ \&\ house(x)) \to visited(x, x)\ )$.

It should be clear that there is a problem with 3). The problem is not *which* of the occurrences of 'x' the outermost quantifier binds, it's that it no longer binds any of them, because of the intervening '$(\forall x)$'. A particular occurrence of a variable is bound by the *closest* quantifier which can bind it (i.e. which uses the same letter). The first occurrence of '($\forall$x)' is vacuous, and so can be dropped. 3) amounts to this:

4)   ($\forall$x)[(politician(x) & house(x)) $\rightarrow$ visited(x, x)],

In other words, what 3) really says is: for any x, if x is both a politician and a house, then x visited itself. Clearly, this is not what is intended by 1).

The equivalence of 3) and 4) is guaranteed by the **Laws of Vacuous Quantification**. These state that if in any wff, e.g. of the form ($\forall$x) A, the quantifier binds no occurrence of the variable within A, then the quantifier is redundant - the wff is equivalent to A. So the law for $\forall$ (the same holds for $\exists$) is:

5)   ($\forall$x)A $\leftrightarrow$ A   (if A contains no free occurrence of x)

We can show that this equivalence is a logical law by deriving it from no premises:

1)   ($\forall$x) A   ASS.   W.i.A.
2)   A $\forall$E, 1.   1, 4
3)   ($\forall$x)A $\rightarrow$ A $\rightarrow$I, 1, 2.
4)   A   ASS.
5)   ($\forall$x) A $\forall$I, 4
6)   A $\rightarrow$ ($\forall$x)A $\rightarrow$I, 4, 5.
7)   ($\forall$x)A $\leftrightarrow$ A $\leftrightarrow$I, 3, 6.

The first sub-proof involves a vacuous application of $\forall$E - choose a name, and substitute it for all free occurrences of x within A (by hypothesis, there are none). The second sub-proof involves a similarly vacuous application of $\forall$I.

While on the subject of 1), note that

6)   ($\forall$y)($\forall$x)[(politician(y) & house(x)) $\rightarrow$ visited(y, x)],

is essentially exactly the same formalization of it as 2). The point of variables is to establish a link between quantifiers and a pattern of predication - as has been emphasized with Prolog, what matters is not the particular lettering chosen for a variable, but the pattern of cross references that it establishes. The basic pattern which is common to both 2) and 6) is this:

$$(\forall\ )(\forall\ )[\ (\text{politician}(\ )\ \&\ \text{house}(\ ))\ \rightarrow\ \text{visited}(\ ,\ )\ ]$$

(What *is* different to 2) is this:

7) $(\forall y)(\forall x)[\ (\text{politician}(y)\ \&\ \text{house}(x))\ \rightarrow\ \text{visited}(x,\ y)\ ]$,

which says that every politician was visited by every house.) There
are principles of quantifier logic to confirm the equivalence of 6) with
2), the *Laws of Alphabetic Variants*. For universal quantification:

8) $(\forall x)\ P(x)\ \leftrightarrow\ (\forall y)\ P(y)$,

(provided the variables do not clash within P.) In other words, if two
wffs differ only in that one has one variable in exactly the places the
other wff has another, they are equivalent - they are merely
alphabetic variants of one another. Again, we can show the
equivalence is a logical law. It suffices to look at the entailment in one
direction, since the other is obviously symmetrical:

1)	$(\forall x)\ P(x)$	ASS.	W.i.A.
2)	$P(a)$	$\forall$E, 1.	1
3)	$(\forall y)\ P(y)$	$\forall$I, 2.	
4)	$(\forall x)\ P(x)\ \rightarrow\ (\forall y)\ P(y)$	$\rightarrow$I, 1, 3.	

Another equivalent reformulation of 2) is this:

9) $(\forall y)(\forall x)[\ (\text{politician}(x)\ \&\ \text{house}(y))\ \rightarrow\ \text{visited}(x,\ y)\ ]$,

which differs only in that the order of the quantifiers have been
switched to $(\forall y)(\forall x)$. Again, there are laws of quantification theory
to underwrite the equivalence, the *Laws of Quantifier Shift*. These
say that if two wffs differ only in the order of two adjacent quantifiers
of the same kind, they are equivalent. So, for example:

10) $(\forall x)(\forall y)\ R(x,\ y)$ is equivalent to $(\forall y)(\forall x)\ R(x,\ y)$.

This is the first law we have looked at which involves more than one
quantifier. One of the simplest principles involving multiple
quantifiers is:

$$(\forall x)(\forall y)\ R(x,\ y) \quad \text{entails} \quad (\forall x)\ R(x,\ x),$$

if everything bears R to every object, then everything bears R to itself. To prove this, we simply instantiate the same name twice, then generalize:

1)	$(\forall x)(\forall y)\ R(x,\ y)$	ASS	W.i.A.
2)	$(\forall y)\ R(a,\ y)$	$\forall$E, 1.	1
3)	$R(a,\ a)$	$\forall$E, 2.	
4)	$(\forall x)\ R(x,\ x)$	$\forall$I, 3.	

If $(\forall x)\ R(x,\ x)$ is true, R is termed a ***reflexive*** relation.

The logic of multiple quantifiers comes into its own when relations are involved. Since there are various important kinds of relations - such as the reflexive relation - it helps to have a taxonomy. Here are some more kinds:

R is symmetric iff $(\forall x)(\forall y)(\ R(x,\ y) \rightarrow R(y,\ x)\ )$.
R is asymmetric iff $(\forall x)(\forall y)(\ R(x,\ y) \rightarrow \neg R(y,\ x)\ )$.
R is non-symmetric iff R is neither symmetric nor asymmetric.

So for example, *being the same height as* is symmetric, and *being taller than* is an asymmetric relation. *Loving* is non-symmetric: in some cases, love is reciprocated (asymmetry fails), and in others, it is not (symmetry fails).

R is transitive iff $(\forall x)(\forall y)(\forall z)(\ (R(x,\ y)\ \&\ R(y,\ z)) \rightarrow R(x,\ z)\ )$.
R is intransitive iff $(\forall x)(\forall y)(\forall z)(\ (R(x,\ y)\ \&\ R(y,\ z)) \rightarrow \neg R(x,\ z)\ )$.
R is non-transitive iff it is neither of these.

Can you think of relations which exemplify these last three kinds? These are some of the more obvious categories of relations, but many others are possible, for example:

R is euclidean iff $(\forall x)(\forall y)(\forall z)(\ (R(x,\ y)\ \&\ R(x,\ z)) \rightarrow R(y,\ z)\ )$.

There are many laws which relate relations. For example, if a relation is transitive and symmetric, it is euclidean. Let us consider how to prove this. When reasoning with quantifiers, it is important to think strategically about the structure of the proof, just as it is in the propositional case (section 4.2). To think strategically about a proof involving generalizations means: having assumed your general premises, don't immediately start instantiating them without first thinking about the conclusion you're aiming to prove. In this case the conclusion is $(\forall x)(\forall y)(\forall z)((R(x, y) \& R(x, z)) \rightarrow R(y, z))$. To prove this we need to establish, on purely general grounds, a particular instance of it, such as $(R(a, b) \& R(a, c)) \rightarrow R(b, c)$. Since this is a conditional, we need to set things up for $\rightarrow$I. In other words, the derivation should take this shape:

$R(a, b) \& R(a, c)$	ASS
$\vdots$	
$R(b, c)$	
$(R(a, b) \& R(a, c)) \rightarrow R(b, c)$	$\rightarrow$I
$(\forall x)(\forall y)(\forall z)((R(x, y) \& R(x, z)) \rightarrow R(y, z))$	$\forall$I

When the $\rightarrow$ Introduction is made, the assumption we make about a, b and c will be discharged.

So now the task has become: given $R(a, b)$, and $R(a, c)$, how can we derive from these $R(b, c)$, by appealing to the general properties we are allowed to assume about R, viz. transitivity and symmetry? Symmetry allows us to reverse $R(a, b)$ to $R(b, a)$, and $R(a, c)$ to $R(c, a)$. So we now have four relational statements to make use of. Thinking about transitivity: this will enable us to prove the statement we are currently aiming for, $R(b, c)$, if we can find some x such that $R(b, x)$ and $R(x, c)$. Is there such an x - can we find an x satisfying these requirements from amongst these four statements? Yes, a fills that role: b bears R to a, and a bears R to c. So the heart of the proof will essentially involve these transformations:

i)	$R(a, b) \& R(a, c)$	ASS
ii)	$R(a, b)$	&E, i
iii)	$R(b, a)$	From ii, by symmetry
iv)	$R(a, c)$	&E, i
v)	$R(b, c)$	From iii and iv, by transitivity

In the full derivation, instead of instantiating symmetry and transitivity more or less at random, our choice of instances will be motivated by a proper understanding of the essential steps. All that remains is to fill in the details:

1)	R(a, b) & R(a, c)	ASS	W.i.A.
2)	R(a, b)	&E, 1	+, 3, 8
3)	(∀x)(∀y)(R(x, y) → R(y, x))	ASS	
4)	(∀y)(R(a, y) → R(y, a))	∀E, 3	
5)	R(a, b) → R(b, a)	∀E, 4	
6)	R(b, a)	→E, 2, 5	
7)	R(a, c)	&E, 1	
8)	(∀x)(∀y)(∀z)((R(x, y) & R(y, z)) → R(x, z))	ASS	
9)	(∀y)(∀z)((R(b, y) & R(y, z)) → R(b, z))	∀E, 8	
10)	(∀z)((R(b, a) & R(a, z)) → R(b, z))	∀E, 9	
11)	(R(b, a) & R(a, c)) → R(b, c)	∀E, 10	
12)	(R(b, a) & R(a, c)	&I, 6, 7	
13)	R(b, c)	→E, 11, 2	
14)	(R(a, b) & R(a, c)) → R(b, c)	→I, 1, 13	
15)	(∀z)((R(a, b) & R(a, z)) → R(b, z))	∀I, 14	
16)	(∀y)(∀z)((R(a, y) & R(a, z)) → R(y, z))	∀I, 15	
17)	(∀x)(∀y)(∀z)((R(x, y) & R(x, z)) → R(y, z))	∀I, 16	

Let's take one more example: if a relation is euclidean and reflexive, it is symmetric. As in the previous example, we need to prove a specific instance of the conclusion, e.g. R(a, b) → R(b, a). So we assume R(a, b). The reflexivity of R gives us, for example, R(a, a). But if a bears R to b, and a bears R to a, if R is euclidean it follows that b bears R to a. In more detail:

1)	R(a, b)	ASS.	W.i.A.
2)	(∀x) R(x, x)	ASS.	+, 2, 5
3)	R(a, a)	∀E, 2.	
4)	R(a, b) & R(a, a)	&I, 1, 2.	
5)	(∀x)(∀y)(∀z)((R(x, y) & R(x, z)) → R(y, z))	ASS.	
6)	(∀y)(∀z)((R(a, y) & R(a, z)) → R(y, z))	∀E, 5.	
7)	(∀z)((R(a, b) & R(a, z)) → R(b, z))	∀E, 6.	
8)	(R(a, b) & R(a, a)) → R(b, a)	∀E, 7.	
9)	R(b, a)	→E, 4, 8.	
10)	R(a, b) → R(b, a)	→I, 1, 9.	
11)	(∀y)(R(a, y) → R(y, a))	∀I, 10.	
12)	(∀x)(∀y)(R(x, y) → R(y, x))	∀I, 11	

The proof illustrates the importance of strategic planning. If you simply assumed the euclidean principle, and then started instantiating, choosing three separate names to instantiate for 'x', 'y' and 'z', you would miss the crucial point that you have to use the same name for both 'x' and 'z'. We instantiate with 'a' at line 6, and again at line 8.

4.4.3   The logic of identity

We use the identity symbol '=' to express the strict identity relation: for any x and any y, x = y just in case x is *exactly the same individual as* y. So when we say, for example, that

1)   Lewis Carroll is Charles Dodgson,

the 'is' here is strict identity - Carroll (the author of *Alice in Wonderland*) was *none other than* Dodgson (the Oxford don who taught logic). So this has the form:

2)   c = d.

Identity is such a special relation that it is treated as a logical constant, with its own symbol, semantics and rules of inference. Like the other special relation, '<' (cf. exercise 2.5 D), it is standard to express identity in infix form. So note its syntax. The identity sign must be flanked by two terms - by names (as in 2), or variables, as in $(\forall x)(x = x)$, which says that everything is self-identical.

   Some people have difficulty with the idea that identity is a relation between objects. Perhaps they think that a *relation* should relate two objects, but where an identity holds, only one object is involved. But there are many relations which relate each object to itself, e.g. being the same height as. (The main difference is that unlike being identical in height, being identical is also a relation that no object bears to any other.) Moreover, most would agree that distinctness is a relation between objects - that when we say

3)   Budapest is not Bucharest,

we refer to two entities, and say that they differ. Distinctness, which can be symbolized with '$\neq$', is just the contradictory relation to identity. '$x \neq y$' is just an abbreviation for '$\neg (x = y)$'. If distinctness is a genuine relation, why not identity?

   The introduction rule for identity is quite straightforward: at any stage in a proof, a self-identity may be introduced:

$$\frac{}{a = a}$$

There is nothing above the line: a self-identity requires no premise to be inferred from (compare the discussion of Excluded Middle, on p. 184). Nor does it count as an assumption about the world. The elimination rule for identity is a version of Leibniz's Law, that if x is y, then anything true of x is true of y (and vice versa):

$$(\forall x)(\forall y)\ (\ x = y\ \rightarrow\ (P(x) \leftrightarrow P(y))\ ).$$

This formulation of the law is *schematic* - it should be read: whatever predicate P you choose, if x = y, P applies to x just in case it applies to y. This is also known as the Indiscernibility of Identicals, i.e. if x and y are identical, they will be indiscernible in all respects. Notice how this uses a biconditional to express the notion of indiscernibility: given any predicate P, if x = y, then P(x) iff P(y), i.e. they'll either both be P, or both not be P. As a rule of inference, we have:

$$\frac{P(a),\ a = b}{P(b)} \qquad\qquad \frac{P(a),\ b = a}{P(b)}$$

There are two versions, because if a is b, it doesn't make any logical difference which way round you say it, a = b, or b = a. Substitution of one co-referring name for another does not have to be uniform. That is, if P contains two or more occurrences of 'a' then you can substitute the name 'b' for as many, or as few, of those occurrences as you like. For if P(a) is true, and a is b, then any sentence resulting from such a substitution must be true.

Identity is reflexive, symmetric and transitive. The proof that it is a reflexive relation is immediate, given =I. We can also prove, for example, that distinctness is symmetric, $(\forall x)(\forall y)(\ x \neq y \rightarrow y \neq x\ )$. The proof illustrates both identity introduction and elimination; it is clearer if we use '$\neg(x = y)$' instead of '$x \neq y$':

1)	¬(a = b)	ASS.	W.i.A.
2)	b = a	ASS.	1, 2
3)	¬(a = a)	=E, 1, 2.	
4)	a = a	=I.	
5)	¬(b = a)	RAA, 2, 3, 4.	
6)	¬(a = b) → ¬(b = a)	→I, 1, 5.	
7)	(∀y) (¬(a = y) → ¬(y = a))	∀I, 6.	
8)	(∀x)(∀y) (¬(x = y) → ¬(y = x))	∀I, 7.	

We assume ¬(a = b) and, for Reductio, b = a. This identity allows us to use =E to substitute 'b' for 'a' in line 1), obtaining the denial of a self-identity. This has to be false; by making the =I at line 4, the contradiction is made explicit, and we infer ¬(b = a).

Exercise 4

A.   Some sentences of natural language don't make their quantifiers explicit, and so are potentially ambiguous. Nevertheless, one reading is often far more plausible than the others, so we correctly guess what is intended. Formalize these three sentences, on the most plausible reading:

1)   Giraffes don't eat lions.
2)   Chemical events are caused by physical events.
3)   Physical events cause mental events.

B.   Formalize all three sentences in this argument in terms of ∀ (rather than ∃), and produce a derivation of the conclusion:

4)   Every snake is a reptile.   No reptile is homoiothermic. Therefore: No snake is homoiothermic.

C.   An *enthymeme* is an argument in which one or more premises is not explicitly stated, because assumed to be obvious. For instance:

5)   John is a brother of Mary, therefore: Mary is a sister of John.

The missing premise here is not simply that, for any x and y, if x is brother to y, y is sister to x. There can be two brothers. We need to specify that y is female. So this argument not only tacitly appeals to the general principle that a female who has a brother is his sister, it

also needs the particular premise that Mary is female. Using 'B(x, y)'
for 'x is brother to y', 'F(y)' for y is female, etc., we can formalize it as:

$$(\forall x)(\forall y)((B(x, y) \& F(y)) \rightarrow S(y, x)),\ B(j, m),\ F(m)$$
So: S(m, j).

Derive the conclusion from these premises.
          Supply what you consider to be the missing premises in the
following three arguments, stating them as generalizations wherever
appropriate and possible:

6)   a is not a knave, therefore: a is a knight.
7)   Any dog likes Mary if she likes him. Fido doesn't like Mary.
        Therefore: Mary doesn't like Fido.
8)   a is left of b, and b is left of c. Therefore: c is right of a.

Supply a proof of each conclusion, making use of the additional
premises.

D.   Show that an asymmetric relation is irreflexive.

4.5 Reasoning with existence

4.5.1 Reasoning with ∃

∃ **Introduction**:   Universal statements are relatively strong.
Consequently, it's easy to state what follows from one, and harder to
state just when it is correct to infer one. ∀E is simple, and the I rule is
complex.   With ∃ it's the reverse.   Existential statements are
relatively weak, so it's difficult to state what follows from them, but
easy to state how to introduce them. So I'll start with the easy rule,
∃I, also known as existential generalization. For any name n, any
predicate P (whether simple or complex), and almost any variable v:

$$\frac{P(n)}{(\exists v)\ P(v)}$$

That is, provided the variable chosen does not clash with any already
in P(n) (this is the same as constraint iii) on ∀I).
          For example, from 1) we may infer 2)

1)   Paderewski is a pianist and also a prime minister,
2)   There exists a pianist who is also a prime minister.

The inference is simply this:

1)   P(a) & Q(a)   ASS.   W.i.A.
2)   (∃x)(P(x) & Q(x))   ∃I, 1.   1

Notice that ∃I, unlike ∀I, makes no requirement that all occurrences of
the name be replaced by the quantified variable. It is equally correct
to infer from P(a) & Q(a)

3)   (∃x)(P(x) & Q(a)),

that there exists a pianist and Paderewski is a prime minister, or that

4)   (∃x)(P(a) & Q(x)),

in effect, that Paderewski is a pianist and someone is a prime minister.
If 1) is true (as it is), then both of these are.
        The point of the prohibition against clash of variables can be
illustrated by starting with the premise that Socrates is not the only
thing there is,

        (∃x)(x ≠ socrates).

If we were to perform existential generalization on this using the same
variable, we would initially obtain (∃x)(∃x)(x ≠ x). But the outermost
(∃x) here is vacuous, since all the variables which follow it are bound
by the inner quantifier. So what we really obtain is (∃x)(x ≠ x). In
other words, from the true premise that something is distinct from
Socrates, we would obtain the logically false conclusion that
something is distinct from itself.
        Any system which has ∃I in this form assumes, in effect, that
every name names something real, something which exists. This is
convenient, but ultimately an over-simplification. Logical systems
which do not embody this assumption, which do not have such a
liberal form of ∃I, are known as *free* logics.

∃ **Elimination**: We can know that something is P without knowing its
identity - without knowing which thing it is which is P. The police

can know that someone murdered Jones, but not know who. They know that

5)   (∃x)(person(x) & murdered(x, jones)),

but know no such particular fact as, say,

          murdered(smith, jones).

If we can know such things as 5), we can reason with them - we can reason about the existence of some P, without knowing which P. Reasoning about some P in this way is reasoning from an ∃ premise - it's what's involved in the rather complex rule of ∃E.

Suppose we know there is some instance of a concept P, but don't know which thing it is - we don't know its name. The way to proceed is to pick some individual at random, and let it *play the role* of this P instance. It's like the detective re-enacting the murder with an assistant playing the role of the murderer, in the hope of establishing something about the crime. The detective says "Let's suppose you murdered Jones. You would have climbed in through the window over here, and then hidden yourself in this small cupboard for three hours. So you would have to be quite agile, and not very tall ..." The assistant gives him a peg on which to hang his reasoning and his conjectures about whoever it was who did murder Jones. In the formal rule, we have a premise (∃x) P(x), but start by assuming P(a), for some arbitrarily chosen a. Nothing we conclude must depend on any facts peculiar to the individual chosen - the only assumption about a we can rely on is just P(a). Suppose now the conclusion we want, A, can be derived. So we have a proof of A, on the assumption that P(a). If we *knew* that a was the P instance - if P(a) could remain undischarged as a premise - that would be the end of the matter (we would have the conclusion we want, from a premise we were assured of). But we don't - we just know that there is some P. What the rule of ∃E says, in effect, is that you can swap the premise P(a) for (∃x)P(x): you can exchange the dependence of your conclusion on P(a) for dependence on the weaker premise (∃x)P(x).

Before stating the rule, it will be helpful to work through an example semi-formally:

          Active volcanoes exist   Therefore: Volcanoes exist.

The inference has the form $(\exists x)(P(x)$ & $Q(x))$ So: $(\exists x)P(x)$. It is valid: if at least one thing has both P and Q (the properties of *being a volcano* and *being active*), then at least one thing has P. Assume the existential premise:

1)   Active volcanoes exist   ASS $(\exists x)(P(x)$ & $Q(x))$

The information we have is that something is an active volcano, but we don't know which thing it is. We choose an object at random, to play the role of that volcano - Mount Snowdon, say:

2)   Snowdon is an active volcano   ASS $P(s)$ & $Q(s)$

Note: we do not *infer* 2) from 1). It doesn't follow. Rather, we make this as a further *assumption* - by supposing that Snowdon is an active volcano, we let it play the role of the unspecified active volcano which the premise tells us exists. It gives us something to reason about. What is important for this inference is that it exposes the &, which in 1) lies within the scope of $\exists$. In 2) 'and' is the dominant connective, and we may thus apply & Elimination:

3)   Snowdon is a volcano   &E, 2 $P(s)$

From this it follows that there is at least one volcano:

4)   Volcanoes exist $\exists I$, 2 $(\exists x)\, P(x)$

This is the conclusion we are aiming for. But we have derived it from 2), not 1). So far, 1) has played no real part in the proof. Line 4 has come from the assumption that Snowdon is an active volcano, line 2. We don't know this - it isn't the premise we are given. We need to change the conclusion's dependence on 2) for dependence on 1) - and this is just what $\exists E$ allows:

5)   Volcanoes exist $\exists E$, 1, 2, 4 $(\exists x)\, P(x)$.

We can do this because we chose Snowdon arbitrarily. We only made one assumption about it - that it stand in for the unspecified thing which the existential premise tells us about.

The rule can be schematically represented:

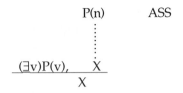

Provided n is arbitrary, in the sense provided by these constraints:

i)   In proving X from P(n), the only assumption n occurs in is P(n) -
i.e. we don't appeal to any further facts specifically about n.

ii)   n occurs neither in the conclusion X nor the existential wff,
(∃v)P(v).

iii)   P(n) is an assumption - which is discharged by the application
of ∃E. (If we knew that P(n) - if that was a premise of the argument -
we wouldn't need to go through this rigmarole of ∃E.)

It is worthwhile going through another example:

> If Pedro owns a donkey, he beats it. Pedro owns a donkey.
> So: Pedro beats a donkey.

The logical form of this, in LQE, is:

> (∀x)((donkey(x) & owns(pedro, x)) → beats(pedro, x)).
> (∃x)(donkey(x) & owns(pedro, x)).
>
> So: (∃x)(donkey(x) & beats(pedro, x)).

We want to reason about this unspecified donkey of Pedro's, which the
second premise tells us exists. So in the proof (at line 2) we pick some
individual a at random and say, "Suppose this were a donkey of
Pedro's ...". With the universal premise, we can infer that it would be
beaten by Pedro (line 6)), from which it follows that there is a donkey
which Pedro beats - the conclusion we want. So now we assume the
second premise, at line 8), and apply ∃E to it, discharging assumption
2) and deriving the conclusion:

1)	$(\forall x)((D(x) \& O(p, x)) \to B(p, x))$	ASS.	W.i.A.
2)	$D(a) \& O(p, a)$	ASS.	1, ~~2~~, 8
3)	$(D(a) \& O(p, a)) \to B(p, a)$	$\forall$E, 1.	
4)	$B(p, a)$	$\to$E, 2, 3.	
5)	$D(a)$	&E, 2.	
6)	$D(a) \& B(p, a)$	&I, 4, 5.	
7)	$(\exists x)(D(x) \& B(p, x))$	$\exists$I, 6.	
8)	$(\exists x)(D(x) \& O(p, x))$	ASS.	
9)	$(\exists x)(D(x) \& B(p, x))$	$\exists$E, 2, 7, 8.	

Notice that although we end up with an existential conclusion, this is
$\exists$ Elimination, because what is essential is reasoning *from* the
existential premise, line 8). (The conclusion of a deductively valid
argument can't be stronger than the premises - with a weak, $\exists$, premise,
one is liable to get a weak, $\exists$, conclusion.)

4.5.2 The form of everything

It has previously been noted (section 2.5) that there is a tendency for $\forall$
to be associated with $\to$, and for $\exists$ with &. The association is at its
strongest when we are translating into predicate logic English phrases
such as 'any P' or 'some P'. We translate along these lines:

1)	... every P ...	translates into:	... $(\forall x) P(x) \to$ ...
2)	... there is a P ...	translates into:	... $(\exists x) P(x)$ & ...

where the dots are meant to suggest that these phrases occur within
some surrounding context. In cases involving multiple quantification,
for instance,

3)   All teachers, in all their lectures, interest all those who
attend.

we can recover their structure by taking each quantifier phrase in turn
and formalizing in the spirit of those translation principles. 3) is a
very strong claim, because each of its quantifiers is universal - so strong
that it is obviously false. Notice that for 'lecture' we really need a
two place predicate, 'y is a lecture of x', to relate lecture to teacher.
For each teacher, we are only talking about the lectures which that
person gives. Similar considerations apply to 'attend', to relate a
person to the lecture they are attending. So we have:

3´)   (∀x)(teacher(x) → (∀y)(lecture-of(y, x) →
                    (∀z)(attends(z, y) → interests(x, z)))).

Take any teacher x, then: take any lecture of x, then: take anyone z
who attends such a lecture, then: x interests z. Alternatively, one could
go to the other extreme and make a very weak claim, 4). This is weak,
because all the quantifiers are existential:

4)   Some teachers, in some of their lectures, interest some of those
who attend.
4´)   (∃x)(teacher(x) & (∃y)(lecture-of(y, x) &
                    (∃z)(attends(z, y) & interests(x, z)))).

There is at least one teacher x, and: at least one lecture of x's, and: at
least one person z who attends, and: x interests z.   Between the
incautious (3) and the anodyne (4) a whole range of intermediate
statements can be made - for instance, the relatively mild 5). Here the
pattern is ∃∀∃; still, ∃ combines with &, and ∀ with →:

5)   Some teachers, in all their lectures, interest some who attend.
5´)   (∃x)(teacher(x) & (∀y)(lecture-of(y, x) →
                    (∃z)(attends(z, y) & interests(x, z)))).

        These translation principles require some comment and
elaboration. The predicative phrase P in 1) and 2) should not be
vacuous. By this I mean to exclude such words as 'thing', which apply
unrestrictedly to everything. Consider an unrestricted claim:

6)   Everything either is coloured, or is not coloured.

We could introduce a vacuous predicate, 'thing', and translate in
accordance with the above scheme:

7)   (∀x)(thing(x) → (coloured(x) v ¬ coloured(x))).

But 'thing' is vacuously satisfied by everything - we could formalize it
using 'x = x', since every thing is self-identical. So the antecedent of
this conditional is redundant. There is no genuine *restriction* on the
variable, on the sorts of things it can take as values. Compare 3´),
where, for example, 'x' is restricted to teachers.   So 6) is simply
equivalent to this:

6´)   (∀x)(coloured(x) v ¬ coloured(x)).

This is how we represent the logical form of 6), and it illustrates why the association of ∀ with →, and ∃ with &, is only a *tendency* - it does not apply in every case.

Another qualification concerns structurally ambiguous sentences. In some sentences, like 5), there is no ambiguity about the relative scopes of the quantifiers, and so the translation principles can be applied in a fairly mechanical way. By contrast, there is more than one way of understanding the relative scopes of their quantifiers in a sentence like

8)   A soldier went into every house.

'A soldier' means 'At least one soldier', and so is to be formalized by '(∃x)(soldier(x) & ... x ...)'. 'Every house' is universal, and so will take the form '(∀y)(house(y) → ... y ...)'. But which comes first - the existential phrase or the universal? Either order is possible for 8). It can be understood as

9)   (∃x)(soldier(x) & (∀y)(house(y) → entered(x, y))),

there was at least one soldier - the same soldier - who went into all the houses. Alternatively, it can be taken to have this structure

10)   (∀y)(house(y) → (∃x)(soldier(x) & entered(x, y))).

On this reading, each house was visited by some soldier, but perhaps different houses were visited by different soldiers. One way to bring out the difference is in terms of the instructions you would give to someone who wanted to check the truth value of the sentence. The instructions relate to the way objects can be selected. Putting '(∀y)(house(y)' first means that you must consider all the houses in turn - for each one, you must be able to find some soldier, not necessarily the same soldier, who went into it. The choice of soldier can come after, can depend on, the choice of house. Putting '(∃x)(soldier(x)' first, as in 9), means that you must consider each soldier in turn, checking whether he went into all the houses. You must be able to find a particular soldier such that, no matter what house you then pick, that soldier went into it.

10) is a weaker reading than 9); it's easier for 10) to be true than for 9). Compare the two scenarios:

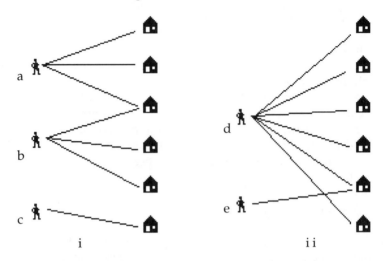

i   ii

In situation i, 10) would be true, but 9) would not be. This is just what
we would expect of a genuinely ambiguous sentence - a possible state of
affairs in which it would be true on one reading, and false on another
(cf. section 2.1.3). What is needed for 9) to be true is a situation like ii,
where we can point to at least one soldier - d in this case - who went
into all the houses. Notice that in any such situation in which 9) is
true, 10) must also be true. Every house was visited by some soldier or
other - as it happens, the same one. What all this suggests is that 9)
entails 10), but not conversely. We can demonstrate that the
entailment holds. It is one of the laws of multiple quantification - the
Law of Quantifier Exchange. Simplifying the forms to their bare
essentials, we have that

$$(\exists y)(\forall x)\, R(x, y) \quad |\!- \quad (\forall x)(\exists y)\, R(x, y).$$

The proof is as follows:

1)	$(\exists y)\, (\forall x)\, R(x, y)$	ASS.	W.i.A.
2)	$(\forall x)\, R(x, a)$	ASS.	1,2
3)	$R(b, a)$	$\forall$E, 2.	
4)	$(\exists y)\, R(b, y)$	$\exists$I, 3.	
5)	$(\forall x)\, (\exists y)\, R(x, y)$	$\forall$I, 4.	
6)	$(\forall x)\, (\exists y)\, R(x, y)$	$\exists$E, 1, 2, 5.	

At line 2 we assume an instance of the existential wff of line 1. This
instance is a universal generalization, which we instantiate at line 3.

By then making an ∃I followed by an ∀I, we switch the order of the quantifiers. So whereas with two quantifiers of the same kind - with a wff of ∀∀ form, or of ∃∃ form - it doesn't matter which of the two comes first (the laws of quantifier exchange, section 4.4), an ∃∀ wff is definitely stronger than the corresponding ∀∃ wff.

Another respect in which our initial translation schema 1) is a little simplistic is that it ignores the subtle differences between the ordinary quantifiers 'every', 'any', 'each', 'all'. At first sight, it may not be clear how these differ, since they all convey the concept of universality. But it's when they interact with other expressions that their different preferences for the relative scope of that concept of universality become apparent. Compare for instance,

11)   No soldier went into every house
12)   No soldier went into any house

The first means that there was no one soldier who went into all the houses:

11´)   ¬ (∃x)(soldier(x) & (∀y)(house(y) → entered(x, y))).

Someone who asserts this is denying 9) - is ruling out type ii situations. The second is a much stronger assertion. It means that no matter what house you choose, there is no soldier who went into it:

12´)   (∀y)(house(y) → ¬ (∃x)(soldier(x) & entered(x, y))).

Both 'any' and 'every' express universality, but what this pair of examples suggests is that 'any' has a preference for wide scope. That is, where there is a possibility for a scope interaction with another connective - here, negation - there is a tendency for 'any' to take wider scope. We see this also with conditionals:

13)   If John wins every game, he will be content.
14)   If John wins any game, he will be content.

The former of these says, in effect

     If it's the case that: for every game, John wins it, then ...

i.e. it requires the → to have wider scope than the ∀. Formally,

13´)   [(∀x)(game(x) → wins(John, x))] → [content(John)].

With the latter, it is the reverse:

          Take any game: if John wins it, then ...
14´)   (∀x)[game(x) → (wins(John, x) → content(John))].

The former clearly makes out John's standards of contentment to be more stringent - he needs to win all the games; whereas in the latter case, as long as he wins *a* game, he is content. Indeed, the thought behind 14) can be equally well put like this:

15)   If John wins some game, he will be content.

What this suggests is an ∃ with scope narrower than the conditional:

15´)   [(∃x)(game(x) & wins(John, x))] → [content(John)].

          The fact that the English sentences 14) and 15) seem equivalent is no coincidence - their underlying forms can be proved to be equivalent. The essential equivalence is this:

16)   (∀x)(Px → A) ↔ ((∃x)(Px) → A)

The equivalence has already been stressed in connection with Prolog - that a universal quantifier with wide scope over a conditional is equivalent to an existential quantifier within the antecedent, provided the variable is not free in the consequent. The following proof is official confirmation of the point. The order in which the E and I rules are applied is closely dictated by the relative scopes of the logical connectives.

1)	(∃x)P(x) → A	ASS.	W.i.A.
2)	P(a)	ASS.	1, 2, 8,
3)	(∃x)P(x)	∃I, 2.	9, 10
4)	A	→E, 1, 3.	
5)	P(a) → A	→I, 2, 4.	
6)	(∀x)(P(x) → A)	∀I, 5.	
7)	((∃x)P(x) → A) → (∀x)(P(x) → A)	→I, 1, 6.	

8)	$(\forall x)(P(x) \to A)$	ASS.
9)	$(\exists x)P(x)$	ASS.
10)	$P(a)$	ASS.
11)	$P(a) \to A$	$\forall$E, 8.
12)	A	$\to$E, 10, 11.
13)	A	$\exists$E, 9, 10, 12.
14)	$(\exists x)P(x) \to A$	$\to$I, 9, 13.
15)	$(\forall x)(P(x) \to A) \to ((\exists x)P(x) \to A)$	$\to$I, 8, 14.
16)	$(\forall x)(P(x) \to A) \leftrightarrow ((\exists x)P(x) \to A)$	$\leftrightarrow$I, 7, 15.

One of the most important things to keep in mind when formalizing English sentences which have an underlying predicate logical structure, is to pay attention to one's intuitive understanding of them, rather than just looking at what appears on the surface. The sense of a sentence is a better guide to its logical structure than its superficial form. Consider, for example,

17)   For both students and pensioners, admission is free.

It would be wrong to assume from the position of the 'and' here that its form is:

18) $(\forall x) ((S(x) \& P(x)) \to F(x))$.

18) means: for anyone who is *both* a student *and* a pensioner, admission is free. This is too stringent - too few people satisfy both predicates. There is a sense in which conjunction is involved in 17), since it means that for students admission is free *and* for pensioners admission is free:

19) $(\forall x)(S(x) \to F(x) \ \& \ (\forall x)(P(x) \to F(x))$.

Alternatively, we can compress this into a single generalization by using disjunction: for any person who is either a student or a pensioner, admission is free:

20) $(\forall x) ((S(x) \lor P(x)) \to F(x))$.

19) and 20) are equivalent. Either we use 'and' other than in the place where it superficially appears (19), or we use disjunction in that place (20).

The indefinite article 'a' provides another example of this point about formalization. In most cases, as in example 3), it has existential force. But with an example like

21)   If John wins a game, he will be content,

it *can* be represented by a universal quantifier, as 13) testifies. Indeed, there are cases where 'a' *must* be represented by $\forall$ - for example, in **generic** uses. Generic uses are found, for example, in definitions. A well-known example of Wilde's:

A cynic: someone who knows the price of everything and the value of nothing.

Perhaps Wilde would have added that a logician is someone who knows the form of everything and the content of nothing. But I shall persist in being literal minded and say that what this means is that *anyone* is a cynic if and only if he or she knows ... etc. Here the universal quantifier, to bind the variable across the biconditional, is obligatory:

$$(\forall x)[\text{cynic}(x) \leftrightarrow ((\forall y)(\forall z)(\text{price-of}(y, z) \rightarrow$$
$$x \text{ knows}(\text{price-of}(y, z))) \; \& $$
$$(\forall y)(\forall z)(\text{value-of}(y, z) \rightarrow \neg x \text{ knows}(\text{value-of}(y, z))))].$$

4.5.3 Reasoning with $\forall$ and $\exists$

The two quantifiers $\forall$ and $\exists$ are related as **duals**, which is to say they are related by this law:

22) $(\forall x) P(x) \leftrightarrow \neg(\exists x)\neg P(x).$

If everything is finite, then there is nothing which isn't finite, and conversely, if it is not the case that there exists something which is not finite, then all things are finite. This equivalence means that we could take 'exists' as primitive, and define 'all' in terms of it. Alternatively, we could take $\forall$ as the fundamental quantifier, and explain $\exists$ in terms of it:

23) $(\exists x) P(x) \leftrightarrow \neg(\forall x)\neg P(x).$

Let us consider the proof of this equivalence. Starting with the left to right direction, we assume (∃x) P(x). To make use of this with ∃E, we also assume a specific instance of this form, e.g. P(a). We further assume, for Reductio, that everything is not P. Since this assumption entails ¬P(a), contradicting P(a), we can negate it. This is the conclusion we want, ¬(∀x)¬P(x), but since at this point it depends on Pa rather than (∃x)P(x), we use ∃E to discharge P(a):

1)	(∃x) P(x)	ASS	W.i.A.
2)	(∀x) ¬P(x)	ASS	~~1, 2, 3~~
3)	P(a)	ASS	.
4)	¬P(a)	∀E, 2	
5)	¬(∀x)¬P(x)	RAA, 2, 3, 4	
6)	¬(∀x)¬P(x)	∃E, 1, 3, 5	
7)	(∃x) P(x) → ¬(∀x)¬P(x)	→I, 1, 6	

In the other direction, we start with ¬ (∀x) ¬ P(x) and assume the negation of the conclusion for Reductio, ¬ (∃x) P(x). The Reductio depends on establishing the contradictory of the first premise, (∀x)¬P(x). We can prove this generalization if we can show ¬P(a), discharging any assumptions about a. To do this, show that P(a) can't be true:

1)	¬ (∀x) ¬ P(x)	ASS	W.i.A.
2)	¬ (∃x) P(x)	ASS	~~1, 2, 3~~
3)	P(a)	ASS	
4)	(∃x) P(x)	∃I, 3	
5)	¬P(a)	RAA, 3, 2, 4	
6)	(∀x) ¬ P(x)	∀I, 5	
7)	(∃x) P(x)	RAA, 2, 1, 6	
8)	¬(∀x)¬ P(x) → (∃x) P(x)	→I, 1, 7	

(The proof has a bearing on the intuitionist interpretation of quantification. Recall that intuitionist propositional logic does not contain the negation elimination form of RAA (cf. section 4.3.1). The major Reductio here is of that form, the inference of line 7 from line 2. It is significant that Intuitionists do not accept this half of the quantifier equivalence 23). Intuitionists understand (∃x) P(x) to be true only when we are capable in principle of finding something which is P, i.e. providing an example. Merely knowing that (∀x) ¬P(x) is not true does not suffice for this - we may not have any positive conception of how to find some instance of P.)

Traditional logic classifies a number of ways of reasoning as fallacies (such as affirming the consequent, section 4.1.1) - patterns of argumentation which may seem plausible, but which are in fact invalid. Because of the way modern logic abstracts out the semantic and inferential rules governing each logical particle, there is a quite general mistake in applying these rules which people are sometimes tempted into. It does not correspond to an informal fallacy, a mistake one might make in informal reasoning, but it is a fallacious move which can lead to an argument going astray. The mistake is to notice the occurrence of some logical expression embedded within a wff, and to apply the rule for it *out of turn*. We might call this the fallacy of the embedded connective. If we have a generalization - of the form, say, $(\forall x)(D(x) \& B(x))$ - then it is correct to infer any instance, e.g. $D(f) \& B(f)$. But if that generalization occurs within the scope of a negation, ¬ $(\forall x)(D(x) \& B(x))$, it is *not* correct to infer the corresponding negated instance, ¬$(D(f) \& B(f))$. What presumably motivates someone who makes such a move is the belief that they are making an application of $\forall E$ within the scope of the negation. But this is a misunderstanding of the rule. $\forall E$ says: when, but only when, you have a wff of the form $(\forall x) P(x)$, you may infer any instance $P(a)$. In other words, the universal quantifier must be the dominant connective in the wff. It must have widest scope. In the above misguided application, this is not so - the $\forall$ lies within the scope of ¬. $\forall E$ is not a rule of substitution - it does not say you may replace $(\forall x) P(x)$ by $P(a)$ in any context whatsoever. (Roughly speaking, you can only substitute one expression for another within some context if they are logically equivalent, and a universal statement is certainly not equivalent to a specific instance.) It is not hard to show that this example is fallacious. The premise might be: Not everything is both a dog and barks, and the conclusion might be: Fido is not a dog which barks. The premise is true, the conclusion false, so the inference is invalid.

The converse mistake is also possible - we might call this the fallacy of embedding the connective. Here an introduction rule is misapplied, introducing a connective within the scope of another. For instance, from ¬ $H(f)$ to infer ¬ $(\exists x) H(x)$. $\exists I$ says that from a particular statement, of form $P(a)$, one may infer the less specific existential statement, $(\exists x) P(x)$. And this means: the existential quantifier must take widest scope, over the whole wff. It is incorrect to think one can somehow perform the whole manoeuvre within the scope of some other connective:

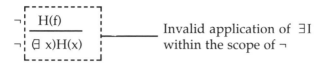

Invalid application of ∃I
within the scope of ¬

Here the premise might be: Fido is not human, and the conclusion: nothing is human. The correct application of ∃I to ¬H(f) produces (∃x)¬H(x); if Fido is not human, then it is correct to infer that something is not human.

Notice that both these mistakes may result in inferences which are in fact valid. For instance, to say that one infers (∃x)P(x) directly from (∃x)(P(x) & Q(x)) by &E is to make the fallacy of the embedded connective. It betrays a misconception about the inference rules. &E applies to wffs of the form X & Y, i.e. to conjunctions. But (∃x)(P(x) & Q(x)) is not a conjunction. The dominant connective is ∃, within the scope of which occurs &. The relative scopes of the expressions determines the order of application of the corresponding rules. The derivation (p. 209) is shaped overall as an ∃E, within which occurs the &E. Similarly, saying that from P(a) & Q(b) one may directly infer P(a) & (∃x)Q(x) by ∃I involves embedding the connective. Here we should look at the structure of the conclusion: ∃ occurs within the scope of &. Correspondingly, one must make an ∃I *before* an &I:

1)	P(a) & Q(b)	ASS	W.i.A.
2)	Q(b)	&E, 1	1
3)	(∃x)Q(x)	∃I, 2	
4)	P(a)	&E, 1	
5)	P(a) & (∃x)Q(x)	&I, 3, 4	

Exercise 5

A.   Formalize 1) and 2) into LQE, using 'dances_with' for both 'dances with' and 'will dance with'

1)   If John dances with everyone, he will dance with Mary.
2)   If John dances with anyone, he will dance with Mary.

Each of the following sentences contains the same quantifier phrases, but with different scope orderings:

3)   For every essay I write, and every person I show it to, there is at least one sentence in it to which they object.

4)   For every essay I write, there is at least one sentence in it to which every person I show it to objects.

5)   There is a sentence which is in every essay I write, to which every person I show it objects.

Formalize them. (Hint: use one place predicates 'essay', 'sentence', 'person'; two place predicates 'write', 'in'; 'objects-to'; and a three place predicate 'show-to'.) State which of them is the least plausible (the strongest), and which the most plausible. Briefly explain in your own words what the difference is between them.

B.   According to the square of opposition (section 2.2.2), the generalizations 'All swans are white' and 'All swans are not white' are contraries. In part this is because the traditional analysis holds that either is true only if swans exist. The modern account does not require this existence condition, and in consequence allows that both could be true - both would be trivially true if there were no swans. Indeed this is the only circumstance in which they could both be true. 6) reflects this fact.

6)   Any unicorn is four-legged.
        Any four-legged thing is not a unicorn.
        Therefore: Unicorns do not exist.

Formalize this and derive the conclusion. (Hint: the proof is simpler if you formalize the conclusion as 'everything isn't a unicorn', rather than 'it is not the case that there exists a unicorn'.)

C.   Set theory was originally founded on the Axiom Schema of Abstraction:

7) $(\exists y)(\forall x)(P(x) \leftrightarrow x \in y)$.

This says that, no matter what predicate P you take, there is a set y such that for any x, x is in y just in case P(x). Intuitively, the principle seems correct: any predicate P delimits a set y of just those things x of which it is true. But Russell showed that the principle leads to contradiction, by using the predicate of not being a member of oneself, i.e. '$\neg(x \in x)$'. This is a paradox - an apparently a priori true principle entailing a contradiction. Since set theory is discussed later (see section 5.1.2), let us focus on an informal version of Russell's paradox. In a certain hotel there is a waiter, Manuel, of whom we are told:

8)   For any of those who are either guests or members of staff, Manuel serves them if and only if they don't serve themselves.
9)   Manuel is a member of staff.

i) Formalize these, and derive the conclusion that Manuel both serves and doesn't serve himself. ii) What should we conclude about Manuel from this?

D.   We can now formally analyse the world of knights and knaves, and make explicit our reasoning about them. Use 'a', 'b', 'c', ... as names of individuals, and the predicate letters H, D, N, for *honest* knight, *dishonest* knave, and normal, respectively. Consider, for illustration, an island populated only by knaves (Crete, according to that old knave Epimenides). Of this island we would say:

10) $(\forall z)\ D(z)$.

We also need a special expression, z says X, which relates an individual z to a proposition X. With this expression, we can schematically express, for example, the thought that whatever anyone says is not the case:

11) $(\forall z)(z\ \text{says}\ X \rightarrow \neg X)$.

This is a schema - it is not a specific sentence, but rather a template for producing sentences. Understand it as: whatever sentence X you take, the result of instantiating it in 11) will be a truth.
        The status of these principles would be that of contingent empirical generalizations - not true by definition, but true of everything on that island. We can only appeal to them so long as we assume we are on that island. Suppose a says that b is a knight:

12)   a says H(b)   ASS

We can *Instantiate* schema 11) and get:

13) $(\forall x)(x\ \text{says}\ H(b) \rightarrow \neg H(b))$ Inst, 9

The rule Inst thus takes us to a definite sentence ('If anyone here says that b is a knight, it is not so'), from something which gives the form of all such sentences. From 13) we can go on in the familiar way, for example to:

14)   a says H(b) → ¬H(b)   ∀E, 11.

and thus, with 12), obtain ¬H(b).

      Suppose now we are dealing with the island of knights and knaves. Formalize the principles that no-one is both knight and knave, that everyone is one or the other. Is there a difference in the status of these principles? Then, using 'z says X', formulate partial definitions of the predicates H, D.

      Prove (by reductio) that, in a land where there are only knights and knaves, no-one can say of himself that he is a knave.

      You come across this character c, who says that either he's a knave, or Socrates is not Socrates. What should we conclude? Produce a derivation of your conclusion.

4.6 Further topics

4.6.1 Identity and definite descriptions

A simple predication like 1) should ordinarily be formalized as 2)

1)   Fido is a dog,
2)   D(f).

This is sometimes paraphrased as: Fido falls under the concept *dog*. But with identity, an alternative formalization is possible:

3)   (∃x)(D(x) & x = f),

Fido is identical to some dog. We can show that these forms are inter-derivable. Firstly, from 2) to 3):

1)	D(f)	ASS.	W.i.A.
2)	f = f	=I.	1
3)	D(f) & f = f	&I, 1, 2.	
4)	(∃x)(D(x) & x = f)	∃I, 3.	

And now the reverse direction:

1)	$(\exists x)(D(x) \ \& \ x = f)$	ASS.	<u>W.i.A.</u>
2)	$D(a) \ \& \ a = f$	ASS.	1, 2
3)	$D(a)$	&E, 2.	
4)	$a = f$	&E, 2.	
5)	$D(f)$	=E, 3, 4.	
6)	$D(f)$	$\exists$E, 1, 2, 5.	

Needless to say, given the inferential complexity of $\exists$E, the simpler formalization is far easier to work with, and should always be preferred.

Although this last example does not show it, the identity symbol adds to the expressive power of predicate logic. By way of background, consider again the treatment of 'exists' in terms of $\exists$, rather than as a predicate. To understand the treatment of 4) using the existential quantifier, 5)

4)   Physicists who understand relativity exist
5) $(\exists x)(P(x) \ \& \ R(x))$,

we might compare it with

6)   Physicists who understand relativity are numerous.

The latter can be understood as saying that the first order property of being a physicist who understands relativity has the higher order property of *being numerous* - of having numerous exemplifications. As Lewis Carroll noted, "the Attribute 'numerous' cannot be applied to an individual man" - as evinced by his example: Men over five feet high are numerous, Men over ten feet high are not numerous, Therefore: Men over ten feet high are not over five feet high. (*Being a colour* is another instance of a second order property, which can be predicated of first order properties, like redness, but not of particulars.)   Existence, likewise, is not treated as a simple property of individuals. It can be thought of as the second order property of having at least one instance. *Being a physicist* has this property, *being a unicorn* does not.

And yet we do assert and deny the existence of individuals - for example:

7)   Vulcan does not exist.

Having identity enables us to formulate such (negative) singular existential judgements:

8)   ¬ (∃x)(x = a),

there is no thing which is Vulcan. So just as 5) can be understood as saying that the first order property expressed by P(x) & R(x) has some instance, so this can be read as meaning that the property of *being Vulcan* has no instance.

Another example of an occurrence of a name requiring combination with identity would be 9), which can be formalized as 10):

9)   Only Einstein understands relativity,
10)   (∀x)(R(x) ↔ x = a).

Notice the biconditional; we need to say both i and ii:

10i)   (∀x)(x = a → R(x)), that Einstein understands,
10ii)   (∀x)(R(x) → x = a), that no-one else does.

The latter on its own would be consistent with Einstein not understanding relativity, the former, with others understanding it.

Identity and distinctness are tied up with counting. To say that a and b are distinct is to say that they are two things, not one. Quantificational logic without identity lacks such numerical precision. We cannot formalize 11) as 12):

11)   At least two physicists understand relativity
12)   (∃x)(∃y)(P(x) & P(y) & R(x) & R(y)).

For this just says what 5) says, but repeats it - it's as if one said 4), and then said it again. We have to specify that x and y are distinct (cf section 3.3.2):

13)   (∃x)(∃y)(P(x) & P(y) & x ≠ y & R(x) & R(y)).

Likewise, a claim of 14)'s form will require three variables, each distinguished from the other: 15).

14)   At least three ...
15)   (∃x)(∃y)(∃z)(x ≠ y & y ≠ z & x ≠ z & ...).

Correlatively, a claim that there is not more than one of a kind, as in 16), can be understood as a denial that there are at least two, 17):

16)   There is at most one unicorn,
17)   ¬ (∃x)(∃y) (U(x) & U(y) & x ≠ y).

Equivalently, it can be taken as saying that if any things x and y satisfy the concept *unicorn*, they are one and the same:

18)   (∀x)(∀y)((U(x) & U(y)) → x = y).

And so on: to say that there at most two ... is to say that there are not more than three, i.e. to deny something with 18)'s form.   Exact numerical claims, such as 19), can be analysed as a combination of existence and uniqueness: there is at least one unicorn, but only one, 20):

19)   There is exactly one unicorn
20)   (∃x)(U(x) & (∀y)(U(y) → x = y)).

More generally, to say that just n Ps are Q is to say that at least n Ps are Q, and at most n Ps are Q.
        Russell's analysis of definite descriptions is a natural extension of these ideas: a combination of the quantificational treatment of *in*definite descriptions with the use of identity to express uniqueness. An occurrence of an indefinite description, as in 21), is treated, not as something which *names*, but as a quantifier, 22):

21)   A king of France was bald,
22)   (∃x)(K(x) & B(x)).

Russell's proposal is that when the description becomes definite, as in his famous example 23), what gets added, from the logical point of view, is uniqueness:

23)   The present king of France is bald
24)   (∃x)(K(x) & (∀y)(K(y) → x = y) & B(x)).

So by his theory, if you assert something like 23), there are three components to your assertion: i) there exists a king of France, ii) it is unique, and iii) it is bald.
        A noticeable difference between definite and indefinite descriptions is that an inference such as this is valid:

25)   The volcano is large.
26)   The volcano is active,   So:
27)   The volcano is large and active.

It was observed in section 2.4 that the corresponding inference involving existential quantification ('some volcano') fails of validity. By contrast, if the two premises of this inference are true, there is just one volcano (or just one volcano relevant to the current discussion), so the conclusion must also be true. The crucial feature of Russell's account is that if a description 'the P' is being correctly used - that is, if there exists a P, and only one - then it achieves the same effect as a proper name, in singling out a unique thing in the world. But it acts in a totally different way from a name - not by referring directly to the particular, but through this combination of quantification, predication and identity.

The difference between names and quantifiers is reflected in logical form. Since the logical form of a name is simple ('a', 'b', etc.), inferences involving them, e.g. identity inferences, are simple and immediate. In the case of identity, one can directly apply $=$E. Definite descriptions have the same sorts of inferential consequences - if, for example, the P is the Q, then anything true of the P is true of the Q - but the complexity of their underlying Russellian forms makes achieving these effects that much more complex. To illustrate, here is the full dress version of the preceding inference:

		W.i.A.
		1,2, ~~3, 4~~
1)	$(\exists x)(\,V(x)\ \&\ (\forall y)(V(y) \to x = y)\ \&\ L(x))$	ASS
2)	$(\exists x)(\,V(x)\ \&\ (\forall y)(V(y) \to x = y)\ \&\ A(x))$	ASS
3)	$V(a)\ \&\ (\forall y)(V(y) \to a = y)\ \&\ L(a)$	ASS
4)	$V(b)\ \&\ (\forall y)(V(y) \to b = y)\ \&\ A(b)$	ASS
5)	$V(a)$	&E, 3
6)	$(\forall y)(V(y) \to b = y)$	&E, 4
7)	$V(a) \to b = a$	$\forall$E, 6
8)	$b = a$	$\to$E, 5, 7
9)	$A(b)$	&E, 4.
10)	$A(a)$	$=$E, 8, 9
11)	$V(a)\ \&\ (\forall y)(V(y) \to a = y)\ \&\ L(a)\ \&\ A(a)$	&I, 3, 10
12)	$(\exists x)(V(x)\ \&\ (\forall y)(V(y) \to x = y)\ \&\ L(x)\ \&\ A(x))$	$\exists$I, 11
13)	$(\exists x)(V(x)\ \&\ (\forall y)(V(y) \to x = y)\ \&\ L(x)\ \&\ A(x))$	$\exists$E, 2, 4, 12
14)	$(\exists x)(V(x)\ \&\ (\forall y)(V(y) \to x = y)\ \&\ L(x)\ \&\ A(x))$	$\exists$E, 1, 3, 13

At lines 1 and 2 we assume the two premises - these dictate that the overall form of the inference will be ∃ Elimination, and play no further role until the applications of ∃E at the end. At lines 3 and 4 we assume the corresponding instances of 1 and 2, for individuals a and b. Although we must choose distinct names for the two instances, to satisfy constraint i) of ∃E, the uniqueness condition of the definite description (line 6) enables us to prove that these are one and the same (line 8). Once we have established the identity of a with b, we can prove that the same volcano is both large and active, line 11. At line 12 we re-introduce the definite description, and then successively discharge assumptions 4 and 3 in favour of 2 and 1. Another aspect of this difference in complexity between names and definite descriptions is that the logical simplicity of a proper name leaves no room for scope interactions with other expressions. It was noted in section 2.4 that there is no difference in the forms of 'Etna is large and Etna is active' and 'Etna is large and active'. The scope interaction with conjunction - which we have just had to *prove* to be unimportant in the case of definite descriptions - simply does not exist in the corresponding sentences containing names.

In 'On Denoting', Russell said that his theory could deal with three puzzles involving definite descriptions, concerning identity, existence, and the Law of Excluded Middle. Let us look briefly at the last of these. A sentence such as

28)   Either the present king of France is bald or he isn't

looks to be an instance of the Law of Excluded Middle, and so its truth should be guaranteed by logic. But if it's true, one or other disjunct must be true. It seems we must either assert baldness of the present king of France, or deny it - either way, we seem committed to there being a present king of France. On an account which takes grammatical form to be a sure guide of logical or semantical form, a noun phrase picks out something, the subject of the sentence, and the verb phrase predicates something of it. Since there is in actuality no present king of France, we must say that the subject of this sentence is a possible, but non-actual entity.

Russell's theory of definite descriptions avoids the postulation of such entities; it avoids making ontology (our account of what there is) subservient to grammar, by divorcing logical and grammatical form. There is more than one way to negate a sentence with a definite description, on his analysis. Whereas names allow no scope interaction with negation (cf. 'London is not small' in section 2.4), the interaction between descriptions and negation is all important. To say that the king of France is not bald is, for Russell, to say something with a potential scope ambiguity. It could mean:

29) $(\exists x)(K(x) \& (\forall y)(K(y) \to x = y) \& \neg B(x))$.

This gives the definite description wider scope than the negation (Russell would call this a primary occurrence of the description). It's to say something false, viz. that there is a unique king of France who isn't bald. The other plausible way to place the negation is

30) $\neg(\exists x)(K(x) \& (\forall y)(K(y) \to x = y) \& B(x))$.

Russell terms this a secondary occurrence of the description. The negation takes wider scope, and we get something true: it's not the case that there is a king of France, and only one, who is bald.

By building the existence claim into the content of what gets asserted, Russell's account preserves classical logic. Sentences containing a definite description are either true or false, even when the description fails to single out anything in the world, because part of what is asserted is that the thing in question exists. 28) could mean one of two things. It could be the disjunction of 24) with the false 29):

31) $(\exists x)(K(x) \& (\forall y)(K(y) \to x = y) \& B(x))$ v
$(\exists x)(K(x) \& (\forall y)(K(y) \to x = y) \& \neg B(x))$

This is not a genuine instance of the Law of Excluded Middle. It is not a tautology - on the contrary, it is false, since both disjuncts require the existence of a king of France. Classical logic is not committed to 31), but to the disjunction of 24) with 30):

32) $(\exists x)(K(x) \& (\forall y)(K(y) \to x = y) \& B(x))$ v
$\neg(\exists x)(K(x) \& (\forall y)(K(y) \to x = y) \& B(x))$

This is a genuine instance of Excluded Middle, and it is true.

In the formalization of uniqueness, two new symbols are worth noting. Firstly, it is sometimes convenient to have a quantifier expressing unique existence. Standardly, '$\exists!$' is used. Thus '$(\exists! x)\, U(x)$' means 'there exists a unique x such that $U(x)$'. In other words, '$(\exists! x)\, U(x)$' is, by definition, the abbreviation of 20). The second piece of notation is a rival to Russell's way of formalizing definite descriptions. Instead of analysing a definite description into a combination of quantifiers and identity, we can treat it as a genuine singular term. In order to convert a predicate like K(x), 'king of France', into a singular term, we need a **term-forming operator**. Like a quantifier, the *description operator* ι can bind a variable to produce a complex expression, thus: (ιx) K(x). Unlike a quantifer, the resulting complex expression is a singular term ('the K', i.e. the thing x which satisfies the condition K(x)), not a sentence. Since '(ιx) K(x)' is a singular term, we can use it directly in identity inferences (e.g. from (ιx)K(x) = a, and P(a), infer P((ιx)K(x)).) Since the description operator is a logical constant, it can be characterized by I and E rules, e.g. for introducing a description:

$$\frac{(\exists x)(K(x) \text{ \& } (\forall y)(\ K(y) \to x = y\ )}{K(\ (\iota x)\ K(x)\ )}$$

4.6.2 Modality

In section 2.2.3, we saw that the notions of necessity and possibility could not be incorporated into simple truth-functional logic. They are the alethic *modalities* (*modes* of truth), and a branch of logic is devoted to their inferential relations: modal logic. We shall now briefly consider the introduction of modalities into our logical language, symbolizing 'Necessarily A' by □A and 'Possibly A' by ◊A. One of the first things we noted about these modalities (section 2.2.1) is the way they are inter-related:

33)   □A ↔ ¬◊¬A.

This means that we could take possibility as primitive, and by defining necessity in terms of it, eliminate all talk of necessity in favour of 'not possibility not'. Alternatively, we could take necessity as the privileged concept, and define possibility in terms of it: ◊A ↔ ¬□¬A. But it is more revealing to have both concepts explicit in the language, and we shall accordingly pay the cost of a certain amount of reduplication in rules by not eliminating one modality in favour of the other.

So necessity and possibility are duals. Given the way necessity was defined as truth in all possible states of affairs, and possibility as truth in at least one, the fact that the modalities are duals simply reflects the fact that the quantifiers are so related (cf. 22 in section 4.5.3.) Indeed any principle which is the modal manifestation of such a truth about quantifiers will also be true. For example, the fact that ∀

distributes over → guarantees that □ distributes over →, a law which is commonly referred to as K:

K) $\Box(A \rightarrow B) \rightarrow (\Box A \rightarrow \Box B)$.

Likewise, the fact that ∀ does *not* distribute over v can be taken to explain the distinction we want between □(A v ¬A) and □A v ¬□A. (Recall exercise 2, D; determination is a kind of necessity.) It's a truth of logic that

34)   Tigers exist or tigers don't exist.

If it's a truth of logic, it's surely necessarily true,

35)   □(tigers exist v ¬tigers exist).

We appeal here to the rule of □ Introduction, or Necessitation: if X is a theorem of logic, then so is □X. In symbols, (for ' | -', see section 4.3.3)

$$\frac{\vdash X}{\vdash \Box X}$$

35) is true. But we wouldn't want the box to distribute over the disjunction - we wouldn't want it to follow from 35) that

36)   □tigers exist v □¬tigers exist.

For, to repeat a point made in section 2.2.3, the existence of tigers is contingent - it's neither necessary that they exist, nor necessary that they don't.
     ◊ and □ provide an approximate means of formalization for the modal auxiliary verbs of ordinary language 'can' and 'must'. For instance,

37)   John can lift Mary
37′)   ◊ lift(john, mary) .

There are possibilities for scope interaction between ◊ and the quantifiers. Suppose that someone, convinced of John's great strength, believes that John could lift several people at once - all the people gathered in a certain room, perhaps. He might say:

38)   John can lift everyone.

In other words, John's lifting everyone, $(\forall x)$ lift(john, x), is asserted to be possible:

38') $\Diamond\,(\forall x)$ lift(john, x) .

(To bring out the essential logical structure, assume that 'x' only ranges over people in that room.) However, someone might not think that John is so strong - they might believe, for instance, that John could lift each person one by one, but not all together. They would prefer the weaker statement:

39)   John can lift anyone.

As noted before (section 4.5.2), 'any' has a preference for wide scope:

39') $(\forall x)\,\Diamond$ lift(john, x)

In other words: for whichever individual you choose, it is possible that John lifts that individual. (Notice also that if you think of $\Diamond$ in terms of existential quantification over possible worlds, that the weaker 39' corresponds to the weaker $\forall\exists$ form.) In traditional logical terms, 38') would count as modality *de dicto* - the proposition, or dictum, that John lifts everyone, is asserted as possible. In 39', by contrast, no complete dictum lies within the scope of the $\Diamond$. Rather, what falls within its scope has a free variable: lifts(john, x). This is a mark of the modality *de re* - the way an entity possesses an attribute - necessarily, or in this case, possibly. For any of those entities x, it is possible that John lifts x.

       Some of the most controversial aspects of modal logic arise when $\Box$ and $\Diamond$ combine in these ways with quantifiers, and identity. For example, if we can perform $\Box$ Introduction on theorems of predicate logic, we can prove that identity is necessary:

1)	$h = h$	$=$I.	W.i.A.
2)	$\Box\, h = h$	$\Box$I, 1.	~~3~~
3)	$h = p$	ASS.	
4)	$\Box\, h = p$	$=$E, 2, 3.	
5)	$h = p \rightarrow \Box\, h = p$	$\rightarrow$I, 3, 4.	
6)	$(\forall y)(\, h = y \rightarrow \Box\, h = y\,)$	$\forall$I, 5.	
7)	$(\forall x)(\forall y)(\, x = y \rightarrow \Box\, x = y\,)$	$\forall$I, 6.	

Line 3) states the empirical discovery that Hesperus, the first star to appear at dusk, is none other than Phosphorus, the last star to disappear at dawn. Line 4) comes by the most controversial move in the argument - that a 'Necessarily' context such as line 2) is fit for substitution on the basis of an identity, of one of these co-referring names for the other. We thus have the result that since Hesperus and Phosphorus are identical, they are necessarily identical. Lines 6) and 7) merely generalize the point.

4.6.3 Truth and meaning

Meaning, like necessity, but unlike truth, is not a truth functional notion. Consider the French sentence a):

a)   La neige est blanche.

This sentence is true (in French) if snow is white, and only if snow is white. We can thus state its material truth conditions as follows:

40)   true(a) $\leftrightarrow$ snow is white.

'Snow is white' is materially equivalent to, for example, 'grass is green', so this biconditional is true:

41)   snow is white $\leftrightarrow$ grass is green.

By 40) and 41), the following is therefore an equally correct statement of the material truth conditions of sentence a:

42)   true(a) $\leftrightarrow$ grass is green.

The notion of meaning is not so liberal. What a *means* (in French) is that snow is white, it doesn't mean that grass is green.

The story about knights and knaves provides a model for these more abstract concepts of truth and meaning. Instead of talking about people being *knights* or *knaves*, we can talk of sentences being *true* or *false*. Instead of having: someone *says* that A, we can have: a sentence *means* that A. (The main difference is that a person can say many things, whereas a sentence, if it's not ambiguous, has only one meaning within a given language. So with the unambiguous sentences we are concerned with, nothing corresponds straightforwardly to a normal - something which says things both true and false.) So for instance,

43)   a means that snow is white.

Notice that the context 'means that' relates a sentence named - we use 'a', 'b', ... to refer to sentences, just as we used them as names for knights and knaves - to a sentence used. We refer to a particular French sentence with 'a', we use a certain English sentence, 'snow is white', to state what it means.

Further parallels follow. No-one is both knight and knave; and

44) $(\forall s) \neg (\text{true}(s) \ \& \ \text{false}(s))$.

Variables s range over sentences in what follows. And just as we conjectured that everyone on the island was either knight or knave, so we have in classical logic the **Principle of Bivalence**:

45) $(\forall s)(\text{true}(s) \ v \ \text{false}(s))$.

The semantic principle 44) surfaces as the logical Law of Non-Contradiction, and 45) as the Law of Excluded Middle. In a trivalent logic (cf. exercise 2.2 D), Bivalence fails - truth and falsity are not the only options, so for example, if a sentence is not false, it doesn't follow that it's true. (If normals are present, if someone isn't a knave it doesn't follow that he's a knight.)

Suppose we came across an island where, as far as we can tell by checking up on the inhabitants, there are only knights and knaves. We never get any evidence that there are normals present. But some of the natives say things (e.g. about undecidable mathematical problems, or about the remote past) it is just impossible for us to check up on. We can't tell whether what they say is the truth or not. The correctly cautious response on this island would be: we have no evidence that there is anyone other than a knight or knave here, but we can't be sure that only knights and knaves are present. So we had better abstain on the principle $(\forall x)(H(x) \ v \ D(x))$ - we have no right either to assert or deny it. Some philosophers maintain the corresponding thesis about language (cf. section 4.3.1). They don't accept bivalence, and the inferential principles it underpins, but they don't reject it either.

But let us return to the connection between literal meaning and conditions of truth. A true sentence is like an honest knight: things are the way it says they are. Paralleling (but marginally stronger than) the definition of an honest knight, we have the schema:

46) $(\forall s)(\text{ s means that } X \rightarrow (\text{ true}(s) \leftrightarrow X))$.

An instance of this schema would be:

47) $(\forall s)(s \text{ means that snow is white } \rightarrow (\text{true}(s) \leftrightarrow \text{snow is white}))$.

Instantiating the generalization for our French sentence we get:

48) $a \text{ means that snow is white } \rightarrow (\text{ true}(a) \leftrightarrow \text{ snow is white })$.

So this, together with 43), gives 40). a is true just in case things are the way it says (and what it says is that snow is white).

46) embodies a principle that goes back to Aristotle ("to say of what is that it is, or of what is not that it is not, is true"). Its formulation as a logical principle about truth is due to Tarski - 46) is a version of what Tarski called **Convention T**. Tarski's concern was a logical investigation of truth, and he proposed Convention T as a constraint which any acceptable formal theory of truth should meet: if sentence a of a particular language means that A, a theory of truth for that language should entail the corresponding statement of its truth conditions, $\text{true}(a) \leftrightarrow A$.

Any theory of truth has to contend with the possibility of a sentence which means that it itself is false:

b)   false(b).

The trouble this creates is shown in the following derivation. (Now that our interest is not so much inference per se, but the concept of truth, it can obscure the important points of the reasoning to make every step explicit - we can afford to elide one or two inferential steps, as I do below.)

1)	b means that false(b)	ASS.	W.i.A.
2)	($\forall$x)(x means that false(b) $\rightarrow$		1,5
	$\qquad\qquad$ (true(x) $\leftrightarrow$ false(b)))	Inst, 52	
3)	b means that false(b) $\rightarrow$ (true(b) $\leftrightarrow$ false(b))	$\forall$E, 3.	
4)	true(b) $\leftrightarrow$ false(b)	$\rightarrow$E, 1, 4.	
5)	true(b)	ASS.	
6)	false(b)	$\leftrightarrow$E/$\rightarrow$E, 4,5	
7)	true(b) & false(b)	&I, 5, 6.	
8)	$\neg$ (true(b) & false(b))	$\forall$E, 49.	
9)	$\neg$true(b)	RAA, 5, 7, 8.	
10)	$\neg$false(b)	$\leftrightarrow$E/$\rightarrow$E, 4,9	
11)	$\neg$true(b) & $\neg$ false(b)	&I, 9, 10.	

On the assumption that b means what it appears to mean, we must conclude that it is neither true nor false. One response to this result is to drop that assumption. Or rather, prevent it from being formulated. This is in effect Tarski's solution - to rule out the possibility of sentences ascribing truth or falsity to any sentences in the same language. Another way of dealing with it is to accept the conclusion, and drop bivalence for these sentences.

4.6.4 Prolog and logic

In this section we examine the way in which Prolog can achieve, mechanically, an approximation to what we have been doing in this chapter: making derivations in first order logic. The problem is that if we gave a machine a full set of deduction rules, it might, if it hit, for example, & Introduction, validly derive from a premise A the conclusion A & A, and from that (A & A) & A, and so on. Prolog avoids this by and large (it can still go into loops!), in virtue of: a) restricted syntax (the general form of a Prolog statement is a conditional with an atomic consequent); b) restricted inference - it employs a single rule, Resolution, which is an *elimination* rule: a generalization of $\rightarrow$E and $\forall$E combined; and c) reasoning backwards, i.e. inference is constrained through being goal directed. We start by looking at the underlying logical syntax of Prolog.

$\qquad$A wff is in *Conjunctive Normal Form* (C.N.F.) if it is expressed as a conjunction of disjunctions, where each disjunct is either an atomic wff or the negation of an atomic wff. By disjunctions we include limiting cases such as an atomic wff A (since A is equivalent to A v A). Likewise for conjunctions (since any wff X is equivalent to X & X). So the following five wffs all exemplify C.N.F:

¬B, ¬A v B, C & B, ¬A & B & (C v D), (A v ¬B) & (C v ¬A v B).

What is distinctive about C.N.F., therefore, is that *if* a wff contains both &s and vs, all the vs are within the scopes of &s, and *if* it contains vs and ¬s, all the ¬s are within the scopes of vs. Wffs in C.N.F. have certain useful features - for instance, they are amenable to a very simple procedure for deciding whether they are logical truths or not. Moreover, a generalization of C.N.F. to predicate logic provides the underlying forms for the wffs of Prolog. So it is an important feature of propositional logic that all its wffs can be put into C.N.F. There are various mechanical procedures for making the transformation.

One method for conversion into C.N.F. is as follows. i) Eliminate any occurrences of → and ↔. For instance, any occurrence of the form X → Y should be replaced by its logical equivalent, ¬X v Y. E.g. 49) becomes 50):

49)   ¬(A → (B & (A v ¬B)))
50)   ¬(¬A v (B & (A v ¬B)))

ii) Drive negations inwards using De Morgan's Laws, erasing any double negations. So 50) becomes, successively,

         ¬¬A & ¬(B & (A v ¬B))
         A & ¬(B & (A v ¬B))
         A & (¬B v ¬(A v ¬B))
         A & (¬B v (¬A & ¬¬B))
51)   A & (¬B v (¬A & B))

What we arrive at is a collection of conjunctions and disjunctions - but where there may be, as here, &s within the scope of vs. So the final stage is iii) Use the Distributive Laws to get conjunctions outside the scopes of disjunctions:

52)   A & ((¬B v ¬A) & (¬B v B))

We can drop any grouping of conjunctions within conjunctions, since an unbracketed series X & Y & Z & ... is semantically unambiguous. We can regard the resulting wff as a set of separate statements, or *clauses*, which, like a program, are conjunctively combined:

53)   A.
         ¬B v ¬A.
         ¬B v B.

The general form of each separate clause, if we group all the negated disjuncts together, and place them before all the unnegated disjuncts, is:

$$¬A v ¬B v ¬C v ... v D v E v F v ...$$

Consider this restriction on the form of clauses: they may contain no more than one unnegated atomic component. This is essentially the restriction on Prolog, the restriction to the so-called **Horn Clause** subset of logic, since any such disjunction

$$¬A v ¬B v ¬C v ... v D$$

is equivalent to ¬(A & B & C & ...) v D, which is equivalent to a conditional with an atomic consequent,

$$(A \& B \& C \& ...) \rightarrow D.$$

We can now state the propositional part of the Resolution rule of inference, as it pertains to such clauses:

$$\frac{¬A v ¬B v ... v D, \quad ¬D v ¬E v ... v G}{¬A v ¬B v ... v ¬E v ... v G}$$

Our rule of v Elimination can be seen as a special case of this rule (with ¬B ..., ¬E ..., G, all empty: from ¬A v D, ¬D, infer ¬A). Alternatively, thinking of the disjunctions as conditionals, we can think of Resolution as generalized →E: from D, D → G, infer G. Let us put it in Prolog's notation:

$$\frac{D :- A, B, ... \quad G :- D, E, ...}{G :- A, B, E, ...}$$

Notice these special cases. Any unnegated wff X is unconditional, i.e. conditional upon a vacuous antecedent, X :- . Conversely, a negated atomic wff ¬X, seen as vacuous disjunction ¬X v , can be expressed as a conditional with no consequent, :- X. Resolution can be applied to any two conditionals when the consequent of one (D, here) is in the antecedent of the other - we form a new conditional combining all the remaining antecedent conditions (if any) and the other consequent (if any).

Prolog's reasoning is goal-directed in that Resolution is not applied to a set of premises in a forwards direction, undirected by the goal to be proved. Instead, the negation of the goal is added as a further premise, and we aim to derive a contradiction. In other words, we aim to prove the goal by a Reductio of its negation. Obtaining a contradiction by Resolution means deriving the empty clause, :- . At this point, it is helpful to work through a specific example. Consider this propositional subset of the nutritional advice program,

54)   **needs(john, vitamin_C) :- .**
55)   **found_in(vitamin_C, oranges) :- .**
56)   **should_eat(john, oranges) :- needs(john, vitamin_C),**
                                   found_in(vitamin_C, oranges) .

queried with 'Should John eat oranges?',

57)   **:- should_eat(john, oranges) .**

56) and 57) resolve to:

58)   **:- needs(john, vitamin_C), found_in(vitamin_C, oranges) .**

58) and 54) resolve to

59)   **:- found_in(vitamin_C, oranges) .**

which in turn resolves with 55) to the empty clause, :- ., thus establishing the goal.

We need now to consider how this generalizes to predicate logic, starting by extending the notion of normal form to encompass quantification. We can still get wffs into C.N.F. - or more correctly, for predicate logic, *Skolem Normal Form* - if we can adopt a convention for erasing the quantifiers. The case to focus on is existential quantification. Consider this example:

60)   John shot a tiger.
61) $(\exists x)(\text{tiger}(x) \ \& \ \text{shot}(john, x))$.

A technique for replacing the combination of ∃ plus variable was devised by Skolem. In the simplest existential sentences like these we erase the quantifier and replace each occurrence of the variable it binds by a previously unused name. We can't use a name for a tiger we already know about, e.g. 'shere khan', since we can't assume that John shot *that* tiger. But we can introduce a new name for it - say 'o1':

62)   tiger(o1) & shot(john, o1) .

The important point is that each time we encounter a new existential formula, we must choose a new name to replace it. To guarantee an unending supply of such constants we index them with numbers: 'o1', 'o2', ... Suppose we learn that also

63)   Mary shot a tiger.

It could turn out that the same tiger was the object of both shootings, but this would be an extralinguistic fact, not something which follows from the content of 60) and 63). We should use different names when replacing different existential quantifiers, but the same name to link all the predications connected with the same occurrence of a quantifier. In Prolog, 63) becomes

tiger(o2) .
shot(mary, o2) .

(Up till now we had no means to assert such existential propositions in Prolog.)
        Now consider a slightly more complicated case:

64)   Every hunter saw a tiger.

By representing the existential phrase with a constant,

65)   ($\forall$x)(hunter(x) $\rightarrow$ (tiger(o3) & saw(x, o3))),

we only capture one reading of this sentence, the reading on which all the hunters saw the *same* tiger, o3 (cf. the discussion of example 10, section 4.5.2). To get the weaker reading with Skolem's notation, we need to introduce a function. Let f1 be the new function. We can then make clear that the tiger seen depends on x - it is some function f1 of the particular hunter x considered - by denoting the tiger 'f1(x)':

66) $(\forall x)(hunter(x) \rightarrow (tiger(f1(x)) \ \& \ saw(x, f1(x))))$.

(A constant is a special case of a function, a 0 place function - see section 5.3.1. 'o3' in the preceding example is a constant function, which picks out the same tiger - it does not depend upon the hunter, x.) Similarly, if an existential quantifier occurs within the scope of two universal quantifiers, we will need a Skolem function of two arguments. Take the statement that every teacher, in every lecture, interests at least one person who attends,

67) $(\forall x)(teacher(x) \rightarrow (\forall y)(lecture\text{-}of(y, x) \rightarrow$
$(\exists z)[attends(z, y) \ \& \ interests(x, z)]))$.

Then what is maintained is that the person who is interested depends, in general, both on the teacher and on the lecture they are giving. '$(\exists z)$' falls within the scope of both '$(\forall x)$' and '$(\forall y)$' - correspondingly, the Skolem term we replace it by must be a function of both these quantifiers:

68) $(\forall x)(teacher(x) \rightarrow (\forall y)(lecture\text{-}of(y, x) \rightarrow$
$[attends(f2(x, y), y) \ \& \ interests(x, f2(x, y))]))$.

So the general rule for skolemizing existential quantification is: erase the existential quantifier, and replace all occurrences of the variable it binds with a term which is the application of a new function to as many variables as are bound by universal quantifiers which contain the existential quantifier within their scope.

     Having dealt with $\exists$, we can simply erase any occurrences of the universal quantifier in a wff. There is no ambiguity in the quantificational force of the resulting wff, since we understand all variables in it as tacitly governed by universal quantifiers (as in Prolog). So 68) would become:

69) $teacher(x) \rightarrow (lecture\text{-}of(y, x) \rightarrow$
$[attends(f2(x, y), y) \ \& \ interests(x, f2(x, y))])$.

This describes Skolem's method for erasing quantifiers, but we need to integrate that technique with the procedure for transformation into C.N.F. We need to ensure that quantifiers are uniformly outside the scopes of negations, since otherwise a combination such as $\neg(... o3 ...)$ would be ambiguous in force between $\neg(\exists x)$ and $(\exists x)\neg$. So we expand stage ii) of the transformation to drive negations inside the scope of quantification, changing ¬∀ to ∃ ¬, and ¬ ∃ to ∀ ¬. Then comes the new stage, removal of quantifiers, followed by the final stage, distribution of & over v.   In other words, the conversion of 67) to Skolem Normal Form actually proceeds thus:

(∀x)(¬teacher(x) v (∀y)(¬lecture-of(y, x) v
                        (∃z)[attends(z, y) & interests(x, z)])).
(∀x)(¬teacher(x) v (∀y)(¬lecture-of(y, x) v
                        [attends(f2(x, y), y) & interests(x, f2(x, y))])).
¬teacher(x) v ¬lecture-of(y, x) v
                        [attends(f2(x, y), y) & interests(x, f2(x, y))] .
(¬teacher(x) v attends(f2(x, y), y) v interests(x, f2(x, y)))   &
    (¬lecture-of(y, x) v attends(f2(x, y), y) v interests(x, f2(x, y))).

The generalization of Resolution to predicate logic involves the unification algorithm. (For examples of the unification of list patterns, see section 3.4.3.) Unification is an algorithm for finding the most general common instance of two terms, if one exists. For example, the expression **f(a, b, a)** is a common instance of **f(X, Y, X)** and **f(a, Z, W)** - i.e. it is an instance of each - but it is not the most general common instance. **f(a, Y, a)** is a more general common instance than **f(a, b, a)** because it contains a variable. There is no common instance of those two expressions more general than **f(a, Y, a)**, and it is unique - up to choice of lettering for the variable. By the Law of Alphabetic Variants (section 4.4.2), **f(a, Y, a)** is equivalent in this context to **f(a, Z, a)**.

If the terms in question can be unified, the algorithm outputs a list of the substitutions that have to be made for their unification. Otherwise it outputs 'fail' or 'false' - something to indicate that they are not unifiable. It proceeds by recursively breaking down a given unification problem into a series of simpler identities. I shall represent this by means of two Prolog lists - a list of identities to be considered, and a list of substitutions to be output. Initially, the former is the main problem, the identity formed with the two terms in question, and the latter is empty. In this case:

Identities to be considered	Substitutions
[f(X, Y, X) = f(a, Z, W)]	**[]**

The question of whether these two terms can be unified turns immediately on whether their three component arguments can be unified, so we take this identity off the list and replace it with those three simpler identities:

$$[X = a, Y = Z, X = W] \qquad\qquad []$$

Here are three basic identity statements, and the algorithm considers each in turn.

The unification algorithm has a number of basis conditions to cover the different possible basic identities. It might encounter an identity formed with the same constant, e.g. $c = c$, or same variable, $V = V$, in which case nothing needs to be done, and it can move on to the next identity to be considered. Or it might encounter an identity with two distinct constants, e.g. $b = c$, at which point the attempt at unification fails. Or it might be that there is a variable on the left and something else on the right - as with the first of the identities here, $X = a$. Since the algorithm is aiming to find a common instance of the two main expressions, when considering a basic identity like $X = a$ it must always replace the more general term by the more specific. So the rule is to add $X = a$ to the list of substitutions to be made. These substitution statements are to be read as: replace all occurrences of the term on the left of the identity sign - X here - by the term on the right - a. This instruction includes whatever remains on the list of identities to be considered. Since there is one occurrence of X there, in $X = W$, the unification problem changes to this:

$$[Y = Z, a = W] \qquad\qquad [X = a]$$

The two remaining identities are also straightforward. An identity formed with two variables, as with $Y = Z$, is a case where Alphabetic Variants applies - so we can have the algorithm either replace the one on the left by the one on the right, or vice versa. The final identity $a = W$, with a constant on the left and variable on the right, produces the substitution $W = a$, i.e. replace all occurrences of W by a. So the unification succeeds, with a list of three substitutions:

$$[] \qquad\qquad [X = a, Y = Z, W = a]$$

There is one important qualification to this procedure: the *occurs check*. When considering a basic identity involving a variable, whether on the left or the right of $=$, the algorithm should check whether this variable occurs in the term on the other side. The importance of this can be illustrated with a question such as 'Are the terms $g(X, f(X))$ and $g(h(Z), Z)$ unifiable?' As before, we start with the main identity, which then breaks down into two sub-cases:

$[g(X, f(X)) = g(h(Z), Z)]$ $[]$
$[X = h(Z), f(X) = Z]$ $[]$

We first consider $X = h(Z)$. Since $h(Z)$ is more specific than X (it only matches with expressions like $h(a)$, $h(f(b))$, etc., whereas X matches with anything whatsoever), the substitution is $X = h(Z)$. This includes the occurrence of X in the remaining identity to be considered, $f(X) = Z$. So we now have:

$[f(h(Z)) = Z]$ $[X = h(Z)]$

In this form, however, the final identity creates a problem. If we omit the occurs check - ignore the fact that Z occurs within $f(h(Z))$ - and attempt to replace all occurrences of the more general Z by the more specific $f(h(Z))$, instead of solving the main unification problem by having reduced it to a succession of simpler unifications, we generate an infinite regression. Replacing the occurrence of Z within $h(Z)$ (in the substitution statement on the right) by $f(h(Z))$ produces $h(f(h(Z)))$ - which contains an occurrence of Z to be replaced, giving $h(f(h(f(h(Z)))))$, and so on ad infinitum. To preclude this, the unification algorithm contains the occurs check. (However, because of the extra computational cost of the occurs check, most Prolog implementations omit it.)

Unification enables Prolog to perform $\forall E$. It is a directed form of $\forall E$ - the instantiations to be made are directed by the clauses to be resolved. Suppose we make conditional 56) appropriately general, and make the query, 'What should John eat?':

70)   should_eat(X, Z) :- needs(X, Y), found_in(Y, Z) .
71)   :- should_eat(john, W) .

In order for these to resolve, we need unification to generate the substitutions $X = \text{john}$ and $Z = W$. With these substitutions 70) and 71) resolve to 72). This in turn resolves with 54) - given $Y = \text{vitamin\_C}$ - to 73):

72)   :- needs(john, Y), found_in(Y, W) .
73)   :- found_in(vitamin_C, W) .

This and 55) produce the empty clause - provided that W has the value **oranges**.

Exercise 6

A.   Give the logical forms of the following:

1)   Hesperus is not Mars, it is Venus.
2)   Socrates exists.
3)   There is at least one great philosopher other than Socrates.
4)   It is false that everything is distinct from itself.
5)   Every philosopher who drank hemlock is identical to Socrates.
6)   If anyone invented logic, it was either Aristotle or Frege.
7)   Mary has at least two admirers.

B.   Prove that identity is a transitive relation. Is distinctness transitive?

C.   Formalize and prove each of these arguments.

8)   Hyde killed a man. Jekyll is Hyde.
           Therefore: Jekyll killed a man.
9)   If Shakespeare didn't write *Hamlet* then Shakespeare isn't Shakespeare.
           Therefore: Shakespeare wrote *Hamlet*.
10)   At most one person wrote *Alice*. Charles Dodgson wrote *Alice*.
           Lewis Carroll wrote *Alice*.
           Therefore: Lewis Carroll is Charles Dodgson.

Analyse a definite description formed with a superlative, using $\exists, \forall, =$ and the corresponding comparative. For example, from 11) together with 12), 13) should follow:

11)   The smallest elephant is Jumbo,
12)   Dumbo is another elephant,
13)   Jumbo is smaller than Dumbo.

(Also, from 11) it should follow that there is at least one elephant, that Jumbo is an elephant, but not that Jumbo is small, nor that Jumbo is smaller than himself.) Derive 13) from 11) and 12).

D.   So far we have abstracted from considerations about tense, when formalizing sentences. To treat a tensed statement, e.g. 'Caesar was powerful' as a simple predication 'powerful(Caesar)', is to treat it as: Caesar falls under the concept powerful (at some time or other). But logic cannot ignore tense for ever - it would lead to classifying some fallacious inferences as valid, and failing to capture some valid inferences. Lewis Carroll provided this illustration of the former defect: The meat I buy at market is raw meat. The meat I eat at dinner is the meat I buy at market. Therefore: the meat I eat at dinner is raw meat.

Consider how we might try to capture an intuitively valid inference involving time, such as:

14)   Whenever John dreams, he twitches.
        John will dream.
So: John will twitch.

Such inferences involving tense can be formalized in first order logic if we treat predicates as implicitly relativized to times. For example, let 'John ran' be understood as saying that at some past time John runs:

$$(\exists t)(\ past(t)\ \&\ run(john, t)\ ).$$

('t' is a variable which ranges only over moments of time - cf. exercise 2.5 C.) Instead of taking 'run' as simply a predicate of agents (as in 'run(x)'), we take it as a relation between agents and times, 'run(x, t)', meaning that x runs at time t. A temporal expression like 'whenever' can be understood in terms of universal quantification over times. Formalize this inference, and derive the conclusion from the premises.

Chapter 5
Prolog: logic plus control

5.1 Lists and sets

5.1.1 Recursion with lists

Many important list manipulating predicates can be defined recursively. Consider a list which has lists nested within it, [[a], [b, [c]]]. So far we have **member**, or **on**, which get at the top-level members of such a list. The lists [a] and [b, [c]] are the two things on this list. We might also want to get at the members of these lists, and anything which is a member of a member, etc. Call this relation being *within* a list. The basic case is being on a list:

within(X, List) :- member(X, List) .

For the general case, we want to say that x is within a list if it is on something which is on the list, or on something which is on something which is on it, or ... We can compress this series into a recursion by saying that x is within a list if it is within something which is on it:

within(X, List) :- member(Y, List),
                      within(X, Y).

To understand most recursive operations on lists, we have to understand the recursive structure of lists themselves. Any list can be individuated in the following way:

       [item   followed by   remaining list]   - which are
called its
       [head   and   tail   ]

[item   followed by   remaining list]   - which are called its
[head   and   tail   ]

That is, the **head** is the first member of the list, and the **tail** is the list
(possibly empty) of all the other members.   Head and tail are
separated by what is sometimes called the **list constructor**, written by a
vertical bar, | . This structure is recursive because the tail of a list is
itself a list. Since this is central to a proper understanding of lists, but
also potentially confusing to beginners, I will spell it out by means of an
analogy. Imagine that John and Mary are sorting a collection of books,
which have been piled up into a number of stacks on the floor. Suppose
they are taking each stack in turn, John calling out the title of a book to
Mary, who then makes a decision about where to shelve it. Suppose
further that John always proceeds by looking at a stack from above, not
from the side. He gets the title of a book from its front cover. As far as
he is concerned, any stack of books consists of a top book, sitting on top
of a remaining *stack* of books. Suppose, to make the example short,
there is a pile consisting of *The Clouds, Macbeth* and *Waiting for
Godot*. If we represent this with the list **[clouds, macbeth, godot]**, we
are as it were looking at the stack from sideways on - at the spines of
the books. John doesn't see it like this. He sees it from above, as the
stack whose top member is *The Clouds,* sitting on top of a (possibly
empty) remaining stack. He calls out "Clouds", removes it, and is
confronted with a remaining stack, the top member of which is
Macbeth. He does the same with this, and now faces a stack, the top
member of which is *Waiting for Godot*. He calls out "Godot", removes
it, and discovers he is left with the empty stack. At this point his
procedure for processing a stack of books terminates, and he does
something else - has a break, e.g.
        John's procedure for processing a stack of books is recursive,
which parallels the recursive structure which stacks of books have for
him. The procedure is: to *process* a stack of books, announce and remove
the top book, then *process* the remaining stack. And: when you hit the
empty stack, take a break. Using the list constructor notation, we can
describe this with the Prolog-like routine:

```
process([ ]) :- have_a_break .
process([ TopBook | Remainder ]) :- announce/remove(TopBook),
                        process(Remainder) .
```

John's procedure provides a model for a more elegant way of displaying
a list than simply writing the whole thing as a term. We define a

predicate **printlist**, to **write** each member of a list one after the other, putting spaces between them, and to place the cursor on a new line when it gets down to the empty list:

printlist([ ]) :- nl .
printlist([Head | Tail]) :- write(Head),
                              tab(1),
                              printlist(Tail) .

tab(N) prints N spaces, **nl** puts the cursor on a new line. Since the cursor is the point on the screen at which text is displayed, the difference between these two predefined predicates concerns where the next text, if any, will be displayed. If the following text should continue on the same line, use **tab** to space it apart; if it would be clearer for it to start on a new line, use **nl**.

Consider, then, the structure of **[clouds, macbeth, godot]**. We can describe this as the list whose first member is **clouds**, and whose remainder is the list **[macbeth, godot]**. In other words, we have the identity:

[clouds, macbeth, godot] = [clouds | [macbeth, godot]]

Since the tail of a list is always a list, it too can be split using the list constructor: **[macbeth, godot]** = **[macbeth | [godot]]**. Likewise, the one item list **[godot]** is the list consisting of the item **godot**, and whose tail is the empty list, **[ ]**. The **[Head | Tail]** pattern generates the following view of the structure of this list:

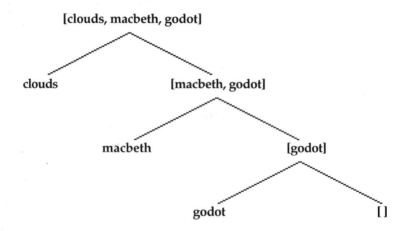

We now have a variety of ways of breaking up a list. Before now we could match a list against the pattern

   [X1, X2, ..., XN]   - the pattern of a list of exactly n members.

This pattern is at odds with the flexibility of lists, since it can only be used to match against lists of fixed length. Or we could use

   append(X, Y, Z)   - can split Z into two lists, X and Y.

This is flexible, in that it can match any list Z, but it doesn't get at the members of Z; it produces two more lists. We can now add

   [X | T]   - the pattern of a list of at least one member, X, plus a
                (possibly empty) tail, the list T.

Further patterns of this sort are possible, because Prolog allows the list constructor to be moved back to allow more than one member of the list to precede it, e.g.

   [X, Y | Tail] is equivalent to [X | [Y | Tail]].

So [X, Y | Tail] is the pattern of a list which starts with the two members X and Y, and a remaining Tail list. It is the pattern of a list with at least two members. So:

   [X, Y | T] - the pattern of a list, with X and Y its first two
                members.
   [X, Y, Z | T] - the pattern of a list with at least three members.

etc. We could use the [X, Y | Tail] pattern if we want to check whether two items are adjacent on a list. X is next to Y on a list if they are the first two things on it:

next(X, Y, [X, Y | T]) .

Otherwise, they will be **next** if they are next to each other on the tail:

next(X, Y, [H | T]) :- next(X, Y, T) .

The great power of the list notation lies in the fact that every list, except for [], can be split into first member and remaining *list*. This is the recursive nature of the list constructing operation, and it enables lists to be of any length. It also means that we can define many important operations on lists in terms of what happens to the head of the list, and then applying the operation recursively to the tail. To put it another way: lists come in two types: [], and those of the form [Head | Tail]. A recursive definition of a predicate of lists p must cover these two types. Simplifying, we can say that it must define i) when p applies to the empty list, and ii) how p applies to an arbitrary list, by matching the list with the pattern [Head | Tail]. Head will pick out the first member of the list, and Tail will be the list which is the remainder - so the recursion will involve applying p to that Tail.

Many implementations of Prolog have a type predicate, list(X), which holds true of X just in case X is a list. We can make use of the recursive structure of lists to reconstruct the definition of this predicate. (If you wish to test your understanding of built-in predicate by explicitly defining it, you may need to spell it differently - for otherwise, even if the definition is identical, it would appear to Prolog as if you were trying to re-define a predicate which is already predefined in your implementation, and this may generate an error message.) The most basic case of a list is the null list. The general case is also straightforward; something is a list provided that its tail is a list:

list([ ]) .
list([Head | Tail]) :- list(Tail).

Understanding the recursive structure of lists also enables us to define many important predicates for manipulating lists. The relations **member**, **length** and **append**, which are predefined in many implementations of Prolog, can be defined using the list constructor, and it helps to understand them to go over these definitions. Taking **member** first, the basic problem is: how to get at all the members of a list using the pattern [Head | Tail]. The fact that the head is the first member of a list provides the basic case:

member(X, [X | Y]) .

X is a member of any list of which it is the head. Now we have to get at all the remaining items; since these are collected in the tail, and the tail is itself a list, we have the recursive clause:

member(X, [Y | Tail]) :- member(X, Tail) .

X is on a list with a certain tail if it is on that tail. We see that the recursive structure of this definition will make Prolog check firstly the head of a list, then the head of its tail, then the head of the tail of the tail, and so on, until it has worked its way through all the members of the list. For length: how many things are on the empty list? None; it's length is zero. What is the length of a list with a Head and some arbitrarily long Tail? It's one more than however long that Tail is:

length([ ], 0) .
length([Head | Tail], N) :- length(Tail, M),
                          N is M + 1 .

This is all that is required to define the length of a list.

The Head and Tail structure of a list makes it easy to get at the first member of a list, but how can we get at the last member of a list? Can we define a relation **last(L, X)**, such that X is the last member of list L, no matter what the length of L is (provided it is not the empty list)? In fact, the recursive structure of a list makes it quite easy to define this relation. Taking the basis case to be a list with one member, the last thing on it is the only thing on it:

last([X], X) .

For the general case of a list with a head and tail, just forget about the head and look for the last thing on the tail:

last([Head | Tail], X) :- last(Tail, X) .

When you work through a number of these recursive definitions, you begin to appreciate the power of the technique. What at first looks like cheating - here, helping oneself to the **last** thing on the Tail - comes to seem wholly natural. We can generalize this relation to find the **nth** member of a list. The central idea is to modify the recursive clause so that Prolog keeps count as it strips down a list:

nth(N, [Head | Tail], X) :- M is N-1,
                       nth(M, Tail, X) .

Thus the task of finding, say, the 3rd thing on **[a, d, b, c]** reduces to the task of finding the 2nd thing on **[d, b, c]** - and this in turn to the task of finding the 1st thing on **[b, c]**. The first thing on a list (whether or not that list has a tail) is just its head:

nth(1, [X | _], X) .

If there is a possibility that a program using this predicate may ask for the Nth thing on a list, where there are less than N things on that list, we can stipulate something to be its Nth member. In logic, a common stipulation would be to take the last member in such a case. Thus asking for the 6th thing on **[a, d, b, c]** is like asking for the 6th thing on **[a, d, b, c, c, c]**. In this procedure for **nth**, this case will be recognized when we get down to a list with a single item X, and the counter N is greater than 1. In this case, we let that last item X be the Nth member:

nth(N, [X], X) :- N > 1 .

(The last two clauses should be placed before the recursive rule.)

More generally, we may want to define an operation which *transforms* one list into another. Such an operation will have at least two arguments: one for the list to be modified, the input list, and one for the resulting, output list. The recursive clause will match the input list to **[Head1 | Tail1]**, and the output list will, in general, be of the form **[Head2 | Tail2]**, where **Head2** bears some specified relation to **Head1**, and **Tail2** is the result of recursively applying the operation to **Tail1**. A simple example would be to double a list of numbers, in the sense of multiplying each number by 2:

double([], []).
double([H1 | T1], [H2 | T2]) :- H2 is H1*2,
**   double(T1, T2).**

A more sophisticated version would check whether the head currently being considered is a number, only multiplying it if it is. The operation leaves the head as it is otherwise. This would require two recursive clauses, to cover these two different cases:

double([], []).
double([H1 | T1], [H2 | T2]) :- num(H1),
                        H2 is H1*2,
                        double(T1, T2).
double([H1 | T1], [H1 | T2]) :- not num(H1),
                        double(T1, T2).

Because **append** is a relation between three lists, it is a little more complex. The basic problem is to define a relation **append(X, Y, Z)** which holds when list Z is the result of adding the contents of list X to the front of list Y. We can hold Y constant and consider what the possibilities are for list X. In fact there are just two cases: X could be the empty list, or it could be an arbitrary list consisting of head and tail. The basis of the recursion will concern the null list. Clearly, adding nothing to the front of a list results in exactly the same list:

append([ ], List, List).

The idea behind the inductive part of the definition is that appending a list with head X and tail T to the front of a list Y will result in a new list, the head of which is X, and whose tail is the result of joining T to the front of Y:

append([X | T], Y, [X | Tail]) :- append(T, Y, Tail) .

To see that this works, consider it for a simple case, such as appending **[a, b]** with **[c]**. The recursive clause says that - because **[a, b]** is **a** followed by **[b]** - these join to a list **[a | Tail1]**, if **Tail1** is the result of joining **[b]** with **[c]**. A second application of the recursive clause tells us that - because **[b]** is **b** followed by **[]** - these join to a list **[b | Tail2]**, if **Tail2** is the result of joining **[]** with **[c]**. But now we have reduced the problem to an append with the empty list. **Tail2** = the result of joining **[]** with **[c]** = **[c]**. And now, as we come out of the recursion, the list is put together: **Tail1** = **[b | [Tail2]]** = **[b | [c]]** = **[b, c]**, and the solution, **[a | Tail1]**, = **[a | [b, c]]** = **[a, b, c]**.

5.1.2   Lists and sets

Lists, bags, and sets are three ways of collecting objects together, three different kinds of totality. They are similar, and differ in the details of their identity conditions. Sets are most familiar to mathematicians and philosophers, but lists are the fundamental structure in Prolog.

Lists obey the strictest principles of individuation. For list L1 to be identical to list L2, not only must they list the same objects, but they must mention them the same number of times, and in the same order. Sets are individuated solely in terms of the things they contain; S1 = S2 iff anything in one is in the other (even if the description of, say, S1 mentions them more times than that of S2, or in a different order). Bags are intermediate: the order in which members are listed is irrelevant, but the number of mentions matters. The following illustrate the difference between lists, bags and sets, using lists to represent all three kinds of structure:

> [a, b, c] and [a, b, d] are different lists, bags and sets.
> [a, b, c] and [c, b, a] are different lists, but the same bag and set.
> [a, b, a] and [a, b] are different lists and bags, but the same set.
> [a, b, c] and [a, b, X] are the same list, bag and set, if X = c.

Sets can be specified in two rather different ways. We can denote a set by listing the things which are in it. The set of planets in our solar system is (currently believed to be) a set of nine things:

{mercury, venus, earth, mars, jupiter, saturn, uranus, neptune, pluto}

Curly brackets are the standard notation for sets. Since the order in which the members are listed is irrelevant to a set, this is the same set as, for instance,

{pluto, venus, earth, mars, jupiter, saturn, uranus, neptune, mercury}

Moreover, since what is essential to a set are just the things in it, and since the Hesperus is the same thing as Venus, this is also the same set:

{hesperus, mercury, earth, mars, jupiter, saturn, uranus, neptune, pluto}

An alternative way of getting at a set is to describe it as the collection of just those things which satisfy a certain condition. Thus, taking the predicate 'planet(x)' to be true of any x which is a planet of our solar system, we can talk of the set of all those things:

{x: planet(x)}

(Alternative notations are sometimes used - for instance, '(λx) planet(x)' is also used to denote the set of things x such that x is a planet.) In naive set theory, given any predicate, we can form the set of all those things which satisfy it. (This can lead to trouble; cf. exercise 4.5 C).

In standard set theory, membership, or being an element of, is written with an epsilon, '∈'. Thus we can say:

venus ∈ {x: planet(x)}

Venus is a member of the set of planets. A special symbol is reserved for the *empty* or *null set*: ∅. So for instance:

{x: unicorn(x)} = ∅.

Since there are no unicorns, the set which the predicate 'unicorn(x)' picks out is the empty set. An important relation between sets is the *subset* relation: A is a subset of B, written A ⊆ B, just in case everything in A is in B. We can take this as definitional:

A ⊆ B ↔ (∀x)(x ∈ A → x ∈ B).

For instance, the so-called terrestrial planets form a subset of the set of all planets:

{mercury, venus, earth, mars} ⊆ {x: planet(x)}

We can approximate set theory in Prolog by using lists to represent sets. We can use the standard relation of list membership for set membership. Corresponding to the idea of collecting together all the things which satisfy some predicate into a set, Prolog has a predefined procedure for lists:

findall(X, C, L) holds iff **L** is the list of all **Xs** which can be shown to satisfy condition **C** (given any way of making **C** true).

For instance, if **planet** is a predicate of individual planets, we can form a new predicate **planetlist**, which is true of a list of all things which can be proved to be planets:

planetlist(List) :- findall(X, planet(X), List) .

The parenthetical condition in the explanation of **findall** means: if **C** contains any further variables, other than X, then any way of assigning values to those variables which makes C true will count - that is, will supply us with a value of X to be added to the list L. To illustrate - suppose we have this record of exam results:

passed(john, logic, b) .
passed(mary, logic, a).
passed(mary, maths, b).
passed(mary, ethics, c).

(The third argument of **passed** is the grade.) If we wish to prepare a list of all those who have passed any exam at any grade -

passlist(L) :- findall(X, passed(X, _, _), L) .

the solution will be **L = [john, mary, mary, mary]**, i.e. the name **mary** is added to the list for as many times as Prolog can prove the condition **passed(mary, _, _).**

One of the most basic operations on sets is that of forming the *intersection* of two sets - the set of all those things common to both. If C is the intersection of A and B, we write $C = A \cap B$. So for instance

{earth} = {mercury, venus, earth} $\cap$ {earth, mars, jupiter}.

The intersection of A and B is the set of all things in A and in B; in Prolog:

inter(A, B, C) :- findall(X, (member(X, A), member(X, B)), C) .

Note that intersection is a function: C is *the* intersection of sets A and B. The use of lists in the dating agency example (section 3.4.2) involved something similar to the intersection operation. To find out whether two people are a good **match**, we had to check whether, in each category of their **likes**, e.g. in sport, there is something common to each of the set of sports they enjoy - whether there is something in the intersection of these sets.

The *union* of two sets is the set of things which are members of one or the other. The union of A with B is written $A \cup B$.
For example:

{mercury, venus, earth, mars} = {mercury, venus, earth} $\cup$ {earth, mars}

Just as intersection corresponds to conjunction, so union corresponds to disjunction; the union of A and B can be defined:

$$A \cup B = \{x: x \in A \lor x \in B\}.$$

In Prolog this becomes:

union(A, B, C) :- findall(X, (member(X, A); member(X, B)), C) .

Using the standard device of thinking of a set as drawing a boundary around the things which are its members, these operations on sets can be depicted as follows (the result of the operation being the area of cross-hatching):

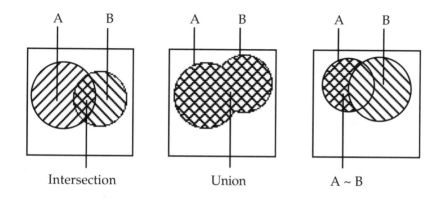

Intersection   Union   A ~ B

The relative *difference* of B in A is the set of members of A which are not members of B. In set theory we write

$$C = A \sim B.$$

An example would be:

{mercury, venus, earth} = {mercury, venus, earth, mars} ~ {mars}

In Prolog the definition is:

diff(A, B, C) :- findall(X, (member(X, A), not(member(X, B))), C) .

We can define a relation **findset** to obtain the *set* of all those Xs which satisfy some condition C,

findset(X, C, S) :- findall(X, C, L), getset(L, S) .

if we have a relation **getset**, to obtain from a list a new list representing the corresponding set, by removing any repetitions. We will define **getset(L, S)** so that it keeps the first member of list **L**, removes any subsequent occurrences of that thing from the tail, and then recursively applies to that thinned out tail:

getset([], []) .
getset([H | T], [H | X]) :- remove(H, T, Y),
                            getset(Y, X) .

This requires us to define **remove(X, List1, List2)**, such that **List2** is the result of removing all occurrences of **X** from **List1**. The definition can be divided into two cases: is the head of the list **X** or not? If it is, we want to remove it - and we can achieve this by simply applying **remove** to the tail of the list:

remove(X, [X | Y], Z) :- remove(X, Y, Z) .

If the head of the list is not **X**, then we want to leave it in place, and apply **remove** to what remains:

remove(X, [H | T], [H | Y]) :- not(X = H),
                              remove(X, T, Y) .

Inevitably, the recursion must be finished off with a basis clause:

remove(X, [ ], [ ]) .

Since any set obtained in this way is still expressed as a list, we will also need to define a relation of set identity which abstracts from the order in which items get mentioned if we want to think of it as a set. There are various equivalent ways of defining the subset and set identity relations. For example, we can say that A is a subset of B iff A is the intersection of A and B. For if A = A ∩ B, there can be nothing in A which it does not have in common with B. There may (or may not) be things in B which are not in A, but if the area of overlap between A and B is not less than A (it couldn't be greater than A), it must be that A ⊆ B. But if we are to define this using the **inter** operation on lists, we need to cut out any redundant members of B using **getset**:

subset(A, B) :- getset(B, C), inter(A, C, A) .

We can then say that A is the identical set to B when each is a subset of the other, for then there is nothing in one which is not in the other. Essentially:

sameset(A, B) :- subset(A, B), subset(B, A) .

We could precede this rule by:

sameset(X, X) .

If the lists are identical, the sets must also be identical, and we can spare Prolog the effort of checking whether each is a subset of the other.

The predefined relations **bagof** and **setof** are slightly more flexible versions of **findall** and **findset**. They are more expressively flexible because they are provided with a means of selectively binding variables with existential quantifiers. If we want the set of those who have passed something - some exam at some grade - we can use the relation we defined above:

findset(X, passed(X, Y, Z), L)

To express this using **setof**, we must bind the variables **Y** and **Z**, whose values we are not interested in, by prefacing **passed(X, Y, Z)** with **Y^Z^**, thus:

setof(X, Y^Z^passed(X, Y, Z), L)

Read this as: find the set L of all those Xs who passed some exam Y at some grade Z. In set theoretic notation,

$$L = \{ \; x: (\exists y)(\exists z) \; passed(x, y, z) \; \}$$

The variables 'x', 'y' and 'z' are all within the scope of the set brackets, and it makes no sense to ask for their values outside that context. Correspondingly, **X**, **Y**, and **Z** are all local to the **setof** operation, and their values are not retained. The solution returned in this instance is **L = [john, mary]**. The simpler **findall/findset** version should be preferred for such a query. But contrast it with the question:

for some exam, find the set of those who passed it (whatever the grade),

setof(X, Z^passed(X, Y, Z), L)

This cannot be formulated using **findset**. It has the logical form

$$(\exists y)(\ L = \{\ x: (\exists z)\ passed(x, y, z)\ \}\ )$$

The variable **Y** is no longer bound locally within **setof**, and its value is accessible outside that operation. There are three ways to answer this query, given the above records: with exam **Y = logic**, the set **L = [john, mary]**, with **Y = maths, L = [mary]**, and with **Y = ethics, L = [mary]**. Similarly, we can ask the question: for some grade Z, find the set of all those who passed some exam at that grade,

setof(X, Y^passed(X, Y, Z), L)

This also has three solutions, since there are three grades mentioned in the records: with **Z = b, L = [john, mary]**, with **Z = a, L = [mary]**, and with **Z = c, L = [mary]**.

Note that throughout we have ignored a fundamental fact about sets, which is that they can contain other sets as members. Just as a list can contain lists as members, so we might have a set

$$\{\ a, c, \{d, b\}, \{b, d, b\}\ \}.$$

Since {b, d, b} contains exactly the same members as {d, b}, these are the same set. So our set is { a, c, {d, b}, {d, b} }. Since this mentions {d, b} twice, its description can be simplified to just: { a, c, {d, b} }. What this shows is that some relations like identity and subset should really be defined recursively, to handle any degree of nesting of sets within sets. For simplicity, I have omitted this point.

5.1.3 First and second order logic

So far the kind of quantification we have employed, in logic and programming, has been *first order*. This means that the variables of quantification range over (first order) things, rather than (second order) properties of things, or (third order) properties of properties of things, or any higher order. The inference from 1) to 2) is a typical first order inference:

1)   Leibniz was a philosopher and mathematician.
2)   Someone was a philosopher and mathematician.

We can formalize this as:

P(l) & M(l) |− (∃x)(P(x) & M(x)) .

Syntactically, in first order logic variables only occur in the same positions as names. By comparison with higher order logics, this is restrictive. Higher order logics are more powerful - more things can be said, and therefore more inferences can be made. Consider the inference from 3) to 4):

3)   Leibniz was a mathematician and Descartes was a mathematician.
4)   There is something which Leibniz and Descartes both were.

The something which Leibniz and Descartes both were was: a mathematician. They shared this common property. There are various ways to treat this inference. One way is to construe 3) in terms of the ontology of sets (cf. the discussion of **is**, section 3.3.1). Thus:

3′)   leibniz ∈ {x: mathematician(x)} &
            descartes ∈ {x: mathematician(x)},
4′)   (∃S)(leibniz ∈ S & descartes ∈ S)

But if we want to formalize 3) in the conventional way,

3′′)   mathematician(leibniz) & mathematician(descartes),

we must capture the inference by using variables which can occupy the same positions as predicates. If we use Greek capitals 'Φ', 'Ψ', ... as such second order variables, we can express what is inferred in this form:

4′′)   (∃Φ)(Φ(leibniz) & Φ(descartes))

4′′) involves quantification into predicate position: there is some Φ such that Leibniz was Φ and Descartes was Φ. So 'Φ' is a variable which ranges over properties of people. We may even want to count such properties - by inferring 6) from 5), for example:

5)   Leibniz and Descartes were both mathematicians and philosophers.
6)   Leibniz and Descartes had two important characteristics in common.

Being important here is a higher order property - a property of properties (cf. the discussion of *being numerous*, section 4.6.1). If we symbolize 'important' by 'Imp', 6) takes this form:

$(\exists \Phi)(\exists \Psi)[\ Imp(\Phi)\ \&\ Imp(\Psi)\ \&\ \Phi \neq \Psi\ \&\ \Phi(l)\ \&\ \Psi(l)\ \&\ \Phi(d)\ \&\ \Psi(d)\ ].$

Here, the apparatus of predication and identity is brought to bear on variables which themselves occupy the position of predicates. The expressive power of Prolog is greatly enhanced by a number of such higher order predicates, predicates which enable other Prolog predicates and wffs to be manipulated as their arguments.
      One of the most central examples of a higher order predicate in Prolog is **call**. **call(X)** calls the Prolog goal **X**, so **X** must be instantiated to a Prolog wff of the appropriate syntax (Edinburgh, we assume). We can use it to define disjunction in Prolog. Suppose we would prefer **or** to the usual semi-colon. Assuming we have fixed the syntax of **or** as an infix binary operator (see operator declarations, section 5.3.1), we can then define it:

X or Y :- call(X) .
X or Y :- call(Y) .

Notice how this definition parallels the natural deduction rule vI: from X, you may infer X or Y; from Y, you may infer X or Y.
      A more weighty illustration of **call** is provided by the definition of another logical connective, **forall**. **forall** is the nearest thing in Prolog to an explicit symbol for universal quantification. Strictly speaking, **forall** is a *binary* quantifier - it takes two wffs to form a wff. **forall(P, Q)** means roughly $(\forall x)(\ P(x) \rightarrow Q(x)\ )$. More accurately,

> **forall(P, Q)** holds iff $(\forall x_1) ... (\forall x_n)\ (P \rightarrow Q)$, where $x_1, ..., x_n$ are all the variables which occur in both P and Q.

Suppose, for example, we supplement the above exam records with this information,

student(john).
student(mary).
exam(logic).
exam(ethics).
exam(maths).

and we want to say that students **qualify** if they pass *all* the exams. We cannot define **qualify** like this:

qualify(X) :- student(X),
                    exam(Y), passed(X, Y, _) .

For this means that someone qualifies if they pass *some* exam. The query **qualify(john)** would succeed, given this rule and the facts, whereas it should fail. We need to introduce universal quantification into the defining condition:

qualify(X) :- student(X),
                    forall(exam(Y), passed(X, Y, _)) .

In other words: for any X, X qualifies if X is a student, and: for every Y such that Y is an exam, X passed Y.

The introduction of **forall** means that Prolog must have some way of proving such generalizations. It does so by Enumeration (cf. the discussion of $\forall$I, section 4.4.1). To see how, consider what do we want it to do in a case like this. To check a goal like **qualify(mary)**, we want Prolog to check, for every Y that is an exam, that the goal **passed(mary, Y, _)** is true (for some grade - we don't mind which). This will be achieved if a list of instances of **passed(mary, Y, _)** is prepared - one goal of this form for each exam Y - and then it is verified that each of these goals is true. To **verify** a list of goals, we simply need to **call** each of them in turn:

verify([ ]) .
verify([Goal | Rest]) :- call(Goal),
                            verify(Rest) .

verify(List) will succeed if all the goals on the list can be proved, otherwise it will fail. The important part of the definition of **forall** involves the preparation of this list of goals - the list forming predicate **findall** can be used:

```
forall(P, Q) :- findall(Q, P, List),
                verify(List) .
```

A goal like **forall(exam(Y), passed(mary, Y, _))** sets the goal

findall(passed(mary, Y, _), exam(Y), List)

Just as the goal **findall(Y, exam(Y), List)** produces a list of each item **Y** for which the condition **exam(Y)** can be proved, i.e. **[logic, ethics, maths]**, so this will produce a list of each goal of the form **passed(mary, Y, _)**, one for each way of proving **exam(Y)**. So **List** is instantiated to something of the form

> **[passed(mary, logic, X), passed(mary, ethics, Y),
> passed(mary, maths, Z)]** .

The list is then passed to **verify**, which recursively calls each of these goals in turn. The corresponding query **qualify(john)** produces a similar list of three goals, and it will fail at the **verify** stage, because not all of them are true.

Exercise 1

A.   Define a printing predicate which will **write** the elements of any list in a column - each item displayed on a new line, indented 3 spaces from the left margin.

B.   Define **substitute(X, Y, L1, L2)** to hold when **L2** is the result of replacing any occurrences of **X** in list **L1** by **Y**. Check:

?-   substitute(the, a, [the, fox, jumped, over, the, lazy, dog], X)

C.   Sometimes we want to know the sum of a series of numbers, where we do not know in advance how long that sequence of numbers will be. Recursively define **addup**, to relate a list of numbers to the number which is the sum total of that list. (Hint: for the basis case, take a list of one number. For the general case, compare how **length** works.) Check that, for example, **addup([3, 1, 6, 5], 15)**.

D.   For the second Grid program: how would you use **findall** to collect a list of all the objects currently in the database? What is the equivalent formulation of this goal in terms of **setof**? How would you ask the following: for some horizontal axis (latitude), collect the set of all those things which are at that axis? Use this to define a relation **horizontal**, which holds between a Y co-ordinate and a list just when the list collects together all the objects which lie along that horizontal axis. Given the Grid as shown (exercise 3.2), your program should generate four solutions to the query

?-   **horizontal(Y, L)**

Define a relation to pick out just the individuals within a list like **[[a], [b, [c]]]** - just those things **within** it which are not lists. Then using **findall**, define a relation which flattens such a list to a list of individuals. Check that, for example, **flatten([[a], [b, [c]]], [a, b, c])**.

5.2   Recursion and control

5.2.1   Recursion in arithmetic

Many familiar arithmetical concepts can be defined recursively. The definition of the natural numbers as the series consisting of 0, and the successor of any natural number, is recursive:

nat(0) .
nat(N) :- nat(M),
          N is (M + 1) .

The natural numbers are the smallest infinite set, and we can get **nat** to generate that set - until the machine runs out of memory - by asking for all solutions to the query **nat(N)**. (**nat** may not work very effectively as a type predicate, to check if an arbitrary argument is a a natural number. Most implementations have a number of predefined type predicates for arithmetic - for example **int(X)** for the integers, **num(X)** for any number.)

The structure of the natural numbers can be used to repeat an operation a given number of times. Suppose we want to draw a line across the page or screen. A line can be thought of as an unbroken succession of underscore characters, '_'. We can use the primitive **put** to display the underscore. Every character is encoded by a number, its ASCII code, and **put(N)** prints on screen the symbol with ASCII code N. Since 95 is the code of the underscore, we want a predicate which will repeat the operation **put(95)** as many times as we want. If the screen is

60 characters wide (i.e. 60 letters can be written on a single line), a line across it will be drawn by 60 **put(95)**s. The following definition will suffice:

```
do_line(1) :- put(95) .
do_line(N) :- put(95),
              M is N - 1,
              do_line(M) .
```

The goal **do_line(60)** will work its way down to **do_line(1)**, by recursively subtracting 1 from the current number and calling **do_line**. As a side effect, each time the subtraction is made an underscore will be printed out. But a program like this, although neat in theory, can be cumbersome in practice. Recursions can be expensive in terms of the amount of memory they demand, and should be avoided if an alternative can be found. (In this case, an appropriately long **write('____')** would be one way to fix it.)

The Fibonacci series is the sequence of numbers which begins: 1, 1, 2, 3, 5, 8, 13, 21, 34, 55, 89, ... At any stage in the sequence, the recipe for generating the next number is: add the last two numbers. This is a recursive procedure - to find the next *Fibonacci number*, you have to know the two preceding *Fibonacci numbers*. Because the general rule looks at two numbers, to start the recursion off we need two basis clauses. We need to say that the first Fibonacci number is 1, and that the second is 1. (An alternative is to take 0 and 1 as the first two numbers in the series.) After that, the general rule will take over: 1 + 1 is 2, 1 + 2 is 3, 2 + 3 is 5, and so on. To think about describing this in a program, it will help if we reflect on what a sequence or series essentially is. To take a collection of objects in sequence is in effect to line those objects up against the natural numbers. It is to say: there is a first object, a second object, a third, and so on. Each object in the series is paired with a natural number n; each n acts as an index for the nth object in the sequence. In the case of the Fibonacci sequence, the pairing is between two collections of numbers:

Index	1	2	3	4	5	6	7	...	N	...
	↓	↓	↓	↓	↓	↓	↓		↓	
Fibonacci	1	1	2	3	5	8	13	...	M	...

So we can think of the Fibonacci sequence as defined by a certain *relation* between numbers, the relation exhibited in this pairing.

In Prolog we define a two place relation **fibonacci**, so that **fibonacci(N, M)** holds just when M is the Nth Fibonacci number. The definition will start with the two basis clauses:

fibonacci(1, 1) .
fibonacci(2, 1) .

To think about what goes into the recursive rule, let us work through a specific example - finding the fifth Fibonacci number (the Prolog goal **fibonacci(5, M)**.) Firstly, we need to determine the two natural numbers which precede 5: 5 - 2 and 5 - 1. Next, we need to determine what numbers in the Fibonacci sequence are paired with these - the goals **fibonacci(3, X)** and **fibonacci(4, Y)**. Working recursively, Prolog will find that the third Fibonacci number is 2, and the fourth is 3. At the final stage, we add these two numbers together, thus obtaining 5 as the fifth Fibonacci number. These three steps are shown on the left, imposed on a segment of the above pairing:

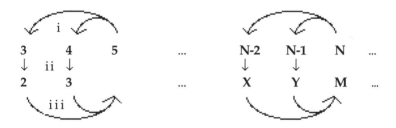

The recursive rule simply generalizes this sequence of calculations:

fibonacci(N, M) :- A is N-2,
                      B is N-1,
                      fibonacci(A, X),
                      fibonacci(B, Y),
                      M is X + Y .

For a more standard recursive operation on numbers, consider exponentiation, the procedure of raising one number to the power of another. Let's concentrate on the series of numbers 2^n (the series of numbers giving the lines on a truth table, for n atomic wffs, cf. section 2.1.3). Raising a number to the power 1 gives just that number: $2^1 = 2$. Raising a number by the power 2, squaring it, is multiplying it by itself. Thus

$$2^2 = 2 \times 2 = 4,$$

($3^2 = 3 \times 3 = 9$; $4^2 = 16$, and so on.) Likewise, cubing a number is multiplying it by itself three times

$$2^3 = 2 \times 2 \times 2 = 8,$$

(and 3 cubed is $3 \times 3 \times 3 = 27$, etc.) A number raised to the power of 4 is multiplied by itself 4 times:

$$2^4 = 2 \times 2 \times 2 \times 2 = 16.$$

Suppose we want to condense this series of facts into a general definition of exponentiation, i.e. of raising one number m to the power of another number n. We can start by noticing that when we want to work out what 2^4 is, for example, we work out what 2^3 is, then multiply that by 2. 2^4 is $(2 \times 2 \times 2) \times 2$, and $(2 \times 2 \times 2)$ just is 2^3. In general, to work out 2^n, we work out 2^{n-1}, and multiply by 2: $2^n = 2^{n-1} \times 2$. And this applies to any number m, not just 2:

$$m^n = m^{n-1} \times m.$$

Thus exponentiation, like many arithmetical functions, can be defined recursively. We can define a three place relation, **exp(M, N, P)**, which holds if **M** raised to power **N** is **P**. The basis of the definition is that

exp(M, 1, M) .

The general case is given by the preceding equation; in Prolog:

exp(M, N, P) :- X is N - 1,
                    exp(M, X, Y),
                    P is Y * M .

Although this captures the logical content of exponentiation, it's not quite right as a program. This is due to the way Prolog searches for solutions to a query. If we ask this program for all solutions to a simple exponentiation like **exp(4, 2, P)**, it will firstly return the correct solution **P = 16**. It does this by making the three calculations in the rule just given for this particular case:

i) **X is (2 - 1)**, giving **X = 1**, and then
ii) **exp(4, 1, Y)**, giving, by the basis clause, **Y = 4**, and then
iii) **P is (4 * 4)**.

But consider what happens if Prolog backtracks to search for further solutions. *We* know there is only one number $P = 4^2$, but nothing in the program says that. As far as Prolog is concerned, there may be further ways to solve goal ii). Not from the basis clause, but perhaps from the recursive clause. The recursive clause suggests that a new way to solve **exp(4, 1, Y)** would come by subtracting 1 from 1, giving 0, and then solving the further goal

iv) **exp(4, 0, Y)**.

And how will it solve iv)? The basis clause does not apply, but the general clause advises: subtract 1 from 0, which gives -1, and calculate

v) **exp(4, -1, Y)**.

How will it solve v)? By subtracting 1 from -1, and evaluating **exp(4, -2, Y)**, which in turn leads to **exp(4, -3, Y)**, **exp(4, -4, Y)**, ... and so on *ad infinitum*.

We need to stop Prolog generating values of **N** below 0. One way to ensure this is to require that **N** be greater than 0, by adding the condition **0 < N**. We revise this part of the definition to prevent it attempting to calculate negative exponents:

exp(M, N, P) :- 0 < N,
             X is N - 1,
                exp(M, X, Y),
                P is Y * M.

Many numerical recursions require us to add such a condition, but there is an additional advantage in this case. Numbers can be raised to negative powers, and these exponentiations are calculated differently. 2^{-4}, for example, is $1/2^4$. More generally, m raised to the power -n is the inverse of m to the power n. So for negative exponents n we make the following calculation. Check that n is negative - less than 0. If n is negative (-4, say), we first want the corresponding positive number (4, in this case). In mathematical terminology, we want the *absolute value* of n. In Prolog,

abs(X, Y) holds iff Y is the absolute value of X.

If x is the absolute value of n, we calculate m raised to the power x - some value y. Finally, we calculate the inverse of y - what number p is 1 divided by y? The equation $m^{-n} = {}^1/{m^n}$ thus becomes the Prolog rule:

exp(M, N, P) :- **N < 0,**
                abs(N, X),
                exp(M, X, Y),
                P is 1/Y .

(As it stands, **exp** is not defined for 2^0, for example. If the power is 0, the result can be defined to be 1, for all numbers. Without affecting the rest of the definition, we can accommodate this by changing the basis from **exp(M, 1, M)** to **exp(M, 0, 1)**.)

5.2.2 Control with the cut

For a variety of reasons, a definition can be logically correct yet inefficient as a program. One way for a program to be inefficient is for it to allow Prolog to look for alternative ways of proving something, when there aren't any further solutions - or when there are, but the first one will do. At best, Prolog will waste a little time finding out that there are no alternative solutions, and then return empty-handed; at the worst, the attempt will send it into an infinite loop or regression. Prolog has a special feature for restricting the search for alternative solutions, the *cut*. In Edinburgh syntax, it is written as an exclamation mark. Despite its name, the cut is a fairly blunt instrument for controlling a program by restricting backtracking. The basic idea is that when Prolog passes an occurrence of !, in trying to solve some query, the cut prevents it re-crossing that point when backtracking. Once Prolog reaches ! at some point within a clause, it becomes committed to the solutions to any goals it obtained in reaching that point, and can only backtrack on goals to the right of the cut.

Suppose that there are several clauses in the definition of some predicate **p**, and that one of them contains an occurrence of !. Imagine that in the course of solving some query, Prolog needs to find a solution to **p(X)**, and gets to the clause with the cut. A rough analogy would be, if we think of Prolog as a vehicle which travels a path back and forth through the program, searching for solutions, that the cut is a special sort of traffic light. Initially, the lights are set to green. When Prolog passes through the lights, in search of a solution, they automatically change to red. Prolog can track back and forth along the road past the lights, in searching for solutions, but it cannot pass back through the lights to try to re-solve goals which precede it. This is why it becomes committed to any solutions obtained in reaching the ! - it can't cross back and look for alternatives to goals to the left of the cut. A slightly closer analogy for the cut would be to think of it as a switch within the program. Initially, the switch is set to **true**, Prolog's vacuous goal. This goal automatically succeeds. But as Prolog passes it, the switch flips to something like **fail**, the goal which always fails, so that any attempt to redo the goal is bound to fail;

switch :- true .
switch :- fail .

But what the cut switches to would be better called **super-fail**. On backtracking, an ordinary failure, as occurs when Prolog encounters the predefined **fail** goal, will simply cause Prolog to track further back. This still allows it to find further solutions, if they exist, e.g. by successfully redo-ing a preceding goal, or going on to the another clause in the definition of **p**. The **super-fail** effect of cut does not permit this - it causes all attempts to re-do preceding goals to fail. Backtracking can no longer succeed, and so the attempt to find further solutions ceases at this point.

Since the cut is a notoriously unintuitive feature of Prolog, I will introduce it by returning to a very simple example of backtracking, the program for pairs of truth values (section 3.2):

tv(t).
tv(f).
pair(X, Y) :-   tv(X), tv(Y) .

Syntactically, the cut can be added as an atomic condition anywhere in the body of a rule. For example, we can place it thus:

pair(X, Y) :-   tv(X), !, tv(Y) .

There are three places where the cut could be placed in this rule, which I shall mark as follows:

pair(X, Y) :-   (iii) tv(X), (ii) tv(Y) (i).

None of these three positions corresponds to a realistic use of the cut, but together they well illustrate its effect on backtracking. If we conjoin ! at the end of the clause, in position (i), Prolog is committed to the solutions it obtained for **tv(X)** and **tv(Y)** in getting there; it can't backtrack at all. If we shift the cut back to position (ii), this frees it to backtrack on solutions to **tv(Y)**, but not on **tv(X)**. Putting it in position (iii) means that Prolog crosses the cut as soon as it tries to solve **pair**, and is committed to that clause. It can backtrack on all the goals to the right - just as in the original, cut-free program. But if there were further clauses to the definition of **pair**, a ! in position (iii) would make them redundant - the cut would prevent Prolog going on to try them out. We can show these positions as three different barriers across the tree of solutions:

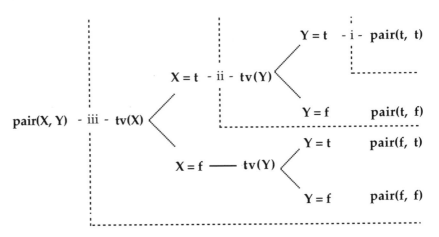

Position (i) allows this program just one solution, (ii) allows it two, and (iii) allows all four.

As mentioned, this example is not intended as a realistic application of the cut, and the program could either do without it totally (position iii), or a simpler, cut-free equivalent could be written (e.g. just **pair(t, t)**, for i). An example of how it can be put to good effect is provided by the definition of factorial. The factorial function is one of the simplest examples of a numerical recursion. Roughly, the factorial of a number n - which by a coincidence of notation, mathematicians write with an exclamation mark, n! - is the result of multiplying that number together with all the natural numbers which precede it. For example,

$$5! = 5 \times 4 \times 3 \times 2 \times 1.$$

But since 4! is $4 \times 3 \times 2 \times 1$, this means that

$$5! = 5 \times 4 \times 3 \times 2 \times 1 = 5 \times (4 \times 3 \times 2 \times 1) = 5 \times 4!$$

In other words, the factorial of any number is that number multiplied by the factorial of its predecessor. Adding to this the basis fact that 1! is 1, we have a recursive definition of factorial. In mathematician's notation:

1! = 1.
n! = n × (n-1)!

To calculate the factorial of some number N, first find the number X which is 1 less than N, then find the factorial Y of X, then multiply Y by N. In Prolog:

fact(1, 1).
fact(N, M) :- X is N - 1, fact(X, Y), M is N * Y .

Although this is essentially correct, the same problem which arose with **exp** on backtracking will occur here: if further solutions are sought, **fact** will generate an infinite regression. We can prevent this with the strategy adopted for **exp**: by inserting **1 < N** as the first condition in the antecedent of the general clause, we make explicit the condition that **fact** applies only to numbers greater than 1. There is, however, a completely different way of securing this effect. Rather than building into the definition the condition that **fact** applies only to positive numbers, we aim to make it part of the definition that **fact** is a *function*. On this way of looking at it, the problem is that although *we* know that factorial is a functional relation - that for any N, there can only be one M such that **fact(N, M)** - nothing we have put into the program tells Prolog this. We know, for instance, that the only solution to **fact(1, M)** is M = 1. But if Prolog is searching for solutions to that goal, nothing in the program so far tells it that this is the only instance of that relation.

The cut enables us to secure this effect - to tell Prolog not to attempt to look for alternative solutions to **fact(1, M)**. Since ! is syntactically just an atomic condition, if we wish to add a cut to an unconditional sentence, we have to make it conditional:

fact(1, 1) :- ! .

In general, it is best to think of the cut as having no effect on the declarative reading of a sentence, i.e. to read this as:

> The factorial of 1 is 1, unconditionally   (i.e. if ... nothing).

This is essentially the same as before. Because it is concerned with control, i.e. in restricting backtracking, the cut doesn't really show up in the logical content of a program. Where it makes a significant difference is in the procedural reading:

> To prove that the factorial of 1 is 1, do nothing (this is the same as without !) - but fail totally on attempting to re-solve this goal.

However, in this case the presence of the cut is slightly special, in that we can think of it as affecting the descriptive content of the definition, viz:

> The factorial of 1 is, uniquely, 1.

That is, we can think of it as telling Prolog that **fact** is a function in the case of the number 1 - the only M for which **fact(1, M)** is 1 (and the only N for which **fact(N, 1)** is 1.) Because this is the basis of a recursion, uniqueness here has the effect of ensuring uniqueness for all other numbers.

To see the way it has this effect, of preventing **fact** going into an infinite regression on backtracking, it helps to follow the way a factorial is computed in a particular case, e.g. finding that the factorial of 3 is 6. We display the path to the solution as follows. Each time **fact** recursively calls itself, we show the values obtained in the calculations as successive instantiations of the general rule, until the basis condition is met:

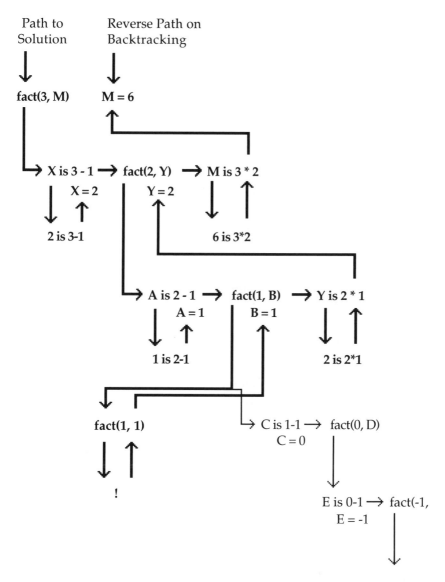

Path to Solution

Reverse Path on Backtracking

fact(3, M)   M = 6

X is 3 - 1 → fact(2, Y) → M is 3 * 2
X = 2   Y = 2

2 is 3-1   6 is 3*2

A is 2 - 1 → fact(1, B) → Y is 2 * 1
A = 1   B = 1

1 is 2-1   2 is 2*1

fact(1, 1)   C is 1-1 → fact(0, D)
                         C = 0

!   E is 0-1 → fact(-1,
                         E = -1

What's important here is to follow through the path Prolog takes on backtracking. Because Prolog is tracking *back* to look for a goal it can redo in a new way, the goals are re-considered in the reverse order: the last one solved becomes the first one to be re-consulted. We need to follow the solution path, the darkened line, from M = 6 *backwards*. The last goal solved was **M is 3*2**. Because multiplication is a function, the original solution is the only solution to this goal. Since there are no alternatives to the last goal, Prolog will check back to the penultimate goal, i.e. **fact(2, Y)**. Whether this can be re-satisfied depends on whether the defining condition, the antecedent of the recursive clause, can be re-satisfied. So Prolog checks back to the last goal solved in solving that - another multiplication. Since this has a unique solution, again it checks back to the preceding goal - **fact(1, B)**.

We have now reached the crucial point. In the cut-free version of the program, **fact(1, 1)** having already been used to obtain the original solution, Prolog would now consult the recursive clause for an alternative, and fall into a bottomless pit, trying to calculate the factorial of 0, of -1, of -2, ... In the version with the cut, **fact(1, 1)** is conditional, and when Prolog re-checks the antecedent of the conditional, it encounters the cut. Since it passed the cut *en route* to the original solution, the switch has been thrown to super-fail, and this causes Prolog to fail henceforward - in effect, to abandon the backtrack. This also shows why it has to be 'super-fail'. **switch** here (as in the **pair** program) would be ineffective. If Prolog encountered a plain **fail** at this point, it would try out the other clause in the definition, and be off into the endless regression.

A typical use of the cut in a possibly non-recursive context occurs when the kind of things which satisfy a certain predicate naturally fall into a number of distinct types, at least some of which are mutually exclusive. So the definition can be split into a number of rules, such that if an object satisfies the predicate under the condition covered by one rule, we know in advance that it won't satisfy it under another. Logically, we should distinguish two quite distinct uses of the cut here: for contrary conditions, and contradictory conditions. I shall explain both by developing a single example. Again, the example is intended as a simple illustration, rather than a realistic application. Suppose we have a database of facts such as these:

female(eve) .
male(adam) .
male(cain) .
parent(adam, cain) .
parent(eve, cain) .

and we are interested in checking the type of parent a person is. A goal could be **p_type(adam, Y)**, and the possible solutions **Y = father** or **Y = mother**. The following definition captures the intended meaning of **p_type**:

```
p_type(X, father) :- male(X), parent(X, _) .
p_type(X, mother) :- female(X), parent(X, _) .
```

The predicates **male** and **female** are contraries - they are mutually exclusive. Nothing can be both - if something is male, it is not female:

1) $(\forall x) (\text{male}(x) \rightarrow \neg \text{female}(x))$.

The procedural significance of this is that if X successfully passes the **male** test, there is no need for Prolog to backtrack to check whether X is female - we know in advance that the latter test will fail. We can prevent Prolog wasting effort on a pointless backtrack by inserting ! after **male(X)**:

```
p_type(X, father) :- male(X), !, parent(X, _) .
p_type(X, mother) :- female(X), parent(X, _) .
```

In this and the first definition of **p_type**, Prolog will hit the **female** condition when the **male** test fails. By adding a cut, we ensure that Prolog will hit that condition *only* when the **male** test fails. We lose nothing from the logical content of the definition. If anything, we add the information in 1), by securing it procedurally: we commit Prolog to X's being male, not being female, if it gets past **male(X)**. 1) is the justification for inserting ! at that point; if the predicates were not contraries, it would be wrong to prevent Prolog from checking whether something satisfies the latter if it satisfies the former.

These predicates are not only contraries, they are also contradictories. That is, every x (in the domain in question) satisfies one or the other - if x is not male, x is female:

2) $(\forall x) (\neg \text{male}(x) \rightarrow \text{female}(x))$.

The procedural significance of this is that if X *fails* the **male** test, there is no need to test whether X is female. Given that the two predicates are exhaustive, if something fails to satisfy the first it must satisfy the second. This means that we can omit the condition **female(X)** altogether:

```
p_type(X, father) :- male(X), !, parent(X, _) .
p_type(X, mother) :- parent(X, _) .
```

If we know that some test will succeed when and only when we make it, then we know that that test is redundant - it can be omitted. Two factors combine to make the **female(X)** goal redundant in the second definition of **p_type**. Firstly, the insertion of **!** ensured that Prolog would check that condition when and only when the **male(X)** goal fails. Secondly, since we are assuming these conditions are contradictories, we know that the check on **female(X)** will *succeed* when and only when **male(X)** fails. So that check will succeed when and only when it is made. In this third definition, we in effect add the information in 2) by a certain omission. Unlike the second definition, we cannot remove the cut without altering the content of the program. An example of this use of the cut would be to change the **remove** program (section 5.1.2):

remove2(X, [ ], [ ]) .
remove2(X, [X | Y], Z) :- !, remove2(X, Y, Z) .
remove2(X, [H | T], [H | Y]) :- remove2(X, T, Y) .

The cut at the neck of the second rule tells Prolog that any solution obtained for a goal which matches the head of that rule is unique. Suppose Prolog is set the goal **remove2(c, [a, b, c, d, e], X)**. Working recursively, it reaches the sub-goal **remove2(c, [c, d, e], Z)**. This cut commits it to the solution it obtains by the second rule (namely, **Z = [d, e]**) being the only solution for this sub-goal. It prevents Prolog backtracking to re-solve this sub-goal by the third rule (which would generate the incorrect solution **Z = [c, d, e]**.)

We see here a connection between the cut and negation - it secures the effect of, for example, **not male(X)**. In fact **!** is used to define Prolog's negation by failure. Assuming we have declared **not** as a unary prefix operator (see section 5.3.1), we can define it by the combination of cut and **fail**. Whenever Prolog encounters the predefined condition **fail** in a rule - and thus attempts to verify it - the call is guaranteed to fail.

not X :- call(X), !, fail .
not X .

So, to continue with the above database, a goal such as **not male(eve)** will succeed. This is because the **call** to **male(eve)** in the first rule will fail, causing Prolog to backtrack to the second **not** rule, which succeeds. By contrast, **not X** (e.g. **not female(eve)**) will fail when the embedded goal **X** succeeds. When **call(X)** succeeds, Prolog will cross the cut, preventing backtracking, and committing it to the final **fail**. **fail** can be thought of as the logically false proposition $\perp$, which is often defined as '0 = 1'. In systems which take $\perp$ as primitive, negation is defined in terms of it: $\neg X \leftrightarrow (X \rightarrow \perp)$. This can be likened to saying, for instance, 'If that politician is honest, then I'm a chinaman' as a way of saying 'That politician is not honest'. In Prolog, ! secures the effect of this biconditional - that **not X** succeeds when, and only when, **X** fails.

5.2.3   Recursion and iteration

It is instructive to compare various ways of defining a recursive function.   The calculation of cumulative interest is essentially recursive.   To take a simple example: suppose one starts with a £100 deposit, at a rate of 10% per annum.   At the end of the first year one receives £10 interest.   This is added to the deposit, and is thus fed in to the recursion: the cumulative interest for the next year will be 10% of £110, i.e. £11.   So at the end of the second year one will have £121, and - assuming a constant rate of interest - at the end of the third year 10% of that will be added, giving 133.1.   And so on.   Let us take cumulative interest to be expressed by a three place predicate, relating initial deposit, number of years, and final total, holding the rate of interest as a separate fact:

rate(10) .   /* percent */

(Alternatively, add the rate as an extra parameter to the main predicate.)   One might take the basis of the recursion to be given by the first year:

interest1(Initial, 1, Final) :- !,
**   rate(R),**
**   Final is Initial + (Initial* R/100).**

This contains what I shall call the central operation in calculating cumulative interest: at each year one takes the total so far, here the **Initial** sum, and adds to it the appropriate percentage of itself. However, in terms of the program this approach involves some redundancy.   Since the central operation must be contained in the recursive clause, we can simplify the basis by realizing that the cumulative interest for zero years will add nothing:

interest1(Initial, 0, Initial) :- ! .

As with the Towers of Hanoi problem, and exponentiation, we should define the basis case for 0, the first natural number, rather than 1.

The way of recursively defining cumulative interest which is most likely to occur to one first is to say: for a given number of **Years**, find the penultimate sum **P**, the amount totalled up to the preceding year, and then perform the central operation on that to obtain the **Final** amount:

interest1(Initial, Years, Final) :- X is Years - 1,
                                           interest1(Initial, X, P),
                                           rate(R),
                                           Final is P+(P*R/100) .

However, this is not an efficient form of recursive definition. Intuitively, any calculation of cumulative interest must, at some point, start working forwards in time - as we did above, from the first year, to the second, to the third ... But **interest1** does not operate like this initially. Because it says "To find the interest for N years, find the interest for N-1 years", it sets up a stack of goals that look backwards in time; a goal such as **interest1(100, 5, X)** sets up the sub-goal **interest1(100, 4, X)**, which in turn passes to **interest1(100, 3, X)**, and so on back to the basis.

Because **interest1** grows a big stack of goals, it makes an expensive demand on memory. We can eliminate this by realizing that the order in which the interest is calculated does not have to follow the literal sequence of years. We still subtract 1 from the number of years each time we apply the central operation, but we use this parameter as a counter for the number of times the central operation is to be applied:

interest2(Final, 0, Final) :- ! .
interest2(Initial, Years, Final) :- rate(R),
                                          Next is Initial + Initial*R/100,
                                          X is Years - 1,
                                          !,
                                          interest2(Next, X, Final) .

This is *tail recursive*. A tail recursive definition of a predicate P is one in which the use of P in its own definition is reserved until the last goal of the last clause. Because of this positioning, **interest2** makes the calculation *before* it recursively calls itself, and thus starts stepping through the sequence of increments straight away, without first building up a stack of goals. Although the basis clause is superficially of the same form as that for **interest1**, its significance is wholly different. It reads not as "The total sum, after 0 years of cumulative interest, is just the initial deposit" but as "When the counter reaches 0 - when there are 0 applications of the central operation remaining - then the amount calculated (instantiated to the first argument) is the final amount."

We can achieve tail recursion and have the counter record the number of calculations made, rather than the number still to go, if we slightly modify the form of the main predicate involved. To do this, we need to keep track of both the number of calculations made and the total number of years, and compare them - stopping when the former value reaches the latter. This requires an additional argument: one for the changing counter and another for the fixed (relative to any given interest calculation) number of years. **interest3** hands the calculation over to a four place predicate, in which the counter is initially set to zero:

```
interest3(Initial, Years, Final) :-  accumulate(Initial, 0, Years, Final) .
accumulate(Final, Same, Same, Final) :- ! .
accumulate(Initial, N, Years, Final) :-
        rate(R),
        Next is Initial + (Initial * R/100),
        M is N + 1,
        accumulate(Next, M, Years, Final).
```

This technique of defining one predicate in terms of another which accumulates a value until it hits a termination condition, is useful in providing efficient tail recursive definitions of some list operations. I will illustrate the process of producing definitions of this form with a simple example. Consider a predicate to recover the smallest number on a list, as in **minimum([2, 4, 1, 2, 3], 1)**. We might try the following as a first shot:

```
minimum([H | T], N) :- min_so_far(T, H, N) .
min_so_far([H | T], X, N) :- X =< H,
                             min_so_far(T, X, N) .
min_so_far([H | T], X, N) :- H < X,
                             min_so_far(T, H, N) .
min_so_far([], N, N) .
```

min_so_far holds the smallest number so far encountered as its middle argument. This starts off as the head of the given list, which by default is the smallest number encountered at the outset. **min_so_far** successively strips down the given list, testing to see whether the next number **H** it encounters is smaller than the current smallest **X**. If it isn't, **X** is left in place, otherwise **H** replaces it. The third argument of **min_so_far**, the answer **N**, is uninstantiated until we get down the empty list, at which point **N** can be equated with the minimum so far.

However, this is not a properly tail recursive definition. To get it into this form, we need to pack the two recursive clauses into one. This can be achieved by disjoining the two test conditions, using an extra variable to carry the outcome of the test, as in

$$((X =< H, X = Y) ; (H < X, H = Y))$$

and placing the new variable in the appropriate argument place of the recursive condition: **min_so_far(T, Y, N)**. In general, such disjunctions of tests or operations will produce less readily comprehensible code, but in the present instance we can define a predicate which naturally covers the disjunction of cases: minimum. Minimum is simply that function which, when supplied with a pair of numbers, returns the lesser of the two. We define a relation **min(X, Y, Z)**, such that Z is the lesser of X and Y:

```
min(X, X, X) .
min(X, Y, X) :- X < Y .
min(X, Y, Y) :- Y < X .
```

We can now state a properly tail recursive definition of **min_so_far**, with **min** presenting the disjunction of tests in an intuitively clear form:

```
min_so_far([], N, N) .
min_so_far([H|T], X, N) :-  min(H, X, Y),
                            !,
                            min_so_far(T, Y, N) .
```

A tail recursive definition should include a cut as the penultimate goal. Placing a cut after one or more goals has the effect of telling Prolog that those goals are deterministic, i.e. have unique solutions. In general, this can improve efficiency, since those goals do not have to be marked as potential points at which backtracking may occur.

The operation of reversing a list provides another example of this technique. Sometimes a list may be formed in reverse order, and we want to turn it around. A natural thought for defining a relation **reverse**, which holds between two lists just in case one is the reverse of the other, is to use **append**. To reverse a list like **[a, b, c, d, e, f]**, i.e. with head **a** and remainder **[b, c, d, e, f]**, reverse the remainder, and then append **[a]** to the back of that. More generally, then,

reverse([Head | Tail], List) :- reverse(Tail, X),
append(X, [Head], List) .

To complete this, we need to state what it is to reverse the most basic case of a list:

reverse([], []) .

The definition is non tail recursive. Moreover, since it uses **append**, it really involves a recursion within a recursion. As the length of the list to be reversed increases, so the amount of memory required to reverse it will grow disproportionately. Each time **reverse** recursively calls itself, it will require an **append** recursion. Other things being equal, therefore, it would be better if we could define a reversal relation which does not involve this double recursion. There is a way to do so. The central idea is quite intuitive if we return to the comparison of a list with a pile of books. Take the top book on a pile and start a new pile with it, and then repeat the operation, successively taking the top book off the old pile and placing it on the new pile:

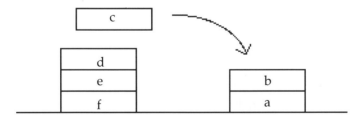

When the original pile has dwindled to nothing, you will have stacked the books up in reverse order. The important thing is that the new stack is built up on a 'first in, last out' basis - the first book placed on the new stack becomes its last member.

So the main operation is successively to strip down the original list, rebuilding it in reverse order. This requires an extra list gradually to accumulate the reverse image of the original - an *accumulator* list. The accumulator starts as the empty list. The program first strips off the head of the original list, making it the first thing on the accumulator. It repeats this, successively taking the head off what remains of the original, and making it the head of the accumulator, until it gets down to the empty list.

```
reversal(List1, List2) :- rebuild(List1, [], List2) .
rebuild([], List, List) .
rebuild([H| Tail], Store, Result) :- rebuild(Tail, [H| Store], Result) .
```

It is best to think of **rebuild** procedurally: its first argument is the given list, as input; the second argument is the gradually increasing accumulator; and the third argument is the reversed list, which is output when the first list has been stripped down to the empty list.

Predicates like **accumulate** and **rebuild** are, of course, recursively defined in terms of themselves. It is tempting to think of them as iterative, since they are used to step through a given operation repeatedly. But at best they are "quasi-iterative". Genuine iteration in Prolog is achieved in a different way - through *failure-driven* or *repeat loops*. These are typically set up using **fail**. Recall that **fail** is the guaranteed unsuccessful goal, which can be thought of as $0 = 1$. We can use it to set up a repeating loop which generates various *side-effects* - operations like writing a message on the screen, or reading characters in from a file, or writing data to a file. To illustrate this idea, take the following very simple failure-driven loop:

```
go :-  repeat,
       write(a),
       0 = 1 .
```

Consider what happens when we set the goal **go**. The first call, to **repeat**, succeeds - exactly how we'll consider in a moment. It then hits the goal **write(a)**, which succeeds with the side-effect of **a** being written to the screen. Having caused this, Prolog moves on to the next goal - which happens to be $0 = 1$ (or **fail**). So Prolog's attempt see if the query **go** is true, by this rule, fails at this point, and it backtracks. It tracks back to the goal **repeat** - and this goal has the effect of repeatedly succeeding. So Prolog goes forward again at this point, re-crosses the **write** goal, causing its side-effect to occur once more, and again it hits the fail condition. And so on, ad infinitum: it keeps bouncing back and forth between the **repeat** and fail goals, repeatedly invoking any goals in between. Here is genuine iteration of the **write** operation.

How, incidentally, should **repeat** be defined? (It is actually predefined, but its definition is simple to state.) If it were defined by the simple atomic statement:

repeat.

it would succeed only once, so when Prolog came to re-invoke it on backtracking, it would not be capable of being satisfied in an alternative way, and Prolog would exit the rule at that point, without going into its loop. On the other hand, if we defined it solely by the rule:

repeat :- repeat.

a call to the **repeat** goal in the rule would set Prolog going off into an infinite loop, and it would never come out of it to progress with the main failure driven loop. So what is needed is the combination of both these statements. The call to **repeat** will succeed the first time around, by the atomic fact, and the rule guarantees that it will succeed on subsequent calls when backtracking.

This predicate **go** does not, of course, illustrate a serious application of a failure driven loop. But it does suggest that if a repeat loop is to terminate, one of several modifications must be adopted. i) Modify the **repeat** condition to a goal that fails after a finite number of calls. We might replace it by some predicate **p** defined for a specific number of instances, so that Prolog will run through all ways of proving **p(X)**. (This ploy is adopted by the expert system in section 5.4.1.) ii) Place a goal within the loop that recognizes a termination condition, e.g. a termination symbol, if the loop is for reading in characters, which then employs cut to abort the loop. iii) Modify the **fail** condition so that it eventually succeeds after a finite number of iterations.

Strategies i) and iii) can be combined if we define a version of **repeat** which counts the number of times N it is called, until N is identical to a number specified in the **fail** condition. For instance, we can modify the definition of **go** to iterate its side-effect ten times:

```
go :-  repeat1(N),
       write(a),
       N = 10 .
```

repeat1(N) is to be defined so that the first time it is called, **N** is 1, the second time, **N** is 2, and so on. This definition provides another illustration of using an accumulator for tail recursion:

```
repeat1(N) :- repeat2(N, 1) .
repeat2(N, N) .
repeat2(N, I) :- J is I+1,
                 !,
                 repeat2(N, J) .
```

We can adopt approach iii) to provide a genuinely iterative definition of cumulative interest. As with **interest3**, we use a number **M** to count forwards with the number of calculations. As with the revised definition of **go**, the equality at the end acts as a generalized version of the 0 = 1 **fail** condition; as long as the counter **M** has not reached the total of **Years**, the inequality will fail, and the calculation will be repeated. The central operation is iterated within the loop - but it does not recursively hand on each new increase it calculates to the same predicate. But nor does Prolog have the means to re-assign a variable a new value within the loop, as in a for ... until loop of a conventional language. Instead, Prolog can use the second order predicates **assert** and **retract** to assert the current value outside the loop, and then pick it up again for the next calculation.

If **X** is instantiated to a syntactically correct Prolog wff, **assert(X)** will write that wff into the program. If you invoke an **assert** goal, e.g. by querying

```
?-     assert( loves(john, mary) )
```

this will have the effect of asserting the statement **loves(john, mary)** as a fact. So when a sentence gets **assert**ed, as far as Prolog is concerned it is as much a truth as any other part of the program. Similarly, if **X** is instantiated to a syntactically correct wff, **retract(X)** will delete from the program the first wff of that form, if there are any. If **X** contains variables, as in

```
retract( loves(john, _) )
```

Prolog will remove the first atomic sentence which instantiates that form. In the present application, temporary facts about interest amounts get asserted outside the loop, held by a relation **total**:

```
interest4(Initial, Years, Final) :-  rate(R),
                                     assert(total(0, Initial)),
                                     repeat,
                                     retract(total(N, Current)),
                                     Next is Current+Current*R/100,
                                     M is N+1,
                                     assert(total(M, Next)),
                                     Years = M,          ~
                                     !,
                                     retract(total(M, Final)) .
```

When the counter reaches the number of years, the **Years = M** condition succeeds, Prolog passes through the cut, making one last **retract** of the **total** condition, thus committing itself to the **Final** amount being the **Final** value picked up by that **retract**.

5.2.4 A connectionist net

A powerful alternative to the symbolic approach to AI programming represented by Prolog is that variously known as *Connectionism*, *PDP* (Parallel Distributed Processing), or *Neural Networks*. This approach is inspired by the network architecture of the brain, in which processing tasks are distributed across a large number of simple processing units, the neurons, working in parallel. Artificial neural networks can be used both for modelling actual brain processes, and for practical applications with no pretence of physiological realism. Much current research is performed by simulating networks in software, using conventional serial computers. Neural networks have proved particularly successful at low-level processing tasks, such as perceptual recognition and classification, but less successful at higher cognitive processes like reasoning. One exciting prospect, at least from the engineering perspective of producing practical applications, is therefore of systems which combine the best of both neural and symbolic approaches. While the description of such a system is beyond the scope of this book, it is important for those working in the symbolic tradition to understand the connectionist alternative. With this in mind, I will outline a network approach to one of the problems we have already considered, the dating agency example of section 3.3. This network will be an example of the interactive activation and competition model of Rumelhart and McClelland. Serial simulations of neural nets tend to make heavy demands on memory, so this will also be an opportunity to implement some of the preceding techniques for optimization.

The basic component of a network is the neuron-like unit. Each unit can be thought of as representing some feature of the environment - in this net, these are either individual people, or attributes of people. Every unit has a certain level of activation, A, which reflects the current confidence of the net in the presence of that feature. One unit can have an excitatory influence on another (i.e. tend to raise its activation A), or an inhibitory influence (i.e. tend to suppress A), or have no direct influence. These influences are embodied in the weights of connections W between units: positive numerical weight for excitatory, negative for inhibitory. Zero weight is equivalent to no connection. The knowledge which a network has of a particular domain is embodied in the pattern of connections between its units. One of the most significant features of neural nets - not reflected in the simple example developed below - is the fact that they can be *trained*. A network can learn, e.g. to perform perceptual discriminations, and this means learning an appropriate pattern of connection strengths.

In general, a unit will receive input from certain other units in the network, and will in turn output to other units. We can represent this schematically:

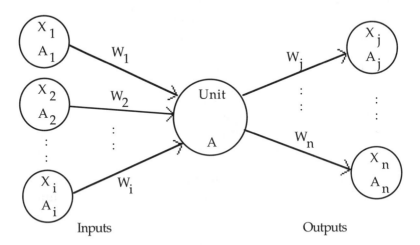

Inputs   Outputs

There is considerable scope for variation on this general theme. In the dating agency network below, all the links are bidirectional, so there is no distinction between input and output connections. In another setup, a unit might have many inputs but only a single output. In networks performing some perceptual recognition task, some units will receive input directly from external sensors. Activation levels may be binary, on or off, or they may take a range of values. In addition, networks which are trained need some way of switching a neuron between 'learning' and 'use' modes. A second major dimension of variation involves the different configurations in which the units can be linked together. The example below is fairly amorphous, but, for example, nets doing perceptual recognition will typically be structured into several layers, with a flow of information from the layer of units connected to sensors, to the output layer in which the units represent significant classifications of the input data. A third major dimension of variation concerns the principles which govern the evolution of a net - the way the patterns of activation levels or connection strengths are updated.

Consider the following extension of the data presented in sections 3.3 and 3.4:

Name	Sex	Build	Char	Age	Music	Sport	Recreation
john	m	large	shy	mature	pop	swimming	cinema
brian	m	medium	shy	mid	pop	jogging	cinema
pete	m	medium	extro	mid	jazz	tennis	travel
mary	f	medium	extro	young	jazz	swimming	travel
jane	f	small	extro	mid	pop	tennis	travel
helen	f	large	shy	mature	classical	swimming	reading

Each particular attribute, such as shy or extrovert, will be represented by a unit in the network. Nodes representing contrary attributes are connected by inhibitory links. In this network, inhibitory links have a connection strength of -0.1:

connects(large, medium, -0.1).
connects(large, small, -0.1).
connects(medium, small, -0.1).

A network could receive conflicting external information confirming more than one of these units, but an inhibitory link between them ensures that the internal connections between the concepts is correct: high confirmation or activation of one will, by the negative connection weight, tend to disconfirm or suppress activation of the others. Thus contrary attributes are represented within groups of mutually inhibiting units. Although attributes such as *liking pop* and *liking classical* are not mutually exclusive per se, we shall take them to represent the preferred or first choice in music. These are exclusive - if pop is your favourite kind of music, then classical cannot also be. So units in the three groups of likes are also connected by inhibitory weights.

In the network we distinguish between the names - 'John' the name is treated as the attribute *being called 'John'* - and the entities named, the individual people. The respective units are **john** and **e_john** (e_ for 'entity'). Although **e_john** represents the individual John, the information about him - that he is large, mature, etc. is not stored in that unit, but in the positive links between that unit and the appropriate attribute units: **m**, **large**, **mature**, etc. Thus the information about Mary, for instance, is distributed across this pattern of connections:

connects(e_mary, f, 0.1) .
connects(e_mary, medium, 0.1) .
connects(e_mary, extrovert, 0.1) .
connects(e_mary, young, 0.1) .
connects(e_mary, jazz, 0.1) .
connects(e_mary, swimming, 0.1) .
connects(e_mary, travel, 0.1) .
connects(e_mary, mary, 0.1) .

As mentioned, all the links in this network are bidirectional, so we define a symmetrical relation:

weight(X, Y, N) :- connects(X, Y, N) ;
                         connects(Y, X, N) .

Other things being equal, activation of, for example, **jazz** will encourage activation of **e_mary**, and conversely; evidence for someone who perfers Jazz is evidence for Mary, and evidence for Mary is evidence for someone who prefers Jazz. Altogether, this network has 6 Name nodes, 2 for Sex, 3 Build, 2 Character, 3 Age, 3 each for Music, Sport and Recreation likes, and 6 representing the individuals, a total of 31. (Ideally, a network of this kind should be larger; it should represent more individuals than just 6.)

There are various numerical parameters which help to determine the overall behaviour of a network. There are the **Max** and **Min** parameters - the maximum and minimum possible activation values which a node can take. Here the range is from +1 to -1. There is also **Rest**, the resting activation level, to which a node will gradually return in the absence of any input. This is 0; all the nodes in the net are initially set to this resting level. The current state of the net - i.e. the different activation levels of all the units - is held as a list of values, a list of expressions such as **value(mary, 0.39)**. In order easily to reset the net for a new task, we record the resting activation levels for the whole net in a statement of the form:

initial([value(m, 0), value(f, 0), value(large, 0), ...

A related parameter is **Decay**, which determines the *rate* of return towards the resting level. Two parameters appeared above: the strengths of excitatory and inhibitory links within the network. These have a scaling effect - to determine the effect of some unit on a unit to which it is connected, you multiply its output by +0.1 if the link is excitatory, -0.1 if inhibitory. For simplicity, the output of a unit X_i is here taken as its activation level A_i. The total input to a unit from within the network is essentially the sum of all these $(A_i{}^*W_i)$. In terms of the single unit depicted above:

1)   Input $= (A_1{}^*W_1) + (A_2{}^*W_2) + ... + (A_i{}^*W_i)$

However, there is one proviso - a threshold may be set on output levels, such that if a unit's output (activation) falls below the threshold, it will fail to have any influence on other units. Here this parameter is set at 0.1. So if A_i is below 0.1, the amount $(A_i{}^*W_i)$ is discounted. To run the network on a particular problem, we need to activate one or more particular units. To give a unit constant external stimulation is known as *clamping* that unit. All the units in this net, apart from those representing individual people, can receive an external stimulus. In the program, we shall clamp a unit by asserting a fact such as

ext_input(brian, 1) .

Such external stimuli are also scaled - in this network, by a factor of 0.4 - and the result added to the net input to the unit.

A listing for the interactive activation and competition model - the general algorithm which drives this net - is given in figure 5.1 below. The top level goal is of the form **cycle(N)**, which will take the net through N processing cycles. The current state of the network **Net** is inspected, and **update** computes from this the **Next** state. The statement recording the current state is then retracted, and this Next state is asserted. Thus all the nodes' activation levels are updated at the same time (the net is *synchronous*). **update** is defined in terms of the tail recursive **up_date**. This accumulates the list of activation levels which will be the **Next** network state, by looking at the existing activation value A of each unit X in turn, calling upon **change** to calculate the next value V of X. The new activation value of a unit is determined by its existing activation level and the total input N to it. **input** computes the current net input to a unit by, firstly, finding all the units X to which it is connected, and the strengths W of the connections. It uses **findall** to collect these into a list of structures of the form **w(X, W)**. It then performs the sum 1): find the activation level A of each X, from the current state of the Net, multiply each A by the weight of connection W, and add all these individual influences together. This is performed by **total** and its tail recursive partner **totup**. More precisely, each multiplication is carried out by **product**, which incorporates the threshold factor. The value which **total** returns is the total internal influence on a unit - the influence of all the units to which it is connected in the network. Finally, **input** needs to take into account the effect of any external stimulation of the unit.

With the total input N to a unit now calculated, we can compute the change from its current activation level to the new value V. Essentially, if overall the input is excitatory - that is, if N is greater than 0, V will be given by the formula

$$A + ((Max-A)*N) - (Decay*(A-Rest))$$

For efficiency, we could write the values of the global parameters **Max**, **Decay** and **Rest** directly into the equation. But for perspicuity we hold them separately, in a relation of the form **parameters(Max, Min, Rest, Decay)**. Note that the larger A becomes, the smaller the difference between it and the Max level, (Max-A) - and also the greater the difference between it and the resting level, (A-Rest) - so the smaller will be the increase brought about by a given N. A similar equation governs the decrease in A, if the net input is inhibitory (if N is negative.) Finally, **guard** is there to keep activations within the

bounds of **Max** and **Min** - if the new value comes out above the maximum
or below the minimum, it is set equal to **Max** or **Min** respectively.

```
parameters(1, -1, 0, 0.1) .
reset :- retract(net(_, _)),
         initial(Net),
         assert(net(0, Net)) .
cycle(I) :-  repeat,
             net(J, Net),
              update(Net, Next),
             K is J+1,
              retract(net(J, Net)),
              asserta(net(K, Next)),
             I = K, !, printout .
update(Net, Next) :- up_date(Net, [], Next) .
up_date([], Final, Final) .
up_date([value(X, A) | T], L, F) :- change(X, A, V),
                                    !,
                                    up_date(T, [value(X, V) | L], F) .
change(Unit, A, V) :- input(Unit, N),
                      parameters(Max, Min, Rest, Decay),
                      ( (N > 0, !,
                         X is A + ((Max-A)*N) - (Decay*(A-Rest)) )
                        ;
                         X is A + ((A-Min)*N) - (Decay*(A-Rest)) ) ,
                      guard(X, Max, Min, V) .
input(Unit, N) :- findall(w(X, W), weight(Unit, X, W), L),
                  total(L, M),
                  ext_influence(Unit, M, N) .
total(L, N) :- totup(L, 0, N) .
totup([], N, N) .
totup([w(X, W) | T], I, J) :- net(_, Net),
                              member(value(X, A), Net),
                              product(W, A, V),
                              K is V+I,
                              !,
                              totup(T, K, J) .
product(W, A, 0) :- 0.1 >= A, ! .
product(W, A, V) :- V is W*A .
ext_influence(X, M, N) :- ext_input(X, I), !,
                          J is 0.4*I,
                          N is M+J .
```

```
ext_influence(X, N, N) .
guard(X, Max, Min, V) :- X > Max, !, V = Max .
guard(X, Max, Min, V) :- X < Min, !, V = Min .
guard(V, _, _, V) .
printout :- net(_, L), nl, prt(L).
prt([]) :- nl .
prt([H | T]) :- write(H), nl, !, prt(T) .
```

Figure **5.1**   The interactive activation and competition model

Finally, we can consider some of the interesting properties of this kind of network. Firstly, we can recover the attributes of an individual by clamping his or her name - as in the example of **brian** above. After a few cycles the influence of this will have begun to spread through the network: activation of the other name units will be suppressed, and excitation will spread, via the unit **e_brian**, to the units representing his attributes. After 50 or more cycles, the competing influences in the network should have settled down, with some kind of equilibrium attained, in which there is no significant change in activation values from one cycle to the next. A second feature of the net - of more interest in this application - is that we can recover the individual or individuals who best fit a certain description. Suppose a client of the dating agency would like to meet an extrovert, in the mid age range, who likes classical music and playing tennis. We clamp those four nodes. Although no-one fits this description precisely, after only 40 cycles the name units **pete** and **jane** are significantly high, at over 0.3, whereas the other name units are all negative. They both satisfy three of these attributes. Moreover the **travel** unit has high activation, at over 0.67; the network has 'discovered' that they both share this additional feature. By contrast, a straightforward query to the program of section 3.3,

```
?-      person(X, _, extrovert, mid), likes(X, classical, tennis, _)
```

would fail to find a solution. Thirdly, the network can perform a kind of inductive generalization. Induction is a form of non-deductive inference, in which one reasons from particular data to some general trends. Just as we can ask for **brian**'s attributes, so we can ask, for example, for **m**'s attributes - are there any features significantly correlated with the set of males? If a company had a sufficiently large network of data, trends in it might not be apparent to the human eye, but the network could be left to cycle, to discover if there are any interesting correlations. After 50 or more cycles with **m** clamped, noticeable units are those for medium build, shyness, mid age range, and a preference for pop. Brian emerges as the most typical male.

Exercise 2

A.   Children's times tables reveal the essential recursion in multiplication, or product. For instance:

$$0 \times 6 = 0$$
$$1 \times 6 = 6$$
$$2 \times 6 = 12$$
$$3 \times 6 = 18$$
$$4 \times 6 = 24$$

Notice how, in the six times table, each value is 6 more than the previous one. For instance, 3×6, 18, is 2×6 plus 6. Generalize this into a Prolog program which defines a relation **product** in terms of itself and + (do *not* use *). The definition need only cover natural numbers. (Take multiplication by zero for the basis clause.) Check that your program entails the right solution to **product(3, 6, X)**. Ensure that it does not get into a regressive search for further solutions.

B.   In the Towers of Hanoi problem, it would demand too much memory to compute the sequence of moves involved in the transfer of a stack of 80 discs. But we can do something more modest: we can compute the *number* of moves it would take to transfer such a pyramid. Define a two place predicate **moves**, which relates the number of discs in a stack to the number of moves required to transfer it. Firstly, work out how the recursive nature of **moves** to some extent parallels that of **transfer** - how the number of moves required for N discs relates to the number for N-1 discs. Then translate this into a Prolog program, and check the number of moves required for pyramids of 3, 4 and 5 discs.

C.   Define **addup2**, which converts the predicate **addup** (exercise 5.1 C) to tail recursion, by means of an accumulator. For comparison, define **addup3** in terms of a failure driven loop.

D.   Define a relation **quot**, so that one may ask the question "How many exams did John pass?" with this query:

quot(exam(Z), passed(john, Z, _), N)

(Hint: use **findall** to generate a list of goals, then define a predicate **truths(L, N)** to count the number of provable truths on list **L**.)

5.3 Operators; truth and proof

5.3.1 Relations, functions and operator declarations

Prolog allows one to alter the form in which predicates combine with their arguments. We can illustrate this with the solar system program. We might prefer to increase legibility by having facts about the **orbits** relation follow the natural order of English:

the_moon orbits the_earth .

To do this, we need to declare the predicate **orbits** as having infix form. As it occurs in the original program, its syntax can be described by this rule:

R1   If t_1 and t_2 are terms, **orbits(t_1, t_2)** is a wff.

(Here t_1 and t_2 are meta-variables ranging over Prolog terms, such as names and variables.) The revision we are contemplating is this:

R2   If t_1 and t_2 are terms, t_1 **orbits** t_2 is a wff.

We effect this with an operator declaration:

?-   op(500, xfx, orbits)

The number is not important at this stage; the relevant feature is the term **xfx**, which depicts the symbol **f** we are currently declaring - the third argument of **op** - as lying between its arguments, the two **xs**. Similarly, if we want to make **planet** occur after its argument - perhaps changing it to read more naturally as **is_a_planet**:

the_earth is_a_planet .

the appropriate operator declaration depicts the predicate in postfix position, with **xf**:

?-   op(500, xf, is_a_planet)

It is important to bear in mind that these expressions are still predicates, with whatever meaning we give them in the program, and if we add a fact or rule about one of them, e.g.

X orbits the_sun :- X is_a_planet .

this must be grouped with the rest of the sentences which define that predicate - **orbits**, in this case. Finally, if we want to put a unary predicate in front of its argument, without brackets, as with:

life_is_possible_on the_earth .

we declare it to have prefix form, the relevant term for **op** being **fx**.

Operator declarations can be used to adjust the syntax of what is, from a logical point of view, a wholly different category of symbol: *function symbols*, also known as *operators*. To bring out the important logical difference between a predicate and a function symbol, we can look at a concept which can be expressed as either: fatherhood. This is a essentially a relation between two things: a child and its male parent. Given a statement of a particular instance of that relation,

1) The father of Abel is Adam,

we can separate out the relation-expressing part as a two place predicate, and the names of the two things thus related:

2) father_of(abel, adam).

While this is a perfectly correct formalization of 1), it fails to reflect the fact that fatherhood belongs to that special sub-class of relations, the functions. A function is a relation R which has this property: if one thing x bears that relation to another thing y, then y is the only thing which x is related to by R. In other words, R is a function iff

$$(\forall x)(\forall y)(\forall z)[(R(x, y) \ \& \ R(x, z)) \ \rightarrow \ y = z].$$

It is necessary to be slightly pedantic about this matter, because ordinary language can be confusing. There is a good sense in which the fatherhood relation is not a function - the sense expressed by phrasing it 'x is the father of y'. One organism may father several offspring - the graph of this relation can look like this:

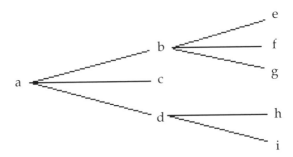

Such a relation, which is **one-many**, is not a function. It is the *converse* of this relation, i.e. that expressed by 'the father of x is y' (as in sentence 1), which is functional. (R′ is the converse of R iff (∀x)(∀y)[R′(x, y) ↔ R(y, x)].) This relation is **many-one**: it may relate many things to at most one thing. (Read the graph from right to left.) A relation such that both it and its converse are many-one is **one-one**. A one-one relation is functional in both directions. An example is the successor function (add 1) on the integers. The successor of any integer is unique, and the converse relation, predecessor (subtract 1), also has this property.

What at first sight may seem an inconsequential feature, the uniqueness property of functions, actually has far-reaching consequences for logical form. We can think of a one place function as taking one object as its argument, and returning a single thing as its value. The value of the function *father of*, applied to, for example Cain, is Adam. To revert to the diagrams of section 2.1.4, the fact that the complex

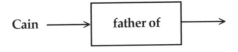

points to a unique thing means that it acts in the same way as a name. For the role of a name is to pick out a single thing. We could depict a name in the same way:

Indeed we can think of a name as a limiting case of a function - a 0 place function, that takes 0 arguments and always returns the same value. This means that the complex 'The father of Abel' can occupy the same place in logical grammar as a simple name like 'Adam'. We formalize it as the application of the function *father* to the argument Abel: father(abel). Whereas a predicate takes the relevant number of terms to form a *sentence* - recall rule R1 above - a function symbol takes the relevant number of terms to form a complex *term*. 'father(abel)' is not something which expresses a complete proposition - it is a complex term, 'the father of Abel'. So just as we formalize 3) as 4)

3)   Adam loves Eve
4)   loves(adam, eve),

so 5) becomes 6)

5)   The father of Abel loves Eve
6)   loves(father(abel), eve).

And 1) becomes the identity statement:

7)   father(abel) = adam

Because uniqueness is inherent in the functional formulation, we can apply the logic of identity. Given 7), by = Elimination we may substitute one of these terms for the other - deriving 4) from 6), or 6) from 4).   These inferences are not available on the relational formulation of fatherhood.

In logic, functions are customarily expressed by symbols f, g, h, ...   So in place of a relational expression $R(x, y)$ we have the inferentially more powerful functional formulation $f(x) = y$. Any function on n arguments, $f(x_1, ..., x_n) = y$ is also a n+1 place relation, $R(x_1, ..., x_n, y)$. We can state, for instance, the general form of a recursive definition (of a unary function):

$$f(0) = g.$$
$$f(x+1) = h(x, f(x)) .$$

g and h are functions which have already been defined (0-place and 2-place, in this case.) Thus in the case of the factorial function (see section 5.2.2), g is the constant 1, and $h(x, y)$ is $(x+1)*y$.

Prolog: logic plus control

We can now turn to consider functions in Prolog. In general, a function symbol cannot be assigned a meaning by directly associating the appropriate function with it. The exceptions are the already defined arithmetical operators *, +, etc., and even a term formed with these must be combined with the evaluator **is** if it is to be evaluated for the number it denotes. (In this one might compare the queries **X is 2*3**, **X = 2*3**, and **X == 2*3**. The first succeeds with **X = 6**, i.e. the value of the function, as applied to those arguments, is returned. The second succeeds with **X = 2*3**, i.e. the identity symbol checks for identity of terms, unifying arguments when possible. The third fails; == checks for strict identity of the structures on either side, without attempting to make them identical if possible. With ==, only a goal such as **X*3 == X*3** will succeed.)

In many cases we may not want or be able to substitute a complex term by a simpler term which equates with it. Suppose, for instance, that we decide that the canonical formulation of an address involves five parameters: personal name, house name or number, street or road name, town or city, and postal code. If we decide that a person's name needs to be structured into three components: title, initial or first name, surname, then a name and address could be a complex term such as this:

address(name(mrs, p, jones), 41, accacia_ave, london, nw3)

This term might be one of several arguments of a predicate recording, say, a patient's medical details. As a complex singular term, it denotes a unique individual, although its usefulness to us would be in holding together a fixed number of items of information, in a fixed pattern, about that individual. In other words, although we are using **address** as a function symbol, we do not intend it to express a function which, when supplied with an appropriate sets of arguments, returns a unique value.

In cases where we do want an operator to express a function, we must assign it this meaning indirectly, by defining an appropriate predicate around it. Imagine you are writing an expert system which must generate a report at the end of its analysis. It might be a financial advice package, explaining its analysis to a client in ordinary English. The system will have a collection of report forms, from which a subset will be selected and filled in for a given client. In this it may need to call on the full range of pronouns - to address the client directly ('you'), to refer to the client's only child ('he' or 'she') or several children ('they'), and so on. An English pronoun is defined by four *features*: person (first, second or third), number (singular or plural), gender (masculine, feminine or neuter), and case (nominative, accusative or genitive). So we might bind examples of these four features together into a complex term, thus:

pronoun(3, singular, f, nom)

We can read this complex term as the definite description 'the third person singular feminine pronoun, in the nominative case'. We know that this description denotes the word 'she' - but so far Prolog doesn't know this. **pronoun** is just a means for it to hold four items of information together. In the present example, we want to invoke the association between the complex term and the relevant item in the context of printing out reports, so we could define the required identities in terms of a printing predicate:

print(pronoun(3, singular, m, nom)) :- !, write(he) .
print(pronoun(3, singular, m, acc)) :- !, write(him) .

and so on, with a catchall default at the end:

print(X) :- write(X) .

However, as Brachman and Levesque point out with a similar example, this is inelegant from the point of view of knowledge representation, in that it does not separate out its grammatical knowledge of pronouns from the procedures which utilize this knowledge. A cleaner style of knowledge representation involves separating out knowledge base,

word(pronoun(3, singular, m, nom), he) .
word(pronoun(3, singular, m, acc), him) .

etc., from printing procedure:

print(X) :- word(X, Y), !, write(Y) .
print(X) :- write(X) .

We should now adapt the definition of **printlist** (section 5.1.1) successively to **print** the items on a list. This will ensure that when a given list pattern - say **[pronoun(3, X, Y, nom), will, receive, an, annuity, on, pronoun(3, X, Y, gen), retirement]** - is instantiated for a

particular client (e.g. with **X = singular, Y = f**), the result of
printlisting it will be the appropriate English.

The fact that a function symbol takes a term or terms and forms
something of the same category means that it must be grammatically
acceptable to iterate the process. In some cases the result may not be
meaningful - e.g. 'the capital of the capital of England' - although this
is at least syntactically well-formed. But it is possible that the
iteration of function symbols introduces an infinity of distinct,
meaningful singular terms into the language. The most central example
is provided by the successor function s. The numeral '1' is the
definitional abbreviation of 's(0)', 2 is s(s(0)), 3 is s(s(s(0))), and so on.
Example 16) in section 2.1.4 was another example of forming a complex
arithmetical term. The ability of complex terms to combine with other
complex terms means that the process of operator declarations for
function symbols has more possibilities to prepare for than in the case
of predicates.

We can illustrate the extra decisions that have to be made by
treating the propositional connectives in Prolog as operators. These
provide another example of operators to which we may want to assign
a meaning, and we shall consider how in the next section. With $\rightarrow$
declared as a binary infix operator, a wff such as 'It's sunny $\rightarrow$ it's
warm' can be simply **sunny $\rightarrow$ warm**. The first new decision to be faced
concerns scope *precedence*. What happens if we get a combination like

1)   **p $\rightarrow$ q & r** ?

Is this i) to be understood as **p $\rightarrow$ (q & r)**, ii) to be understood as **(p $\rightarrow$ q)
& r**, or iii) to be ruled as not well-formed? Any of these stipulations
can be adopted. i) and ii) are conventions for resolving the ambiguity
one way or the other, the third option is to abstain from resolving it -
since 1) could equally mean either of two things, iii) takes it to mean
neither. The generally accepted convention in logic is i). Recall section
2.1.3, where we adopted the policy that a negation always takes
narrower scope than other connectives. In that introductory section, we
avoided taking any further decisions about resolving scope
ambiguities, but now we must adopt a general policy. One standard
ordering of the connectives in respect of scope precedence is this:

$\leftrightarrow$, $\rightarrow$, &, v, ¬,

where the further to the left a connective is, the wider its scope relative to the others. By this convention, a string lacking brackets such as 2) will be taken as 3):

2) $A \rightarrow B \& C \leftrightarrow \neg D \vee C$
3) $(A \rightarrow (B \& C)) \leftrightarrow ((\neg D) \vee C)$.

An alternative convention is to give some connectives equal scope precedence, putting $\leftrightarrow$ with $\rightarrow$, and $\&$ with $\vee$, the former pair taking wider scope than the latter. This is how Prolog standardly treats arithmetical operators, with + and - grouped together, taking wider scope than * and /. You can verify this with a few simple examples. The goal **X is 2+3*5** will return the value **X = 17**, i.e. being read as **X is 2+(3*5)**. The order doesn't matter; **X is 5*3+2** will be read the same way. To get the other scope ordering, brackets have to be explicitly entered: **X is (2+3)*5**, which is the same as **X is 5*(3+2)**. The scope precedence of an operator is declared by assigning it a number. The general rule is: the lower the number, the smaller the relative scope. In other words, an operator which is assigned a higher number will take wider scope than one with a lower number. The particular range of numbers may depend on the implementation. Prolog's own conditional, **:-**, will be declared as an operator with the highest possible number, since it takes widest scope.

The second decision to be made about the syntax of an operator concerns *associativity*, and can resolve any scope conflicts left undecided by the first. Suppose we have a string containing two operators with the same scope precedence, e.g. two occurrences of the same connective:

4) $p \rightarrow q \rightarrow r$.

Again, there are three options for construing this: iv) $p \rightarrow (q \rightarrow r)$, v) $(p \rightarrow q) \rightarrow r$, or vi) neither. Here, the decision concerns how the operator *associates* - to the right, as iv), to the left, as v), or neither. If the operator is non-associative, option vi), then lacking brackets, string 4) will count as not well-formed. Prolog adopts left associativity for numerical operators. Thus **X is 10-5+2** will be treated as **X is (10-5)+2**; to get right association the grouping must be made explicit: **X is 10-(5+2)**. Right associativity is signified by **xfy**, left associativity by **yfx**, and non-associativity by **xfx**. The arguments of **op** are: scope precedence, associativity, and the particular symbol or word being declared. Thus we might have some such declaration as this:

```
?-        op(200, yfx, ↔) .
?-        op(200, yfx, →) .
?-        op(150, yfx, &) .
?-        op(150, yfx, v) .
?-        op(100, fy, ¬) .
```

Notice that a prefix operator can either be right associative, as negation is declared here, or non-associative, signalled **fx**. If ¬ had been declared non-associative, the combination ¬ ¬ **sunny** would be ill-formed, and brackets would be de rigueur: ¬ (¬ **sunny**). Similarly, a postfix operator can either be left associative, declared **yf**, or non-associative.

5.3.2 Truth - three versions

We shall now consider how to set up an elementary language which can be interpreted and manipulated within Prolog. We will suppose that the language of this system has such atomic sentences as **insomnia**, **diabetes** and **pregnant**, which can be taken as possible assertions about a particular patient at a certain time. The logical connectives will be the operators just declared. In this section we shall use Prolog as a metalanguage for stating the semantics of this simple logical system, formulating three versions of a truth definition. The ultimate purpose of this will be to set up the language prior to stating a proof theory for it. By driving inferences with the language, the proof theory will form the basis of a simple expert system.

The truth value of a complex wff depends recursively on the truth values of its parts, and it is straightforward to write that recursion in Prolog. We could define the truth and falsity of complex wffs using one place predicates. Since **true** is a predefined predicate in most Prolog systems, we could use **is_true**, for instance, so that we had clauses such as this:

X → Y is_true :- X is_false; Y is_true .

(This is a fairly direct translation into Prolog of the truth conditions of the material conditional, cf. 2 of section 4.3.2.) However, it is more interesting to treat the truth values as objects, denoted by **t** and **f**, and to define a two place predicate **value**, which relates each wff to its truth value. Here are some of the familiar truth functions:

value(¬ X, t) :- value(X, f) .
value(¬ X, f) :- value(X, t) .
value(X & Y, t) :- value(X, t), value(Y, t) .
value(X & Y, f) :- value(X, f); value(Y, f) .
value(X → Y, t) :- value(X, f); value(Y, t) .
value(X → Y, f) :- value(X, t), value(Y, f) .

Treating the truth values as objects means that we can quantify over them, which enables the semantics of the biconditional to be stated succinctly:

value(X ↔ Y, t) :- value(X, A), value(Y, A) .
value(X ↔ Y, f) :- value(X, A), value(Y, B), A \= B.

It is instructive to work through an example of a definition like this recursively calling itself. Suppose we ask the program to evaluate the wff

$$\text{(insomnia \& } \neg \text{ fall\_asleep)} \rightarrow \text{waking\_up}$$

This can be understood as the conditional: if the patient reports a problem of insomnia and does not report a problem with falling asleep, then the problem is one of waking up in the middle of the night. Suppose that, for a certain patient, we have ascertained this assignment of truth values to the atomic wffs:

value(insomnia, t) .
value(fall_asleep, f) .
value(waking_up, t) .

Since the first clause for each form of wff concerns the conditions for its truth, Prolog will first attempt to show that the conditional is true, t. In other words, it will attempt to prove this goal:

i)   value((insomnia & ¬ fall_asleep) → waking_up, t)

Since the truth conditions of a material conditional are disjunctive, goal i) sets up a disjunction of two sub-goals - either show the antecedent false, or show the consequent true - which we can depict like this:

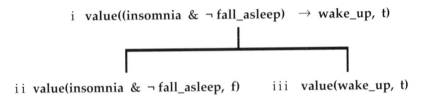

i **value((insomnia & ¬ fall_asleep) → wake_up, t)**

ii **value(insomnia & ¬ fall_asleep, f)**   iii **value(wake_up, t)**

In other words, we have a conditionally affirmative answer to our main question: yes, the main wff is true, *if* either of these goals ii) or iii) can be proved. Both of these sub-goals involve the relation **value**. Just like a circular definition, the question of whether the predicate being defined applies to something is referred to the question of whether that predicate applies to something. The difference is that the problem has not remained at the same degree of complexity, it has been reduced to problems which are a little simpler.

A language designed to be run on hardware which allows parallel processing could, at this point, hand over each sub-goal to a different processor, to be worked on separately. But Prolog must approach its goals in a serial manner, one after the other. The disjunction of i) and ii) in this tree represents the logical space of goals - at this point Prolog won't have 'seen' goal iii), and won't see it until it has finished with ii). Since ii) concerns the falsity of a conjunction, and this is also defined disjunctively, ii) sets up two further sub-goals:

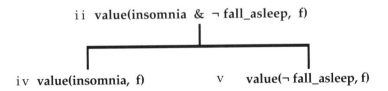

ii **value(insomnia & ¬ fall_asleep, f)**

iv **value(insomnia, f)**   v   **value(¬ fall_asleep, f)**

Given that **insomnia** is true in this particular case, iv) fails, and Prolog will try v). Since this concerns the falsity of a negation, the relevant clause simplifies this to the goal vi) **value(fall_asleep, t)**. Since the value assigned to **fall_asleep** is **f**, this attempt to prove i) via ii) and either iv) or v) fails, so Prolog will backtrack and now try goal iii) - this time with success. The complete logical space of goals, and Prolog's path through it, can be depicted:

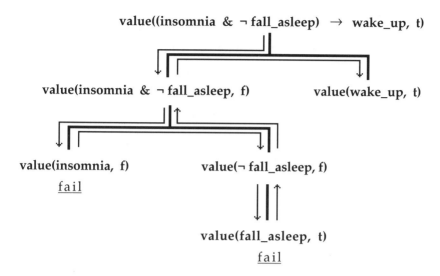

This is the most natural truth definition; it is a fairly direct transcription into Prolog of the propositional component of Tarski's truth definition. The connectives of the meta-language, Prolog's conjunction and disjunction, are used in the most direct way to state the meanings of the connectives of the object language. Although natural, this truth definition is also relatively inefficient. It permits unnecessary backtracking on a goal like **value(fall_asleep)** → **(insomnia v waking_up), X)**. Given the above **value** assignments, this can be proved true in three ways: by proving the antecedent false, or proving the consequent true, by either of its disjuncts. But the first proof should suffice. If we have faith in the consistency of our semantics, it can't be that on backtracking Prolog will find a different truth value for a wff! We can improve this by strategic insertions of the cut - for instance, in a disjunctive condition:

value(X → Y, t) :- value(X, f), ! ; value(Y, t) .

Nevertheless, the program still contains some redundancy. Because it has two clauses for each connective, it may make the same computation twice over. If, for example, it fails to show that a conjunction is true, because it computes that the first conjunct is false, it moves on to the second clause for conjunctions, and re-computes the value for the first conjunct. The larger the sub-wff involved, the greater the waste in reduplication.

We will avoid this reduplication if we state a single clause for each form of wff. To do so, we should calculate the values of the sub-wffs, and then compute the value for the whole in terms of the relevant *truth function* on those component values. The clause for negation illustrates the general idea

value2(¬ X, A) :- value2(X, B), opp(A, B) .

The truth value of a negation is the *opposite* to that of the embedded wff, where **opp(t, f)** and **opp(f, t)**. For the slightly more complicated case of a binary connective, consider the truth table for 'and', with 1 and 0 replacing truth and falsity:

X	Y	X & Y
1	1	1
1	0	0
0	1	0
0	0	0

If we represent the truth values by numbers, we can express the conjunctive truth function as a function on numbers. What arithmetical function corresponds to the above table? Strictly speaking, there are infinitely many functions on numbers consistent with the above table, but two are suggested fairly naturally: multiplication, and minimum. Multiplication obviously fits it: $1 \times 1 = 1$, $1 \times 0 = 0$, etc. Minimum is the relation **min**, defined in section 5.2.3, which finds the smaller of two numbers. If one is happy with the idea of many valued logic (cf. exercise 2.2 D), an advantage of using **min** to define the truth value of a conjunction is that it generalizes to a semantics which allows a range of truth values between 0 and 1.

One of the features of Prolog's inequality relation <, which defines **min**, is that it can also be used to check for alphabetic precedence. The following queries, which will all be answered affirmatively, illustrate the alphabetic 'less than' relation:

?-   **abbz < abca**
?-   **prolog < prologue**
?-   **truE < true**

The first illustrates the point that the lesser of two words is decided by the first place in which an alphabetically prior letter occurs; the second, that the shorter of two words otherwise identical is the lesser.

The third illustrates the convention that capitals are taken to be prior to lowercase letters. The reason for this has to do with the way letters are represented in a computer by numbers. As mentioned in connection with **put**, symbols are usually encoded according to the ASCII standard (with minor variations for such parochial symbols as the '£' sign.) Prolog is actually calculating alphabetic precedence on the basis of the underlying numbers, and the ASCII codes for capitals precede those for lower-case letters. This is why 'truE' is less than 'true'.

      The upshot of these considerations is that the detour via numbers was unnecessary. By a happy coincidence, the < order of **f** and **t** is the same as that of 0 and 1. This means that our definition of **min** will service a definition of the truth value of a conjunction as the lesser of the truth values of the conjuncts, using **t** and **f** as before:

value2(X & Y, V) :- value2(X, A), value2(Y, B), min(A, B, V) .

In the case of the biconditional,

value2(X ↔ Y, C) :- value2(X, A), value2(Y, B), same(A, B, C) .

the relevant truth function is the characteristic function of the identity relation:

same(X, X, t) .
same(X, Y, f) :- X \= Y .

Notice that the account is still recursive, but by halving the number of recursive clauses, it is worked out in a more efficient way.

      However, in a bivalent semantics this second program also contains some redundancy. Consider the evaluation of truth values procedurally. To highlight the issue, imagine evaluating a conjunction of an atomic wff on the left with a very complex wff on the right. If you establish that the first conjunct is false, then you don't need to go through the effort of working out the value of the second - the conjunction must be false. So the recommendation for a procedure would be: only go on to evaluate the second component if you have to. If you know the truth value after looking at the first sub-wff, exit with that value. We can use the cut to commit Prolog to a solution at the earliest possible point:

value3(X & Y, V) :- (value3(X, f), !, V = f) ;
(value3(Y, f), !, V = f) ;
V = t .

To assume bivalence is to assume that **t** and **f** are the only two truth values, and that one or other applies to any given sentence. If we are confident of the completeness of our semantics - i.e. that if we fail to prove that a wff has value **V**, then it definitely doesn't have **V** - then if we fail to prove the conjunction false, we can assume it true. Similarly, for the value of a conditional: if you can prove the antecedent **f**, exit with the value **t**, else prove the consequent **t** and exit with **t**, else its value must be **f**:

value3(X → Y, V) :- (value3(X, f), !, V = t) ;
(value3(Y, t), !, V = t) ;
V = f .

Looking back on this series of truth definitions, we notice that what reads best for humans is not necessarily what reads best to a machine. The readily comprehensible definition is not so efficient, and the more efficient program is not so immediately comprehensible. Of course, a definition produced for human consumption will anyway rely at least tacitly on the control strategies employed by its human readers, and in writing an efficient definition we try to build such control strategies into the program.

5.3.3 Proof

We turn now to the design of a proof procedure for our object language. In this, we face in a very elementary form the problems faced by anyone designing a logical system. From the point of view of logic, a proof theory should be both consistent and complete (cf. section 4.3.3). But from the point of view of building a practical system, completeness may not be such an important desideratum as efficiency. We shall define a one place predicate of wffs, **prove**, which will implement a backwards chaining strategy (cf. section 4.2.2). A forwards chaining strategy would advise, for instance:

F)   If the conditional X → Y is asserted, and X is asserted (and Y has not been asserted), then assert Y.

The bracketed clause is a check which may, or may not, be needed to block repeated application of the same rule. By contrast, a backwards chaining strategy would propose:

B)   If the conditional X → Y is asserted, and we are to prove Y, then aim to prove X.

The same deductive rule is involved in both of these, → Elimination. F) and B) are different meta-rules, strategies for reasoning with →E:

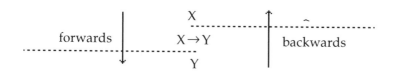

In particular, B) is not to be confused with the fallacy of affirming the consequent. In reasoning backwards, one is searching for the antecedent as an already established premise (or as a consequence of something already established) - whereas in affirming the consequent, the antecedent of the conditional is inferred as a new conclusion.

Negation provides a simple illustration of the competing demands of completeness and efficiency. We could have this rule if it would be of use:

prove(¬ ¬ Wff) :- prove(Wff) .

This might look like a rule of double negation elimination, in that it simplifies a proof problem by eliminating a double negation. But in the context of a backwards chaining proof system, this actually corresponds to the rule of double negation introduction: to prove something of the form ¬¬X - i.e. to introduce a double negation - prove X. We can give the system this rule of DNI, if we wanted to allow for the possibility of it needing to prove a multiply negated wff. But we should certainly not allow it correspondingly unconstrained access to DNE:

prove(Wff) :- prove(¬ ¬ Wff) .

For set to prove any wff, this would send it to prove its double negation, and then the double negation of that, and so on, in an infinite regression. To prevent this, we can either impose the computational burden of checking for regressions, or else omit the rule, thereby impoverishing our means to prove wffs. The easiest control strategy with respect to an elimination rule, in the context of a backwards chaining system, is to drop the rule. In so doing, we risk incompleteness: of there being endlessly many wffs which our semantics would **value** as true, which we are not able to **prove**.

In this context, conditionals provide a more important example. In an expert system, expert knowledge is typically contained within conditional rules, such as the following:

insomnia & ¬ fall_asleep → waking_up .   /* rule 1 */
waking_up & inadequacy → poss anxiety .   /* rule 2 */

Suppose that with insomnia there are two sorts of problems: either failure to fall asleep to begin with, or waking up in the middle of the night (perhaps because the patient is being *woken up*, i.e. the insomnia is a symptom of some other condition, such as chest pains). The first rule says, as mentioned above, that for a patient with insomnia, for whom the problem is not one of falling asleep, we may infer that the problem is to do with waking up in the night. The second rule is to be interpreted as: if a patient wakes up and is preoccupied with feelings of inadequacy, then the problem may be one of an anxiety attack. The important point is that in the context of an expert system based on such rules, we may not be so interested in having the power to prove an arbitrary conditional, as in using pre-established conditionals to draw inferences. The process of establishing conditionals corresponds to the specialist's learning phase - of acquiring the rules that constitute his or her expertise. In building an expert system, the task of establishing conditionals falls to a knowledge engineer, whose job is *knowledge acquisition*: extracting information from a specialist, and formulating it into precise rules. Since this system does not model the ability of an expert to learn new rules, or revise existing ones, it does not need a rule of →I.

Without a rule of →I, the prover will be radically incomplete as a logical system: there will be infinitely many true conditionals which cannot be proved. Notice that this means that we should not make one object language conditional the antecedent of another, as in Prolog itself, for if we try to prove the consequent of the larger conditional, we will have no means of establishing its antecedent. This is not a serious limitation; if we want to say (A → B) → C we can use its equivalent (A & B) → C. Moreover, because we want use conditionals primarily for →E inferences, biconditionals are of marginal value. So again as in Prolog, ↔ can simply be dropped from the language. (If we really need to assert a biconditional relationship we can assert the conditional both ways round; if we need to test for a biconditional dependency in the antecedent of a conditional, we can paraphrase in terms of &, v and ¬.)

This is a good point at which to comment on the syntax of →. We intend it as a sentential connective of the object language, but from the point of view of Prolog it is an infix predicate defined by such clauses as rules 1 and 2 above. It is also declared as a term-forming function symbol, producing terms which may become the arguments of yet larger terms. This is possible because, ultimately, Prolog ignores the distinction between predicates and function symbols and treats both as *functors*. In other words, it treats both atomic sentences and complex terms as the same kind of thing - the expression *structure* is used to cover both. The predefined predicates **functor** and **arg** operate on both sorts of structures. The relation **arg(N, Structure, X)** holds when **X** is the Nth argument of the **Structure**. Thus

?-   arg(2, loves(john, mary), X)

succeeds with **X = mary**. The relation **functor(Structure, Func, N)** holds when **Structure** is of the form $Func(Arg_1, ..., Arg_N)$. If **Structure** is instantiated, **Func** will be recovered;

?-   functor(insomnia & ¬ fall_asleep → waking_up, X, N)

succeeds with **X =** → and **N = 2** (because → is the dominant connective, and is binary). If **Func** and **N** are instantiated, a **Structure** of the appropriate form will be built. Thus the goal

?-   functor(S, loves, 2), arg(1, S, john), arg(2, S, mary)

will return **S** as the wff **loves(john, mary)**.

From the viewpoint of Prolog, then, object language rules 1 and 2 are atomic sentences, and we can generalize over such object language conditionals in rules of **prove**. The backwards chaining principle B becomes the important rule:

prove(Y) :- X → Y, prove(X) .   /* →E */

If conjunctions and disjunctions can occur as antecedents of conditionals, we need introduction rules for them:

prove(X & Y) :- !, prove(X), prove(Y) .   /* &I   */
prove(X v Y) :- !, prove(X); prove(Y) .   /* vI   */

The negation of an atomic wff can be referred to the direct assignment of a truth value:

prove(¬ X) :- value(X, f), !.

An important feature of this ¬ is that it is not negation by failure. (A rule defining negation as failure would be: **prove(¬ X) :- not prove(X).** In other words, you prove ¬ X if you fail to prove X.) By assigning **f** to atomic wffs, we have an explicit representation of negative facts. This is important for an expert system, the informational state of which will evolve during a particular consultation, by interaction with a user. We cannot rely on the closed world assumption, since the system does not start out with a complete description of the case - it must find out whether a particular fact obtains, and explicitly record whether or not it does. For atomic propositions:

prove(X) :- value(X, t), ! .

It is now straightforward to illustrate the backwards reasoning strategy in action. Suppose we have rules 1 and 2 above, and have established these facts:

value(insomnia, t) .
value(fall_asleep, f) .
value(inadequacy, t) .

and set the system to prove that the patient is suffering from anxiety, i.e. with the goal:

?-   prove(poss anxiety)

Since **poss anxiety** is the consequent of rule 2, →E tells us that we can prove this if we can establish the antecedent of that rule. Since the first conjunct of this antecedent, **waking_up**, cannot be established directly, but is also the consequent of a conditional (rule 1), Prolog will use →E a second time. We thus see it chaining backwards from the conclusion to be proved, via a series of intermediate conclusions, to search for premises by which to prove them.

This kind of system can be modified in various ways. For instance, we may want to 'loosen' the connection between the antecedent and consequent of some rules. One way would be to introduce a defeasible conditional => into the object language. If feelings of inadequacy are *symptomatic* for - i.e. a defeasible criterion of - anxiety, then we might prefer to re-express rule 2 as a defeasible connection:

waking_up & inadequacy => anxiety .

We can introduce the defeasible conditional provided we state a rule for its proof-theoretic interpretation. We want to use **A => C** is when C usually but not invariably follows from A - so that given A, it is reasonable to assume that C, unless one definitely knows that not C. So the simplest rule for => is:

prove(C) :- A => C,   /* defeasible →E */
      prove(A),
      not prove(¬ C) .

Another important modification is to allow object language sentences not only the boolean values of **t** and **f**, but to allow them to take a range of numerical values. Care must be taken when assigning numbers to propositions, as they can mean different things in different contexts. I shall assume here that they express subjective probability, degree of belief - a measure of the certainty with which a proposition is established. We can use the relation **prob(Wff, N)**, where **N** can be a real number within the range 0 (definite falsity) to 1 (definite truth). There is no simple formula for evaluating the probability of a complex sentence. The probability of a conjunction can be as low as 0, if it is a contradiction. But it can be as high as 1. Conjoining a sentence with itself does nothing to alter the overall probability - the probability of (A & A) is the same as that of A. However, if A and B are independent, the probability of (A & B) is the product of their probabilities. Two sentences (or the conditions they describe) are independent if neither affects (raises or lowers) the probability of the other. For instance, one throw of a coin is independent of another, so if the probability of throwing heads is a half, the probability of heads this throw *and* heads next throw is $0.5 \times 0.5 = 0.25$. For the conjunction of independents, then, we want:

prob(A and B, P) :- prob(A, X),
                          prob(B, Y),
                          P is X*Y .

However, the conditions we are concerned with are not necessarily independent - waking up with feelings of inadequacy is not independent of waking up. For such dependent conjuncts we might simply take the lesser of the two values - essentially, the **value2** rule for conjunction above. We can combine these two interpretations for conjunction within one system if, as with the two sorts of conditional just distinguished, we use two different conjunction symbols, making sure to use the right one in the right place (e.g. **and** for independents, otherwise **&**).

Disjunctions pose an analogous problem to conjunctions. A disjunction which is an instance of the Law of Excluded Middle has probability 1; the disjunction of a contradiction with itself has probability 0. However, when A and B are contraries, the probability of (A v B) is the sum of their probabilities. This is an instance of a more general principle for disjunctions: the probability of (A v B) is (the probability of A + the probability of B) - (the probability of (A & B)). For when A and B are contraries, they cannot both occur, so the probability of both is 0. (For the disjunction of non-contraries, take the higher of the two values, cf. exercise B below.) For negation: the probability of ¬ A is 1 minus the probability of A:

prob(¬ A, P) :- prob(A, X),
                      P is 1-X .

We re-formulate conditionals by pairing them with a value:

rule(wake_up & inadequacy → anxiety, 0.9) .

In accordance with our interest in using conditionals as rules for proving conclusions, the value is not a measure of the probability of the rule itself, but rather of the strength to which it establishes the consequent, relative to the strength of the antecedent. This is manifest in the rule for using **rule**s:

prob(C, P) :- rule(A → C, X),
                    prob(A, Y) ,
                    P is X*Y .

A conditional establishes its consequent C to a degree X of the value of its antecedent. So if **wake_up & inadequacy** is established with value 0.8, the above rule establishes **anxiety** to a degree of 0.9 of this, i.e. 0.72.

Exercise 3

A.   Modify the definition of **substitute** (exercise 5.1, B) in the following respects. i) Declare operators so that it may be re-written

substitute This for That in List1 => List2

ii) Use the cut (cf. the relation between **remove** in section 5.1.2 and **remove2** in section 5.2.2.) iii) Extend it to cover substitution within nested lists - so, for example,

?-   **substitute a for b in [d, b, [a, b, [b]]] => X**

B.   Give **value**, **value2** and **value3** truth definitions for disjunction. In the case of **value2**, define a relation **max**, to gives the larger of two numbers. Check that each version correctly assigns **t** as the truth value of **p v (q & p)**, given assignments of **t** to **p** and **f** to **q**.

C.   Convert the account of the wffs of propositional logic (section 2.1.2) into a recursive Prolog definition of **wff**, treating wffs as Prolog structures. Check that your program affirmatively answers **wff(p & ¬ q)**, and denies that **wff(p & q ¬)**. Then extend this grammar by adding to it predicates **atomic_wff**, true of just the atomic wffs, **negation**, which applies to negated wffs, and **conjunction**, which picks out just the conjunctions. Check that **conjunction(X)** generates conjunctions. Define a binary relation which relates two wffs just in case one is the negation of the other. Check that **negation-of(¬ p, p)**.
       Finally, extend the grammar with the relation **sub_wff**, which holds between X and Y if X is any sub-formula of Y. **sub_wff** should be defined recursively in terms of itself and a relation **part**. **part** holds between a wff and its immediate constituents - so, for example, **part(X, ¬ p v ¬ r)** holds for **X = ¬ p** and **X = ¬ r**. Define **part** in terms of **functor** and **arg**. Check that the definition generates all five answers to the query **sub_wff(X, ¬ p v ¬ r)**.

D.   One of the important features of expert systems is that they can provide an explanation of the reasoning by which a particular conclusion is drawn. For instance, suppose that when the system records this rule as having fired:

waking_up & going_to_toilet & symptom_of diabetes → poss diabetes

it can report the inference with:

> The patient may be suffering from diabetes
> because:
> the patient reports waking_up and going_to_toilet and symptom_of diabetes

Define a **print** predicate which can display rules in this form. Some other rules it should handle:

waking_up & feelings_of_inadequacy → poss anxiety
difficulty_falling_asleep & drinks_caffeine → should change_drink
over_60 → should sleep_less

5.4 Engines of inference

5.4.1 A simplified expert system

We now turn to developing a very simplified version of a knowledge-based or expert system, utilizing the proof system sketched in the preceding section. It is customary to separate out the different components of an expert system into different modules - specifically, the *knowledge base*, the declarative knowledge which the expert has of a particular domain, from the *inference engine*, a set of inference procedures which enable that knowledge to be applied to a given case. In this insomnia diagnosis program, expertise comes in three forms: knowing what questions to ask, knowing what advice to give in the light of the patients' answers, and general medical principles about, for example, the relation between symptoms and causes. But knowledge base and inference engine are not wholly separable - the former must be organized with a view to its utilization by the latter. Good diagnosis is not simply a matter of knowing the right questions, for instance - one must also know how to ask them in a suitable order.

    Let us start with the inference engine - a listing for which is given in figure 5.2. A diagnosis system needs to build a profile of the case in hand. Each time this program runs, it will build up a store of facts about a patient in statements of the form **proved(X)** or **disproved(X)**. (As an alternative to **disproved(X)**, one could keep to a single predicate by using **proved(¬ X)** instead.) At the start of a session, it will need to ensure that any facts previously proved are erased, so that they don't interfere with the current diagnosis. The top-level predicate **go**, which initiates the inference engine, first wipes the slate clean by invoking the goal **initialise_data**. **initialise_data** uses a variant of **retract, retractall**, which deletes from a program *all* sentences of the form specified - in this case all facts **proved** and **disproved** in the previous session. (Since this wipes out the definitions of **proved** and **disproved**, and since the system will start to call these predicates, for implementations of Prolog in which an error is generated by calling an undefined predicate, we need to provide them with some minimal, innocuous definition. Having **initialise_data** assert something like **proved(start)** and **disproved(start)** achieves this.) **go** then initiates the main procedure **run**, which sets up a failure driven loop. The aim of **run** is to make Prolog keep attempting to state bits of text. It will only succeed in writing a particular **Text** if it succeeds in proving the **Condition** which labels that text. The correlation between texts and conditions is defined by the relation **respond** - the **Text** is the appropriate response or advice if that **Condition** is established. Prolog looks at the first **respond** fact; if it can prove that the condition is satisfied, it writes the text, then hits the **fail** condition, and so backtracks to the next **respond** fact. If it fails to prove a condition, it backtracks immediately to the next **respond** statement, without printing out the corresponding piece of advice.

```
go :- initialise_data,
      run.
initialise_data :- retractall(proved(_)),
                   retractall(disproved(_)),
                   assert(proved(start)),
                   assert(disproved(start)).
run :- respond(Condition, Text),
       prove(Condition),
        nl, write(Text), nl,
       fail.
run.
prove(A & B) :- !, prove(A), prove(B), ! .
prove(A v B) :- !, (prove(A); prove(B)), ! .
prove(¬ A) :- !, not prove(A), ! .
```

```
prove(A) :- proved(A), ! .
prove(A) :- disproved(A), ! , fail .
prove(C) :-  A → C,
             prove(A) ,
             asserta(proved(C)), ! .
prove(C) :- A → ¬C,
             prove(A),
             asserta(disproved(C)), ! , fail.
prove(A) :- question(A, Query),
             quiz(A, Query), ! .
quiz(A, Query) :-  repeat,
                   nl, write(Query),
                   write(' (type y/n)'), nl,
                   read(X),
                   ( X = y,  asserta(proved(A))
                   ;
                     X = n, asserta(disproved(A)), !, fail ) .
```

Figure **5.2**   Inference engine

So **run** makes Prolog work through the **respond** statements in order. For each response, Prolog attempts to **prove** that the condition holds - an extension of the backwards reasoning procedure in section 5.3.3. An important feature of this procedure is that Prolog asserts facts into the working memory as it proves or disproves them. We use here a variant of **assert, asserta**. If the sentence to be asserted concerns a predicate which is already defined by a number of sentences, **asserta** will add it at the front of that definition. Similarly, **assertz** will place its argument at the end of the definition (as does **assert**). To assert a sentence during program execution is to treat it as a *lemma*; the result is available for subsequent use without having to be recomputed. This is important because a given atomic condition, established by asking the user a question, may be relevant to more than one response, if it figures in more than one rule. So by asserting the lemma that it is **proved** or **disproved**, we avoid the need to ask repeatedly whether it obtains.

As this makes clear, the way to **prove** a new fact is to query the user - but only after it has been checked that the condition has not already been **proved**. So the last clause defining **prove** involves asking a question. **quiz** is the procedure for asking a particular **Query** text, and recording the answer. How this is defined will depend on the particular facilities available for data entry by the user. A standard device is the predefined predicate **read(X)**, which takes the next character entered on the keyboard, and assigns it to **X**. After displaying the text of the query, **quiz** prompts the user to respond by typing either 'y' or 'n', and reads in their input **X**. It then acts accordingly, recording the condition **A** as **proved** if **X** is 'y'. (Alternatively, if we allow several characters to be read in together, we could define a predicate **affirmative**, to succeed for values **y**, **yes**, **ok**, etc.) If the answer is negative, not only must **A** be asserted as **disproved**, the **prove** goal which invokes this **quiz** must fail. The cut-fail combination achieves this. To ensure that the call to **quiz** does not fail until the user gives a recognizable response, we can insert a **repeat** at the beginning of the defining condition. With this, if both the **X = y** and **X = n** conditions fail, Prolog will backtrack to the **repeat**, and then rebound forwards, repeating the question.

With no guarantee of medical accuracy, figure 5.3 presents a knowledge base for insomnia diagnosis. The condition labelling a response can be proved in a variety of ways. The most direct way is to have a **question** directly paired with a given **respond** statement, as for **pills**. It may be that some questions are best phrased that a response is given when the answer is negative, as in the case of **exercise**. But in general the connection between questions and responses will be less direct than this; it will be mediated by general rules. Some conditions may have more than one question directed towards them, as with **diabetes_symptom**. And a given condition may generate no specific response, as **diabetes_symptom** again demonstrates. Its role is to contribute to the rule for **poss diabetes**.

¬ fall_asleep → wake_up .
fall_asleep → ¬ wake_up .
fall_asleep & (caffeine v alcohol) → change_drink .
fall_asleep & preoccupied → read .
wake_up & inadequacy → poss_anxious .
wake_up & coughing → poss_smoking .
tired v thirsty → diabetes_symptom .
wake_up & toilet & diabetes_symptom → poss_diabetes .
over_60 → less_sleep .

question(fall_asleep, 'Is it that you have difficulty falling asleep at the beginning of the night?').
question(caffeine, 'Do you drink tea or coffee after 9 p.m.?').
question(alcohol, 'Do you like an alcoholic drink late at night?') .

question(preoccupied, 'Do you find your thoughts preoccupied with problems from work, or personal problems?') .
question(pills,   'Have you recently given up sleeping pills or tranquillisers?').
question(exercise, 'Do you get regular exercise?').
question(inadequacy, 'Are your thoughts preoccupied with feelings of inadequacy?').
question(coughing, 'Are you woken up by bouts of coughing?').
question(toilet, 'Do you wake up several times to go to the toilet?') .
question(tired,   'Do you often feel very weak or tired during the daytime?') .
question(thirsty, 'Do you find that you are constantly thirsty during the day?') .
question(over_60, 'Are you over 60?').

respond(wake_up, 'So your difficulty in sleeping involves waking up in the middle of the night.') .
respond(change_drink, 'This kind of drink is a stimulant, and should be avoided in the late evening or at night.').
respond(read, 'Make sure you always have some light reading by your bedside, to take your mind off your problems.').
respond(pills, 'It may take you a while to adjust back to a regular sleep pattern.').
respond(¬ exercise, 'If your body is not tired, it may be more difficult for you to sleep.').
  respond(poss_anxious,   'You may be suffering from anxiety or depression.') .
respond(poss_smoking, 'If you are a heavy smoker, you should try to cut down immediately.').
respond(poss_diabetes, 'We may need to test you for diabetes.') .
respond(less_sleep, 'You probably need less sleep than you think.') .

Figure 5.3   Knowledge base

Since **run** works its way through the **respond** statements, it is their ordering which is the most crucial to the order in which questions are asked. This is not essential; we can easily modify the definition of **run** so that it works its way through the rules:

```
run :- Antecedent → Consequent,
       prove(Antecedent),
       do(Consequent),
       fail .
run .
```

run will thus check the applicability of every rule. This definition
(and the previous one) suit tasks where the subject can be multiply
diagnosed as satisfying a certain condition - in this application, if we
want to allow for the possibility of their insomnia being multiply
caused. If we want **run** to stop as soon as an acceptable diagnosis is
reached, we should replace the **fail** goal by, for example, **diagnosed, !.**
diagnosed is to fail until a diagnosis has been proved:

```
diagnosed :- diagnosis(X), proved(X) .
```

where **diagnosis** is defined to hold for the appropriate conditions.
This kind of control would suit a task such as testing a subject for
eligibility within a certain category (e.g. of welfare entitlement),
where the first way of proving eligibility will suffice.
        In this second definition of **run** we implement something more
akin to a forwards chaining strategy, in that it looks at each
conditional in turn, looks to see if it can prove the antecedent, and then
'infers' - or rather executes - the consequent:

```
do(A) :- asserta( proved(A) ),
         respond(A, Text),
         write(Text), nl, nl .
```

(With conditions for which there is no response, such as **symptom_of**
diabetes, **do** will still achieve what is required of it - asserting the
condition as **proved** before failing at the **respond** stage.) This control
structure will necessitate some changes in the rules. Whereas before
the connection between the **pills** question and response was immediate,
we must now state a rule for it, if only the trivial seeming

```
pills → pills .
```

If we wish to remove any semblance of a backwards chaining strategy,
we can omit the **prove** clauses for conditionals, but then must re-adjust
the rules to suit forwards reasoning. For instance, we should rearrange
the two rules involving **diabetes_symptom** to something like this:

toilet & (tired v thirsty) $\rightarrow$ diabetes_symptom .
$\neg$ fall_asleep & diabetes_symptom $\rightarrow$ poss diabetes .

5.4.2 Production systems

The idea of a Production System originates in Emil Post's work on defining computability, in 1943. Post's starting point was that strings of symbols are the basic entities to which computations apply, since computations on other entities, such as numbers, can always be seen in terms of operations on symbolic representations of those numbers. So on Post's approach, computations are to be seen as built out of very simple manipulations of strings of symbols. A Post system consists of three components. i) A set of symbols, e.g. {a, b}. This is the alphabet of the system. From this we obtain S, the set of all strings of symbols, e.g. a, aaab, baab, bbb, etc. ii) A finite subset of S: A. Intuitively, the strings in A are the axioms of the system. iii) A set of rules or *productions*, such as XaY -> XbY. This one in effect says "Replace any occurrence of symbol a by symbol b - i.e. for any surrounding strings X and Y." A string here includes the empty string. This can also be read as a kind of conditional: if you come across something of the form XaY, then it may be replaced by something of the form XbY. So these are rules for *producing* strings from strings. If A = { aa }, a single axiom, then this production allows us to convert it into, for example, ab, and this in turn into bb. Post's idea was that the productions are rules of inference for mechanically generating new theorems from A. With these simple concepts we obtain a notion of an effectively - i.e. mechanically - generated set (of strings).

The modern notion of a production system, as it is used in A.I., is a direct descendant of Post's conception. The three main components (not quite the same as the three components of a Post system) are as follows

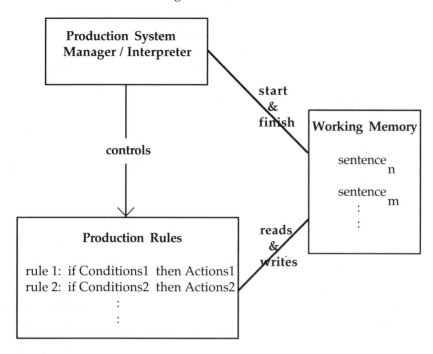

1.   A set of production rules - essentially as before, a set of conditionals. Most production systems name each production (just as we name inference rules, like &E, because it can be important to know which ones are used when.) In the system described below they have the form

rule(Name, if Conditions then Actions)

Production rules are understood as conditional commands: if these *conditions* (or *preconditions*) are met, then do these *actions*. (Productions are also known as condition-action pairs.) Typically, conjunction, disjunction and negation may used in the formulation of both conditions and actions. So note that, unlike in Prolog, there is no restriction that the consequent of the conditional is a logically non-complex sentence - multiple actions may be specified within the action part of a production.

2.   A working memory, which is like a blackboard onto which sentences get written and erased. These sentences record the current state that the computation has reached. Typically, one or more sentences are initially written into the working memory - perhaps as a

result of querying a user. Such sentences correspond to those in the A of a Post system, i.e. a set of axioms, to which the productions are applied.

3.   An interpreter which controls or manages the operation of the system. This works in cycles. At each cycle, the productions are compared against the current state of the working memory. If the conditions of some production rule are satisfied, that rule is said to *fire*, i.e. its actions are carried out: perhaps erasing some statements from the working memory, and writing others in. Depending on how exactly the system is set up, the manager may also connect with the working memory, at the start of a computation - by wiping the slate clean, of anything left over from the last computation - and at the end, if termination is signalled by writing something like 'stop' into the working memory.

The core idea of a production system is thus quite straightforward, and provides a general framework in which many diverse systems of rules can be expressed. The diagnosis system just outlined is close to a production system which cycles through its rules, and could easily be adapted to that control structure (the main difference being that the failure-driven **run** looks at each rule only once, whereas there is no such restriction in a production system.) In this sub-section we illustrate the idea of a production system by developing a rather different sort of example - one which implements *Wang's Algorithm* for deciding the validity of inferences in propositional logic. We start with a description of this algorithm.

We want to be able to tell whether an arbitrary sequent X, Y, Z, ... |- W is deductively valid. For definiteness, let us take the de Morgan transformation ¬p & ¬q |- ¬(p v q) as our example. We can regard a sequent as a pair of lists of wffs, a left list of the premises, [X, Y, Z], and a right list containing the conclusion, [W]. The way Wang's Algorithm tests this is to search for a possible counter-example: if the argument is invalid, it is possible for all the wffs in the left list to be true, and for the wff on the right to be false. The algorithm proceeds by performing a sequence of syntactic reductions of the wffs on these lists, until all that is left are atomic formulae. The rules are determined by the intended meanings of the logical constants, and by the assumption that, if possible, the wffs on the left are to be made true, and the ones on the right false.

a .   Negation. Where a negation ¬X occurs on one list, remove it, and add X to the other list. We can summarize this rule as follows:

Change [..., ¬ X, ...] |- [_ _ _] to [... ...] |- [_ _ _, X].
Change [......] |- [_ _, ¬ X, _] to [......, X] |- [_ _ _].

Clearly, this reduces the complexity of wffs while leaving the overall semantic import of the two lists unchanged. If, for example, ¬p is on the list of wffs to be true, we can replace that by saying: p is on the list of wffs to be false. In the case of our de Morgan specimen, applying the rule changes 7) to 8):

7)   [(¬p & ¬q)] |- [¬(p v q)]
8)   [(¬p & ¬q), p v q] |- [ ].

b.   Conjunction. A conjunction on the left simplifies easily. Just wipe out the conjunction, and write both conjuncts:⁻

Change [..., X & Y, ...] |- [_ _ _] to [... ..., X, Y] |- [_ _ _].

So our sequent becomes 9), and then, by the negation rule, 10):

9)   [¬p, ¬q, p v q] |- [ ],
10)   [p v q] |- [p, q].

A conjunction on the right requires that we introduce two sequents:

Change [... ...] |- [_ _, X & Y, _] to [... ...] |- [_ _ _, X]
                                    and [... ...] |- [_ _ _, Y].

This corresponds to the disjunction of possibilities for the falsity of a conjunction - if X & Y is false, either X is false or Y is false (or both).
c.   Disjunction. A disjunction will be true if either disjunct is true:

Change [..., X v Y, ...] |- [_ _ _] to [... ..., X] |- [_ _ _]
                                    and [... ..., Y] |- [_ _ _].

So our example splits into two sequents:

11)   [p] |- [p, q], [q] |- [p, q].

A disjunction on the right simplifies thus:

Change [... ...] |- [_ _, X v Y, _] to [... ...] |- [_ _ _, X, Y].

Conditionals and biconditionals can be treated in terms of their equivalents involving ¬, v and & (cf. section 2.3). Eventually - as with our example - we arrive at sequents which only contain atomic wffs. The next rule assesses such sequents:

d.   Contradictions. Delete any sequent which contains an atomic wff on both the left list and the right list. For no wff can be both true and false - no consistent counterexample can be presented by such a sequent. Both of the sequents in our example contain an atomic wff on left and right, so both are deleted. Finally, we can come to a conclusion about the inference we are testing:

e.   Verdict. If all sequents are deleted, the sequent being tested is valid. If at least one sequent is left, the original sequent is invalid.

This completes the sketch of Wang's Algorithm, and we may now consider implementing it within the production system framework. A production system interpreter is defined in figure 5.4. **cycle** works as follows. The **rule** goal will match with the first production it finds. **if** and **then**, declared as unary prefix and binary infix operators respectively, are there for presentation - they make the conditional nature of the **rule**s more explicit, but do not affect their content. In this implementation, both antecedent conditions and consequent actions will be lists of goals, and as far as Prolog is concerned, there is no difference between **call**ing a goal on the antecedent and **call**ing one on the consequent. It's just that calling a goal on the antecedent list will have the effect of testing to see whether the condition it describes is true, whereas calling a goal on the consequent will have the effect of making true some condition. Both antecedent and consequent lists, then, can be read by the **verify** predicate defined in section 5.1.3. So the system will attempt to **verify** all the sentences in the Antecedent list of the first production rule. If this fails, Prolog will backtrack and attempt to re-satisfy the **rule** goal, i.e. move on to the next rule listed. The effect of these first two goals in the definition of **cycle** is thus to make Prolog keep looking for a rule such that all of its antecedent conditions are true (given the current state of the working memory). When it finds one, that rule will be fired. Here, this means that the name of the rule (e.g. **left_conjunction**) is **reveal**ed, and then the Consequent list is verified - the actions of the rule are carried out.

```
cycle :- rule(R, if Antecedent then Consequent),
         verify(Antecedent),
         reveal(R),
         verify(Consequent) .
```

```
verify( [] ) .
verify([Head | Tail]) :- call(Head),
                         verify(Tail) .
reveal(R) :- write('Firing rule '), write(R), nl.
test(Left |- Right) :- kill(line),
                       assert(line(Left |- Right)),
                       cycle.
```

Figure 5.4   Production system interpreter

To get the effect of a working memory as a kind of blackboard on which sentences are written, and erased, we can use Prolog's **assert** and **retract**. In this example, these sentences will describe the sequents currently obtained. For instance, when testing the de Morgan transformation, the first sentence to be written into the working memory will be:

line([¬p & ¬q] |- [¬(p v q)]) .

(I shall assume that |-, or something like it, has been declared a binary operator). As with the insomnia diagnosis system, a number of statements may have remained in the working memory from the previous session, all of which must be deleted before the production system is run again. The definition of the main goal **test** needs to do this before it begins to cycle with the new computation. To illustrate an alternative to **retractall, test** uses the predefined predicate **kill**, which takes as its argument a predicate, and which has the effect of wiping out the whole of the definition of that predicate.

A sample of production rules, and the rest of this program, are given in figure 5.5 (conversion of the remainder of Wang's algorithm to the production system format is left as an exercise.) By making the de Morgan sequent the argument of **test**, the **line** statement noted above (corresponding to 7) will be asserted into the working memory. Notice that two production rules will now be applicable - either for the conjunction on the left list, **[¬p & ¬q]**, or for the negation on the right list, **[¬(p v q)]**. A production system program needs a *conflict resolution* strategy - a procedure for selecting a single rule when several could be fired. For instance, a system could maintain a list of rules to be fired, such that the first on the list is the next to be applied. The actions of each production would include instructions for updating the list. Alternatively, productions could influence which rules fired next by writing symbols (e.g. names of rules) into the working memory. The antecedent of each rule would include a check to see if the symbol appropriate to that rule's being fired were currently in the working memory. In the present instance, a production rule could select the next rule by looking at the form of the wff it produces and whether it is placed to the left or right. (If it produces two wffs, it could select two rules.) But there is a tradeoff: the more sophisticated the control structure, the greater the computational effort required for maintaining it. The present problem does not warrant such an increase in effort. We can get by with the simplest possible conflict resolution strategy: first come, first served. The definition of **cycle** ensures that the rules are taken in order, so the first one it comes across with a verifiable antecedent will be chosen.

```
rule(valid, if    [ not(def(line)) ]
            then  [ nl, write('The sequent is valid'), nl ] ).
rule(right_negation,   if [ line(Left |- Right), member(¬X, Right) ]
                       then [ retract(line(Left |- Right)),
                              remove(¬X, Right, NewR),
                              append(Left, [X], NewL),
                              assert(line(NewL |- NewR)),
                              cycle ] ).
          ⋮                            ⋮
          ⋮                            ⋮
rule(contradiction, if    [ line(L |- R), member(X, L), member(X, R) ]
                    then  [ retract(line(L |- R)),
                            cycle ] ).
consistent([], _).
consistent(_, []).
consistent([H | T], R) :- not(member(H, R)), consistent(T, R) .
atoms([]) .
atoms([H | T]) :- atomic_wff(H), atoms(T) .
atomic_wff(X) :- member(X, [a, b, c, d, p, q, r, s, t]) .
```

Figure **5.5** Components of the Wang's Algorithm production system

Let us suppose the first rule to fire is for **right_negation**. The precondition of this rule is a list of two goals. The first of these will be verified provided there is any **line** statement at all in the program, and will instantiate **Left** and **Right** to the two lists of wffs held by it. The **member** goal will then test whether a wff of the form ¬X is a member of the right list. Since these goals will succeed in this case, the rule fires, and Prolog goes on to the five goals in the consequent list.

The first sentence encountered by the higher order goal to **verify** the consequent list is itself second order: to **retract** the line statement currently under consideration. Then the ordinary list processing operation to **remove** ¬X from the right list is called (cf. section 5.2.2). Then X is added to the left list, and a new line statement is asserted into the program - in this case **line([(¬p & ¬q), p v q] I- [ ])**. Finally in the list of actions comes the instruction to **cycle** once more, thus telling the system to look for a new production rule to fire.

One decision to be made is what to do with contradictory sequents - those which contain the same wff on both left and right lists. According to the presentation of Wang's Algorithm above, we simply delete them. This is directly implemented in the **contradiction** rule. This has the consequence that when a valid sequent is processed, ultimately all the **line** statements will be deleted from the working memory. And that is to say, the predicate **line** will become undefined. Prolog has a predefined (second order) type predicate **def**, such that **def(X)** succeeds when X is instantiated to a currently defined predicate. So the production rule which checks for validity should test whether **line** is defined or not. The actions in this case do not include the command to **cycle**, thus ensuring that if the **valid** rule fires, the computation will halt. Given that the other productions all call **line**, and that an error may be generated if an undefined predicate is called, this rule must be the first to be consulted. The rule for invalidity needs to check for a **line** in which both lists contain only atomic wffs, and which are consistent. Consistency is here defined as a property of pairs of lists.

An unrepresentative feature of this system is that although it can face a choice about which rule to apply, the choice it makes is ultimately not important. With a different kind of problem, a choice might lead the system up a blind alley, from which it must be able to extricate itself. To do so, it needs to be able to backtrack to its last choice, and select an alternative. As defined, **cycle** does not allow for this. It 'throws away' the information about how a given line was obtained, and wipes out previous lines. A backtracking production system would need to produce something akin to a natural deduction proof - the sequence of lines it has followed, and the rule by which each line was obtained. It would thus be able to undo a line, look at the rule used, and try an alternative - else track further back.

5.4.3 Search and proof

Search is a very central topic in AI programming. Any program which is going to attempt a task which requires some degree of intelligence is likely to be faced with a wide range of alternative possibilities, amongst which it has to search. Chess playing programs provide a standard example. Faced with a position on a chess board, there will usually be several moves a player can make, and to each of these moves the opponent can make some reply. To each of these responses, the player will in general be able to make several replies, and so on. The further a player looks ahead, the larger the number of ways in which the game could develop to be considered. In terms of the tree of possibilities, the greater the number of stages in the game one considers, the more numerous the branches:

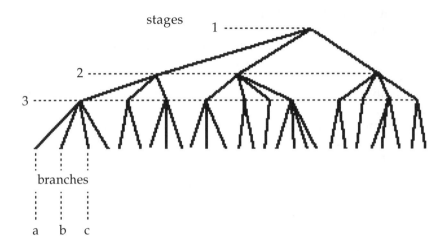

This exponential growth in the number of possibilities is known as the *combinatorial explosion*. The set of all possible states of a system is the *state space*. One or more of these states may constitute the goal of the search; a search routine must find some way of traversing the state space to find its way to a goal state. Different overall strategies can be adopted. Two of the most obvious are:

Depth first. Take each possibility in turn, considering it in as much detail as possible before going on to the next. In terms of trees: explore each branch right down to the end, before tracking back to check the

next branch as far down as it will go, and so on, i.e. investigate each possibility in depth.
Breadth first. Sweep across the broad range of all possibilities available at each stage. Check all the branches produced at the first stage, then check all the branches which extend these at the second stage, and so on.

Other strategies are possible, and each tends to have its advantages and disadvantages. A disadvantage of a depth first approach is that it may lead the searcher down a very long or infinite branch; a disadvantage of a breadth first approach is that it can be expensive in terms of memory to hold all the branching possibilities at once.
    Prolog follows a depth-first approach to solving goals, so routines written directly in Prolog can get depth-first search for free. Let us consider this with a particular search problem. Our example of the Cyclades (section 3.6.1) provides a suitable database. The original problem was simply to find out whether it is possible to **get_to** one place from another. The problem we shall now consider is to produce a list of places describing a path or route from X to Y; thus a typical query will now be:

?-   **route(piraeus, paros, Path)**

It is natural to suppose that the program will incorporate a version of the sort of recursion involved in **get_to** - that it should keep recursively calling itself until it reaches a place which is directly **link**ed to the destination, Y. Recall that a recursion works by producing a stack of intermediate goals, the success of each being conditional upon the success of the next - unless and until the basis is reached and success is unconditional. If it succeeds in hitting the basis condition, Prolog will start to come out of the recursion. Since it will now re-trace its steps through all the intermediate goals, all the intermediate places mentioned therein can be used to build up the path list. The essential point here, then, is that the list grows not as Prolog is finding its way to Y, but only after it has found its way there.
    In this procedure, there will be four parameters to consider: the start X, the destination Y, the path List, and the 'current location' A - the point which the search has now reached. The current location is the point *from* which we are currently trying to get to Y. In other words, the procedure works by holding the destination Y constant, and attempting to shift the departure point A ever closer to it. One way to realize this is with a three place recursion, **goto**. Intuitively, reaching

the destination, Y, provides the basis case: if one can go from A to Y because there is a direct **link** between them, then Y can start off the list of places visited:

goto(A, Y, [Y]) :- link(A, Y) .

However, as we have seen with other recursions, the basis condition can be simplified to a trivial case:

goto(Y, Y, []) .

The general case should successively add places to the front of the path list. If we are trying to go from **X** to **Y**, and we have currently reached point **A**, and if there is a link from **A** to some place **B** from which one can go to **Y** - and **List** is the path from **B** to **Y** - then we can go from **A** to **Y** via [**B** I **List**]:

goto(A, Y, [B I List]) :- link(A, B),
                              goto(B, Y, List) .

This takes care of everything except X, the original departure point. We can add X to the front of the list when the recursion has been successfully completed, connecting up **route** with **goto**:

route(X, Y, [X I Rest]) :- goto(X, Y, Rest) .

We can add this to our program for the Cyclades, and it will exhibit a depth first approach to path finding. But its success is due in part to the rather simplified nature of the problem. Things become a little more difficult if we abandon the assumption that the **links** are unidirectional. We can represent the fact that one may travel in either direction by defining a symmetrical relation:

arc(X, Y) :- link(Y, X) ; link(Y, X).

But if we now substitute **arc** for **link** in **go_to**, the routine will generate looping paths. For instance, in response to the query

?-   route(piraeus, milos, X)

a series of lists will be generated, of which these are the first two:

X = [piraeus, milos]
X = [piraeus, milos, santorini, milos]

The program will go on generating ever longer routes which loop around Santorini and Milos, without ever getting on to any of the interesting alternative routes from Piraeus to Milos.

To block the possibility of generating such loops, the program needs to incorporate a means of checking that it is not revisiting a place it has already been to. The device of keeping a list of places been to - or more generally, of states already passed through - is an important loop prevention technique. The routine will need to hold two lists - the final path list, as before, and the loop detection list. Whereas the former is prepared coming out of the recursion, the latter does its work on the way in. Its role will be to enable a check that the next place chosen is not somewhere already visited. We start with the main predicate, which as before needs only three places:

route2(X, Y, [X| Rest]) :- go2(X, Y, Rest, [X]) .

The important addition is the fourth argument of **go2** - the list of places not to be revisited. The general clause checks that the next place B is not on it:

go2(A, Y, [B | List], Been) :- arc(A, B),
not member(B, Been),
go2(B, Y, List, [B | Been]) .

Note that the **Been** list is added to in the body of the rule. This means that it will grow as Prolog heads into the recursion. Each time **go2** calls itself, **Been** expands to **[B | Been]**, for some B. The path list, by contrast, is larger in the head of the rule - which means that it grows as Prolog comes back out of the recursion. The basis case is similar to that for **goto**:

go2(Y, Y, [], _) .

Notice that this doesn't care about the loop checking list. If Prolog reaches this point, **Been** will have done its work.

These search routines do not actively select successive moves - the next step is determined by the first appropriate link they come across. This is not too surprising - nothing has yet been said about what makes one possible move better than another. Suppose we assign costs to the links in the graph - for instance **link(pireus, milos, 12)** - where this might represent distance, time or financial cost. A simple way of choosing a move at a given point would be to look at all the possible next moves, and select the one with the least cost. This is known as a *hill-climbing* strategy, and **go4**, listed below, implements it. **go4** is in tail recursive form, and adds two arguments to those of **go2** - an accumulator for the cost of the path found so far, and the final Cost total. The basis condition identifies these: when the destination has been reached, the running total is the final total. The main change is the addition of **findnext** to the recursive clause. Using **findall**, **findnext** does a 'breadth first' sweep of all the destinations **C** accessible from the current point **A** which have not yet been visited, preparing a list of items of the form **cost(C, N)**. **minimum** then selects the one with the smallest cost **N**. This is essentially the relation defined in section 5.2.3, adapted to the **cost**s on this list. **findnext** thus takes the current location **A**, the list of places **Been** to, and actively selects the next place **B** with the least cost **M**.

```
gofor(X, Y, [X | Rest], Cost) :- go4(X, Y, Rest, [X], 0, Cost).
go4(Y, Y, [], _, Cost, Cost) .
go4(A, Y, [B | List], Been, N, Cost) :- findnext(A, B, Been, M),
                            P is N+M,
                            go4(B, Y, List, [B | Been], P, Cost) .
findnext(A, B, Been, M) :-
        findall(cost(C, N), (arc(A, C, N), not member(C, Been)), L),
        minimum(L, cost(B, M)) .
findnext(A, B, Been, M) :-
        arc(A, B, M),
        not member(B, Been) .
minimum([H | T], X) :- min_so_far(T, H, X) .
min_so_far([], X, X) .
min_so_far([H | T], X, Z) :- min(H, X, Y), !,
                            min_so_far(T, Y, Z) .
min(cost(X, N), cost(Y, M), cost(X, N)) :- N =< M .
min(cost(X, N), cost(Y, M), cost(Y, M)) :- M < N .
```

Figure **5.6**   Hill-climbing search

Clearly, hill-climbing is not guaranteed to select the cheapest route overall; the most costly route might begin with the least expensive first step. Indeed, **go4** as it stands might not find its way to an accessible destination at all, if it is led astray up a blind alley of inexpensive links. To prevent this happening, **findnext** must be supplemented with a default rule which can fire on backtracking.

In this context, in which search is conducted not in the real world but on some representation of the problem space, search and proof construction are ultimately the same. For proof construction is really a search problem - finding an acceptable path from premises to conclusion. And the search spaces we are concerned with are spaces not of individual states of the system, but of sequences of states. We are looking for a sequence which starts with the initial state of the system, and such that each successive state is obtained from its predecessors by an acceptable transformation, ending with the goal state - in other words, a valid derivation of a description of the goal state from a description of the initial state. To illustrate this equivalence, I will first sketch a proof construction program, and then show how as a special case it can be adapted to the traditional blocks world search problem (cf. section 4.2.2).

To keep things simple, we shall consider proofs only for the logic of the conditional, i.e. sequents such as q→r, p→q |- p→r. Asked to prove |- q→(p→q), the system will deliver the derivation:

1	q	ass
2	p	ass
3	p→q	→I 2 1
4	q→(p→q)	→I 1 3

Each line consists of three items: a line number **N**, a **Wff**, and the **Info** stating how that wff was obtained. These will be held as a structure **line(N, Wff, Info)**. (We shall ignore information about dependency; this could be added easily.)

The program, listed in figure 5.7, will implement the kind of bidirectional approach recommended in section 4.2.2. In order to implement a combined forwards and backwards strategy, four lists will play a central role: a list of lines which is the proof path so far, and a list possibly extending that with a new step, a list of goals representing the (sub-) conclusions being aimed for, and a list possibly extending that with a new goal. Given a proof task specified in the form: list of premises, and conclusion, as in

?-   **proof([q→r, p→q], p→r)**

the first task is to convert the premises into the initial segment of the proof, and to start the goal list off with the conclusion. The **lines** routine effects this, converting this **proof** query into this **prove** goal:

prove([line(1, q→r, [ass]), line(2, p→q, [ass])], Proof, [p→r])

This enters the main recursion, which terminates only when the goal list has become empty, at which point the proof can be identified with the proof so far. Otherwise **prove** recursively processes the four main lists just mentioned.

```
proof(PremList, Conc) :- lines(1, PremList, ProofSoFar),
                         prove(ProofSoFar, Proof, [Conc]),
                         show(Proof) .
lines(_, [], []) .
lines(N, [Wff | T], [line(N, Wff, [ass]) | Tail]) :- M is N+1,
                                                     lines(M, T, Tail).
prove(Proof, Proof, []) :- ! .
prove(ProofSoFar, X, CurrentGoals) :-
        try(ProofSoFar, NewProof, CurrentGoals, NewGoals),
        prove(NewProof, X, NewGoals) .
try(ProofSoFar, ProofSoFar, [X | T], T) :-                    /* 1 */
        member(line(_,X, _), Proof) .
try(ProofSoFar, ProofSoFar, [C | T], [A, C | T]) :-          /* 2 */
        member( line(_, A → C, _), ProofSoFar),
        not member(line(_, A, _), ProofSoFar) .
try(ProofSoFar, Extend, [A → C | T], [C, A → C | T]) :-      /* 3 */
        not member(line(_, A, _), ProofSoFar),
        length(ProofSoFar, M),  N is M+1,
        append(ProofSoFar, [line(N, A, [ass])], Extend) .
try(ProofSoFar, Extend, [A → C | T], T) :-                   /* 4 */
        member( line(N, A, [ass]), ProofSoFar),
        member( line(M, C, _), ProofSoFar),
        length(Proof, P),  Q is P+1,
        append(ProofSoFar, [line(Q, A → C, ['→I', N, M])], Extend) .
```

```
try(ProofSoFar, Extend, Goals, Goals) :-                    /* 5 */
    member( line(N, A → C, _), ProofSoFar),
    member( line(M, A, _), ProofSoFar),
    not member(line(_, C, _), ProofSoFar),
    length(ProofSoFar, P),  Q is P+1,
    append(ProofSoFar, [line(Q, C, ['→E', N, M])], Extend) .
```

Figure **5.7**   Proof as search

The program employs *heuristic search* - by which in general the next step is suggested by a heuristic. The **try** rules embody some of the heuristics informally recommended in section 4.2.2. Rule 2 works backwards, setting things up for →E by extending the goal list: "if you're aiming to show C, and you already have A → C in the proof so far, add A to the list of goals to be proved". The proof so far also provides for loop checking - "provided A is not already in the proof". Rule 2 is complemented by the fifth rule, which works purely forwards, undirected by what is on the goal list. It fires off a modus ponens without looking to see whether the consequent is a goal to be proved. The third rule sets things up for →I: when a conditional is a goal to be proved, extend the proof with the assumption of the antecedent, and add the consequent as a goal to be proved. It is paired with the fourth rule, which makes a directed application of →I, when the consequent has been proved.   Both these rules implement a bidirectional approach, in that they look both at the proof so far and the goal list.   Rule 1 is a 'clean up' rule - it prunes the goal list by removing a wff if that wff occurs on a line of the proof.

The blocks world presents a simpler version of this path-finding problem. Since the problem is symmetrical between search directions, there is no advantage in growing a backwards path as well as a forwards path; the former would be a mirror image of the latter. We need only keep in view the final goal, and grow the forwards path towards it.   Secondly, when considering the next step, we can concentrate on the current state. It is therefore convenient to represent the proof path as a list, the *head* of which is the current state, reversing it when complete. The start of the proof will be a formula which describes the initial state of the blocks world. We can describe each state by a list of items describing its sub-states, of the form **X is_on Y**, where X and Y can be blocks, 1, 2 or 3, and Y can also be a location a, b or c. Thus premise and conclusion are such lists:

?-   proof([1 is_on 2, 2 is_on 3, 3 is_on a], [1 is_on 2, 2 is_on 3, 3 is_on c])

```
proof(Start, Goal) :-  prove([Start], Path, Goal),
                          reverse(Path, Proof),
                          show(Proof) .
prove([Goal | Rest], [Goal | Rest], Goal) :- ! .
prove(ProofSoFar, X, Goal) :-
        try(ProofSoFar, NewProof, Goal),
        prove(NewProof, X, Goal) .
try([Current | Rest], [Next, Current | Rest], Goal) :-
        member(Y, Goal),
        member(X, Current),
        change(X, Y, Current),
        substitute(X, Y, Current, Next),
        not member(Next, Rest) .
try([Current | Rest], [Next, Current | Rest], Goal) :-
        member(X, Current),
        change(X, Y, Current),
        substitute(X, Y, Current, Next),
        not member(Next, Rest) .
change(X is_on A, X is_on B, State) :- (place(B);
                                        (block(B), X \= B) ),
                                        free(X, State),
                                        free(B, State) .
free(X, State) :- not member(A is_on X, State) .
```

Figure **5.8**   Search as proof

try is where the constraints specific to the search problem appear. The first **try** rule is directed by the **Goal**. The heuristic is: try to change a current sub-state X to a sub-state of the goal, if possible. As with **findnext**, we must include a more liberal rule which makes an undirected guess as to what the next state should be. In this case the **try** rule is identical except that it omits the condition **member(Y, Goal)**, and thus fires if no sub-state **Y** of the **Goal** can be reached from the **Current** state. **change** looks to find a permissible transformation of one sub-state into another, e.g. from **1 is_on 2** to **1 is_on b**. Such a change is permissible if the block to be moved is **free** - there is nothing on it - and where it is to be placed is also **free**. So a **change** from one sub-state to another must be relative to a given **State**, since that overall state contains the disposition of the other entities in the blocks world. Notice that changing the condition $X \= B$ to $X < B$ imposes the constraint of the Towers of Hanoi problem (section 3.6.3), and thus provides for its solution by state space search.

Exercise 4

A.   Write a version of the diagnostic system which allows for graded responses, by implementing some version of the probability calculus outlined in section 5.3.3.

B.   Complete the Wang's Algorithm production system, and test it out on both valid and invalid sequents, for example,

   (p & q) v r |- (p v r) & (q v r)
   p v q |- ¬ (p & ¬q)
   (p → q) |- ((p & r) → (q & r))
   (p v q) → ¬ r, s → q |- s → r

C.   In Königsberg, two branches of the river Pregel flow around a small island. Seven bridges cross the river, in this configuration:

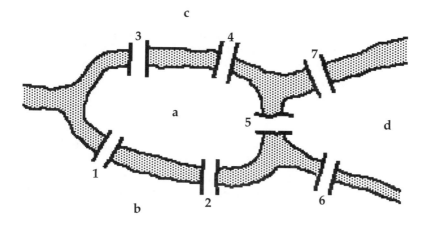

The problem of the Königsberg bridges is this: is it possible to walk in a continuous path across all seven bridges, crossing each one exactly once? The problem famously inspired Euler to provide a topological proof of the impossibility of such a path. If one of the bridges is removed, e.g. bridge 1, then the remaining six bridges can be crossed in a continuous path. Write a program that, for any configuration of bridges, will find a path which crosses all the bridges just once, if one exists, and which returns the path as a list of bridges.

D.   Project: develop a small expert advice system (either backwards chaining or production system). Choose a small, well-defined domain, e.g. a system to advise customers on curtain fabrics. (Relevant considerations include the following. What are the dimensions of the window? What is the length of track on which the curtain is to run? What sorts of pleats are required (pinch pleats need fabric width of double the track length, pencil pleats $2^1/_2$ times, etc.) By how much is the curtain to overhang the window? What is the width of the fabric (perhaps a default width of 120 cms), and cost per metre? Do the curtains need lining? Advise on the total length of curtain fabric, lining material, heading tape and number of curtain hooks.)

5.5   Towards natural language

5.5.1   Parsing

In this section we shall consider various ways of improving the simple grammar of section 3.4.1 (and its extension in 3.6.2). That program correctly identifies, for example, 'John loves a woman' as a sentence, assuming it is presented as the list

1)   [john, loves, a, woman]

But while it can correctly identify a sentence as such, it does not reveal the syntactic analysis which forms the justification for that identification. A syntactic analysis is conveniently summarized in a labelled bracketing structure, which can be expressed as a Prolog list - in this case:

2)   [sentence, [noun_phrase, [p_name, john]], [verb_phrase,
           [transitive, loves], [noun_phrase, [det, a], [c_noun, woman]]]]

This identifies all the constituents of the sentence, and the order in which they are put together. A labelled bracketing is a *structural description* of the phrase it treats; a *phrase structure grammar* for a language or language fragment is any grammar which generates such descriptions for the sentences in it.

A labelled bracketing list can be displayed in a parse tree, or *phrase structure tree* - see figure 3.5 (p. 153). The end of a branch, which connects a word with a syntactic category, represents a particular fact about that word, and is recorded as such in the grammar program, e.g. **p_name([john])**. All the other connections in the tree reflect syntactic generalizations. A single branch linking two syntactic categories corresponds to a rule that anything in the lower category is also classified as falling under the higher category:

noun_phrase(N) :- p_name(N) .

Notice, then, that we doubly classify **[john]**, both as a proper name, and as a noun_phrase. This is because we need the category of noun phrase to divide into two separate sub-categories - those which are unstructured, proper names, and those which are structured out of a determiner and a common noun. We want to capture diverse sorts of expressions, e.g. 'John' and 'a woman', within some unifying syntactic category, since they can occupy the same grammatical position within a sentence. To do this, we classify 'John' according to its basic syntactic category and then, by this rule, relate all expressions of that sort to the more inclusive category. Where two branches come together in a tree, the corresponding general rule is that an expression of the higher category can be formed by **append**ing two expressions from the lower categories, for instance:

noun_phrase(N) :- append(D, C, N),
**   det(D),**
**   c_noun(C) .**

The program in chapter 3 adopts a *top-down* (or hypothesis driven) strategy to the problem of syntactic recognition. That is, asked to prove a goal of the form **sentence(X)**, it attempts to verify this by splitting X into two sub-lists, and attempting to show that these are of the appropriate sub-categories. It starts with the hypothesis that the list X it has been given is a sentence, the topmost category, and works down. It operates *left-to-right*: each time it splits a phrase, it looks at the constituents in a left to right order. Other combinations of strategies are possible. A *bottom-up* (or data driven) approach would start by conjecturing classifications for the words, and then attempt to group these under higher categories, and so on up. It might do this by re-writing the symbols in the list. Grammar rules such as the D.C.G. rules of section 3.6.2,

> prep phrase --> prep, noun phrase
> prep   --> 'of'

can be understood as re-write rules. Instead of reading '-->' as 'can be', we can read such rules in the opposite direction, as saying that the terminal symbol 'of' can be re-written as the non-terminal prep, and so on. Working on the list **[john, loves, a, woman]** *right-to-left*, it would transform this to **[john, loves, a, c_noun]**, and this to **[john, loves, det, c_noun]**, and so on, aiming to re-write it finally as **[sentence]**. For any reasonably complex fragment of natural language, a top-down strategy will need to be able to backtrack not only on the splittings it effects, but also on its grammatical classifications. Consider a sentence such as

> The old man the boats

A program working top-down might split this into 'the old man' and 'the boats', and classify the former as a noun phrase. Finding no verb in the remainder, it should backtrack on that analysis and make the split which recognizes 'the old' as the noun phrase. Similarly, a bottom-up approach might initially put 'man' into the category of common noun, and then find that for this sentence it needs to call on the other way of classifying 'man', as a verb.

One thing we might naturally expect of a grammar is for it to *parse* the expressions which it can recognize, into some structural description such as a labelled bracketing. This could then be handed over to a graphics program for displaying as a tree. To accomplish this, we need to convert the main syntactic predicates into two place relations, which relate a list of words such as 1), to the syntactic analysis (if one exists) 2). If a list can be recognized as a sentence, for example, its analysis will be a list consisting of three things - the atom **sentence**, and two further components corresponding to the noun phrase and the verb phrase. The important thing to bear in mind is that these two items are not simply the respective words or lists of words, they are the *analyses* of those expressions. The basic idea, then, is this:

sentence(List, [sentence, X, Y]) :- append(N, V, List),
                              noun_phrase(N, X),
                              verb_phrase(V, Y) .

A **List** can be classified into a structure **[sentence, X, Y]** if that list can be split by an **append** into a noun phrase **N** and a verb phrase **V**, and **X** is the structure which is the parse of **N**, and **Y** the parse of **V**.

It is helpful to think of this program as a translation manual. A translation manual generally involves three languages - the language being translated from, the *source* language, the language into which expressions from that are translated, the *target* language, and the language in which the manual is formulated, Prolog in this case. The source here is the language of unanalysed lists of words, and the target is the language of labelled bracketing. Notice that the above rule contains the expression **sentence** twice. It occurs as a predicate of Prolog, being used to define a mapping between two languages, and it belongs to the target language, a symbol which expresses a certain classificatory category. All our other grammatical concepts will be required to play this dual role, so for clarity I shall adopt for the target language the common abbreviations 'NP', 'VP', 'IV' etc., for 'noun phrase', 'verb phrase', 'intransitive verb'.

A noun phrase N parses to a structure **[np, X]** if N is a proper name with parse structure X:

noun_phrase(N, [np, X]) :- proper_name(N, X) .

The analysis of the proper name 'John' could be the structure **[pn, [john]]**, but I shall avoid the extra layer of brackets around **john** and simply have it as **[pn, john]**. To achieve this, we can record all the basic lexical items as words, rather than as one word lists:

p_name(john).

and then state a general rule which gives the analysis of all words in this category:

proper_name([N], [pn, N]) :- p_name(N) .

In other words, the basic lexical item **john** becomes the source language list **[john]**, as before, and will be mapped to the structure **[np, [pn, john]]**, when classified at the level of noun phrase.

It remains to complete the account of noun phrases for those compounded out of determiner and noun. An NP of this sort will have a parse structure **[np, X, Y]** with two sub-lists, **X** and **Y**. The principle here is essentially parallel to that for sentences:

noun_phrase(List, [np, X, Y]) :- append(D, C, List),
**   determiner(D, X),**
**   common_noun(C, Y) .**

Again, we need to supplement this with general rules to prepare the parses of the basic items, determiners and common nouns, for instance:

common_noun([C], [cn, C]) :- c_noun(C) .

By making appropriate adjustments to the remaining rules, we can produce a grammar that will translate any list which it can recognize as a sentence into the appropriate labelled bracketing formula. For instance, the query

?-   **sentence([every, woman, walks], X)**

will return **X** as this structural description:

[sentence, [np, [dt, every], [cn, woman]], [vp, [iv, walks]]]

5.5.2 Difference lists

One way to see the parsing problem is to view a sentence as a series of nodes linked by words, the problem being to subsume those links under the appropriate grammatical categories. Thus the sentence

3)   Some farmer beats a donkey

can be described as a series of links:

link(some, 1, 2) .
link(farmer, 2, 3) .
link(beats, 3, 4) .
link(a, 4, 5) .
link(donkey, 5, 6) .

and the parsing of it depicted as the construction of the appropriate graph:

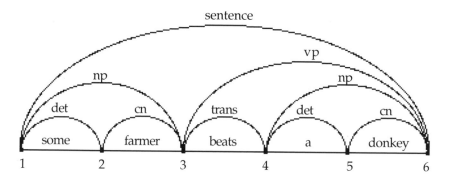

The grammar rules will subsume the basic lexical items under their categories, e.g.

link(det, X, Y) :- link(some, X, Y) .

And a sentence, for example, will link two nodes X and Z if there is a noun phrase which links X with some node Y, and a verb phrase which links Y to Z:

link(sentence, X, Z) :- link(np, X, Y),
**   link(vp, Y, Z) .**

We can combine this way of parsing sentences with the use of lists if we view it in a slightly different light. Instead of thinking of a sentence as the linking together of a noun phrase with a verb phrase, we can view a noun phrase as the *difference* between sentence and a verb phrase. This is the idea behind the apparatus of *difference lists* (or difference pairs), which provides a more efficient way of combining and splitting lists than the use of **append**. We represent a list such as the noun phrase **[some, farmer]**, as the difference between the sentence and the remaining verb phrase:

> **[some, farmer, beats a donkey]**
> **[beats a donkey]**

If we declare a binary infix operator - say **df** - we can bind together a difference pair into a single complex term. Thus **[beats, a, donkey] df [a, donkey]** means: the difference between that pair of lists, i.e. the transitive verb **[beats]**. Notice that any list can be represented in this form as the difference between itself and the empty list - **[beats]** is also represented by the difference pair **[beats] df []**.

Consider how simple the operation of **append** can be for difference lists. Let's call it **join**. In the following diagram, we represent a specific instance of joining two difference lists in the left column. In the middle column we present the general pattern of variables which this instantiates, and in the right column we have a reminder of the more intuitive append between the corresponding conventional lists:

Difference lists join	General pattern	Ordinary lists append
[beats, a, donkey]	X	
[a, donkey]	Y	**[beats]**
with		with
[a, donkey]	Y	
[ ]	Z	**[a, donkey]**
to form:		to form:
[beats, a, donkey]	X	
[ ]	Z	**[beats, a, donkey]**

In other words, the general operation of **append** for difference lists can be defined by the pattern of variables in the middle column:

join(X df Y, Y df Z, X df Z).

Forming a bigger list is simply forming a bigger difference.

A question remains: how can we join two difference lists corresponding to the append of an arbitrarily chosen pair of standard lists - say **[a, b]** and **[c, d]**? If we represent them by the difference pairs **[a, b] df []** and **[c, d] df []**, these pairs will not match the general pattern of **join** - there is no common term **Y**. Clearly, if we represent the former list by the difference pair **[a, b, c, d] df [c, d]**, this will successfully join if we represent the second by the pair **[c, d] df []** - but this specification of the first difference list assumes that we know in advance what the second is going to look like. We would like to represent each of **[a, b]** and **[c, d]** by a difference pair which does not make assumptions about the shape of the other it is to be joined with. The solution is to realize that the ordinary list **[a, b]** also corresponds to the difference list *pattern* **[a, b | X] df X**. The difference pair just mentioned, **[a, b, c, d] df [c, d]**, is one instance of this pattern. Thus the goal

append([a, b], [c, d], Z)

should be represented by the goal:

join([a, b | X] df X, [c, d | Y] df Y, Z)

This will succeed, with **Z** instantiated to the difference list pattern **[a, b, c, d | V] df V**, for some variable **V** (in conventional terms, the list **[a, b, c, d]**, as desired). **X** will be the list pattern **[c, d | V]**, making the first difference list the pair **[a, b, c, d | V] df [c, d | V]**, and **Y** will simply be **V**.

In this section we shall extend the grammar to include noun phrases which include a relative clause, as in this example:

4)   Every man who knows a woman who owns a dog which barks owns a cat that walks.

The D.C.G. rules require extension along these lines:

        common noun phrase --> common noun, rel clause.
        rel clause --> comp, verb phrase.
        comp --> 'who'.
        comp --> 'which'.
        comp --> 'that'.

The grammar sees relative clauses as functioning in the same way as the prepositional phrases introduced in section 3.6.2: as qualifying the description supplied by the common noun. Check your understanding of the grammar by following through the construction of the NPs in sentence 4).

We can now turn to implementing the D.C.G. within the difference lists approach. To distinguish this from the previous programs, let us define a two place predicate **phrase**, which will relate a syntactic type to a difference list. (For clarity, generation of structural descriptions will be omitted from this program.) A listing of the structural rules, and samples from the lexicon, are given in figure 5.9. At the top level, **process** hands over a list of words to **phrase**, converting it to a difference pair. An advantage of using difference lists is that we don't have to separate out the slicing and splicing of phrases in a distinct **append** condition - this will be built into the specification of the constituent phrases as difference lists. Thus for a sentence:

```
phrase(sentence, X df Z) :- phrase(noun_phrase, X df Y),
                            phrase(verb_phrase, Y df Z) .
```

The pattern of variables in these difference pairs is just the pattern in the definition of **join**; it's also the pattern in the **link** rule for sentences. A single word noun phrase, such as **[mary]**, is the difference between, for instance, the lists **[mary, walks]** and **[walks]**. The most appropriate general specification of such a single word list is, as suggested above, a difference list pattern:

[mary | X] df X

As in the previous program, we can record the basic item as a single atom, **p_name(mary)**, and let a general rule prepare the appropriate form of list - this difference list pattern - for all expressions in this category.

```
process(List) :- phrase( Type, List df [] ) .
phrase(sentence, X df Z ) :- phrase(noun_phrase, X df Y ),
                             phrase(verb_phrase, Y df Z ) .
phrase(noun_phrase, [Name | X] df X ) :- p_name(Name) .
phrase(noun_phrase, X df Z ) :- phrase(determiner, X df Y ),
                                phrase(cnp, Y df Z ) .
phrase(verb_phrase, [Verb | List] df List ) :- intransitive(Verb) .
phrase(verb_phrase, [Verb | X] df Y ) :- transitive(Verb),
                                         phrase(noun_phrase, X df Y ) .
phrase(determiner, [Word | List] df List ) :- det(Word) .
phrase(cnp, [Word | List] df List ) :- common_noun(Word) .
phrase(cnp, [Word | X] df Y ) :- common_noun(Word),
                                 phrase(prep_phrase, X df Y ) .
phrase(cnp, [A, B | X] df Y ) :- common_noun(A),
                                 comp(B),
                                 phrase(verb_phrase, X df Y ) .
phrase(prep_phrase, [Word | X] df Y ) :- prep(Word),
                                         phrase(noun_phrase, X df Y ).
common_noun(woman) .
common_noun(father) .
comp(who) .
comp(which) .
comp(that) .
prep(of).
p_name(france) .
```

det(some) .
det(the) .
transitive(owns) .
intransitive(exists) .

Figure **5.9**   A difference lists grammar

Structured NPs consist of a determiner followed by a common noun phrase. The simplest form of common noun phrase is a single common noun, for which the appropriate difference pair can be constructed in just the same way as a proper name - the first rule for **cnp**. The next step up in complexity is a CNP such as 'king of France'. To understand the rule for this, it will help to consider how the parser will encounter this phrase within an arbitrary sentence, say 'The king of France exists'. The sentence will be held as the pair:

[the, king, of, france, exists] df []

which splits, by the rule for sentences, into these two pairs:

[the, king, of, france, exists] df [exists] and **[exists] df []**

We need only consider the former pair, which represents the noun phrase 'The king of France'. The determiner 'the' will be represented by a general pattern like the other single words, **[the | X] df X**, which in this instance will instantiate to:

[the, king, of, france, exists] df [king, of, france, exists]

The CNP we are interested in will here be:

[king, of, france, exists] df [exists]

This is the result of joining the common noun 'king',

[king, of, france, exists] df [of, france, exists]

with the prepositional phrase 'of France',

[of, france, exists] df [exists]

To find the general pattern which these exemplify, replace **king** by the variable **Word**, and the lists **[of, france, exists]** and **[exists]** by **X** and **Y** respectively - thus the second rule for **cnp**. A similar rule can be provided for a common noun phrase such as 'woman who owns a dog', constructed by combining the CN 'woman' with the relative clause 'who owns a dog'. Alternatively, if we want to skip relative clauses as a distinct level of categorization which the parser has to recognize, we can put the constituents of a relative clause, complementizer and verb phrase, directly into the definition of this kind of CNP. To do so we need a slightly different form of difference list pattern, in which we specify the first *two* members of the list, **[A, B | X]**, such that **A** is a CN and **B** a complementizer. This pattern is employed in the third **cnp** rule.

Up to now, the grammaticality of a word has not depended on the sentential context in which it is embedded. But consider the phenomenon of number agreement. Whether an occurrence of the common noun 'man' is acceptable depends on the surrounding sentential context:

> Every man walks.
> All men walk.

In English, the main verb in a sentence must agree in number with the subject - singular with singular, plural with plural. The obvious way to handle agreement is to add an extra parameter to the relevant syntactic predicates, and to require that the values of this parameter - either **singular** or **plural** - for the constituent phrases always agree. For instance:

phrase(N, sentence, X df Z) :- phrase(N, noun_phrase, X df Y),
**   phrase(N, verb_phrase, Y df Z).**

We add this parameter to **phrase** throughout, taking care to ensure agreement only when required. A singular subject can be related to a plural object ('A woman saw the men'), and conversely, so we must not force the object of a transitive verb to agree in number with the verb:

phrase(N, verb_phrase, [Verb | X] df Y) :-
**   transitive(Verb, N),**
**   phrase(_, noun_phrase, X df Y) .**

The same is true of common noun phrases formed with a prepositional phrase ('the mother of the boys', 'the donkeys of the farmer').

The significant alterations to the program involve the basic lexical items. To begin with determiners: some are singular, some plural, and some can be both:

```
det(every, singular).
det(all, plural).
det(the, _).
```

A general rule will subsume all members of the category:

```
phrase(N, determiner, [Word | List] df List ) :- det(Word, N).
```

The determiner 'the' will inherit its plurality from the common noun (phrase) it combines with. If the form of pluralization within a category is highly irregular, we will need to note these irregularities separately:

```
c_noun(woman, women).
c_noun(king, kings).
c_noun(farmer, farmers).
c_noun(country, countries).
```

The general rule is that the word mentioned first is the singular form, and the second is the plural:

```
common_noun(X, singular) :- c_noun(X, _).
common_noun(X, plural) :- c_noun(_, X).
```

Alternatively, where there is a high degree of regularity, we should expect to capture it with a general rule. The present plural of an English verb is usually the infinitive, and the singular form comes by adding an 's'. To capture this regularity, we need to define the operation of adding an 's'. One way to do this is to convert a word into the list of ASCII codes of its letters - thus **talk** becomes **[116, 97, 108, 107]** - append to this the list containing the code for 's' - and then convert back. The predefined relation **name(W, L)** allows us to effect this translation - if **W** is instantiated to a word, **L** will be the list of codes; and if **L** is a list of codes, **W** will be the corresponding word.

addess(Before, After) :- name(Before, List),
                            append(List, "s", New),
                            name(After, New) .

An expression within double quotes denotes the list of underlying
ASCII codes; in place of **"s"** we could have written **[115]**. (Note that
although **name** is invertible, **addess** is not. We need to supply it with a
value for **Before**; if we attempted to supply it with **After**, in the hope
of removing an 's', the call to the first **name** goal would have two
unassigned variables, and fail.) If we now record all intransitive verbs
in their infinitive form, e.g.

intrans(talk) .

the general rules for number will be:

intransitive(Inf, plural) :- intrans(Inf) .
intransitive(X, singular) :- intrans(Inf),
                               addess(Inf, X) .

Similarly for transitive verbs. This essentially completes the
grammar for number agreement.

5.5.3 Extracting semantic information (i): logical structure

If I ask you how to represent in Edinburgh Prolog the queries

5)   Who loves John?
6)   Whom does John love?

you will almost certainly say that 5) is to go into the form **loves(X,
john)**, and 6) into **loves(john, X)**. In an important sense, you will have
extracted the semantic content of the two English questions. And you
will have done so on the basis of the information provided by their
syntactic structure. The word 'who' (or 'whom') acts like a variable in
a Prolog query. Placing it in the subject position of an interrogative
phrased in the active voice tells us that we are being asked for the
subject of the relation; in a passive construction, for the object of the
relation. Any serious natural language processing program will need to
be able to perform this operation of extracting semantic content from
sentences and queries in ordinary English. This is not semantics in the
sense of stating relations between words and the world; we are still

concerned with what is essentially a translation manual between one language and another. But the target language is the language of logical forms, which has a precisely stated semantics and - more importantly here - a well defined set of inferential relations. By translating into a logical language such as Prolog itself, we give a precise representation of the semantic content of a sentence, which can be manipulated by semantically justified (sound) inferential procedures.

In this section **phrase** will be a three place predicate, relating a syntactic category, English words (held in a difference pair), and the new semantic argument. In general the latter will be a list of items carrying the logical or semantical information associated with a phrase; in the case of a sentence it will be the complete logical form. The number of items on the list, and the role they play, will depend on the category of expression involved. Since the full system is quite complicated, we will begin with a fragment containing only the most elementary combinations of verbs and proper names, such as

Mary loves John.
Mary walks.

We want **phrase** to translate these two sentences into the wffs **loves(mary, john)** and **walks(mary)** respectively. Since the syntactic rule for sentences remains the same - they are formed by combining a noun phrase and verb phrase - we want to see their logical forms as the result of combining the logical contributions corresponding to the two constituent phrases. Recall that in section 2.4 the logical notion of a predicate was explained as, roughly, the result of removing a name from a sentence. Now we want to view things from the opposite direction: a sentence wff comes by combining a name with the predicate supplied by the verb phrase. In the former case we want **mary** to fill the vacant position in the predicate **loves(, john)**, and in the latter, **walks( )**. The important point here is that there is not just one pattern which is the logical form of all VPs - and when we introduce quantifier phrases the logical forms corresponding to VPs (e.g. 'loves a man') will be even more varied.

In this simple grammar, a noun phrase such as 'Mary' can be associated with a semantic list with just one item: **[mary]**. Consider 'Mary' as the grammatical subject of a sentence. To get a uniform procedure of slotting the constant **mary** into the appropriate place in the predicate, we will associate a VP with two items of semantic information. There will be a variable **Arg**, to be matched with the

subject term, and a wff which has **Arg** marking its subject argument
place. Thus with the VP 'loves john' we will have the two item list
[Arg, loves(Arg, john)], and for the intransitive verb 'walks', **[Arg,
walks(Arg)]**. **Arg** here is a meta-variable - a variable which ranges
over expressions of the target language. It will be instantiated by
names and, when quantifier phrases are introduced, by first order
variables **x0, x1, x2,** ... The rule for sentences must ensure that the
subject supplied by the NP unifies with this **Arg** of the VP:

phrase(sentence, X df Z, Wff) :-
      phrase(noun_phrase, X df Y, [Subj]),
      phrase(verb_phrase, Y df Z, [Subj, Wff]) .

In other words, the verb phrase supplies a sentence schema which
becomes the complete **Wff** when its missing argument is supplied by the
subject of the sentence. The rule for **sentence** unifies the subject supplied
by the NP with the unfilled argument, marked by **Arg**, in the sentence
schema supplied by the VP - in the case of 'Mary loves john', as
follows:

      [Subj] = [mary] and **[Subj, Wff] = [Arg, loves(Arg, john)]**

The only way to solve these simultaneous equations is with **mary = Subj
= Arg**, and so **Wff = loves(Arg, john) = loves(mary, john)**, as desired.

      To associate the right semantic list with the VP 'loves John',
the rule for combining a transitive verb with a noun phrase needs to be:

phrase(verb_phrase, [Verb | X] df Y, [Arg, Verb(Arg, Obj)]) :-
      transitive(Verb),
      phrase(noun_phrase, X df Y, [Obj]) .

Here the constant supplied by an NP becomes the object of the verb.
The third, semantic, argument to **phrase** can be displayed as a third
layer in a phrase structure tree - figure 5.10 below. The semantic
composition of the wff parallels the syntactic composition of the
English sentence.

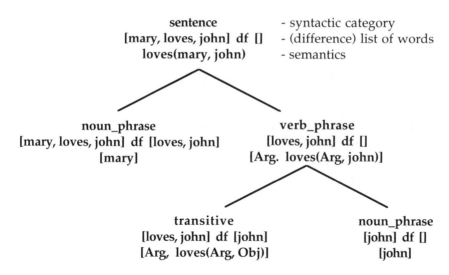

sentence   - syntactic category
[mary, loves, john] df []   - (difference) list of words
loves(mary, john)   - semantics

noun_phrase
[mary, loves, john] df [loves, john]
[mary]

verb_phrase
[loves, john] df []
[Arg. loves(Arg, john)]

transitive
[loves, john] df [john]
[Arg, loves(Arg, Obj)]

noun_phrase
[john] df []
[john]

Figure **5.10   phrase(Cateogry, Difference_list, Semantics)**

Rather than pursue this simple grammar any further, let us move on to the general case involving quantifier phrases. To understand the information we need to associate with a determiner like 'some', it will help if we work back from the logical form we wish to associate with a sentence containing it - example 3):

(∃x0)(farmer(x0) & (∃x1)(donkey(x1) & beats(x0, x1)))

We want the expression 'Some farmer' to be associated with the schema:

(∃x0)(farmer(x0) & PredWff)

PredWff will be instantiated to the wff which expresses what is predicated of this indefinitely specified farmer, i.e. of the variable **x0** supplied by this quantifier. To accommodate this, we shall now associate a noun phrase with three items of information. Firstly, the term it supplies: in the case of a name, the name; in the case of a quantifier phrase, the variable it binds. Secondly, a schema **PredWff**, one of the arguments of which will be filled by that term - maybe as the subject of the predication, or as the object. Thirdly, the schematic form of the wff which will result when all these are put together. (In the case of proper names, which are logically simple and do not introduce a further component into the wff, the distinction between these latter components is idle.) Thus in the case of 'a donkey', the semantic list is:

[x1, PredWff, (∃x1)(donkey(x1) & PredWff)]

In other words, the phrase 'a donkey' will take the wff schema **PredWff** supplied by some verb or verb phrase, and fill an argument in that schema by the variable **x1**. In the present case, since 'a donkey' is the object of the sentence, what will be output from this construction will be the schema associated with the verb phrase 'beats a donkey', that is, **(∃x1)(donkey(x1) & beats(Arg, x1))**.

A determiner such as 'some', expressing existential quantification, will need to be associated with something even more schematic:

(∃x0)(ResWff & PredWff)

ResWff is to be the wff which conveys the restriction on the variable, (cf. section 4.5.2), expressed by the common noun or common noun phrase which the determiner combines with. In the present example it will be **farmer(x0)**, restricting **x0** to farmers. For this, the semantic list associated with the bare quantifier 'some' will contain one more item than that for the quantifier phrase 'some farmer': **ResWff**. Moreover, we need to ensure that each new occurrence of a quantifier introduces a distinct variable, to avoid any possible clash of variables in our logical forms. Edinburgh Prolog contains a predefined predicate **gensym**, for the generation of symbols with a common root. If we declare that root to be **x**, we can get **gensym** to guarantee us an unending supply of symbols **x0, x1, x2, ...** To effect this, we can initialize **gensym** to this root at the start of a parse, when we hand the list over to **phrase**:

```
parse(List, Wff) :-  init_gensym(x),
                     phrase(Type,  List df [],  Wff) .
```

Thereafter, when Prolog encounters a goal of the form **gensym(x, X)**, it will instantiate **X** to the next symbol in the x series.

One further point about 'some' concerns the formation of its schema (∃ x0)(ResWff & PredWff). I assume that all the logical constants have been declared as the appropriate operators - in particular, that ∃ has been declared a unary prefix operator. This means that it will take a variable of the target language like **x0** and form ∃ **x0**. But we want this combination in turn to act as a unary operator on the wff schema which falls within its scope. To achieve this, we can use the structure forming device =.., pronounced 'univ'. This takes a list of atoms, and makes the first one the functor applied to the remainder. Thus the goal

X =.. [func, a, b, c]

succeeds with **X** instantiated to **func(a, b, c)**. It can also be used in the reverse order to take a structure apart;

father_of(adam, cain) =.. X

returns the corresponding list, **X = [father_of, adam, cain]**. We can now state the rule for 'some':

phrase(determiner, [some | List] df List, [X, Reswff, Predwff, Wff]) :-
 gensym(x, X),
 Wff =.. [(∃ X), (Reswff & Predwff)] .

gensym instantiates the Prolog variable **X** to the next target language variable, and =.. puts together the appropriate schema. The treatment of quantifiers has so far followed Montague's 'Proper Treatment', PTQ, but rather than adopt his Russellian analysis of definite descriptions, we shall treat them as genuine singular terms (see the end of 4.6.1):

phrase(noun_phrase, [the | X] df Y, [Term, Wff, Wff]) :-
 phrase(c_noun_phrase, X df Y, [Z, Pred]),
 gensym(x, Z),
 Term =.. [(ι Z), Pred] .

We can also follow the policy of sections 2.5.2 and 4.6.1, of making a special case of the VP 'exists', treating it not as an unanalysed predicate but in terms of quantification:

phrase(verb_phrase, [exists | List] df List, [Arg, Wff]) :-
 gensym(x, X),
 Wff =.. [(∃ X), (X = Arg)] .

This completes the informal explanation of this approach to translation into logical form. For ease of reference, I include below a representative listing for the definition of **phrase**:

```
phrase(sentence, X df Z, Wff) :-
        phrase(noun_phrase, X df Y, [Arg, VPWff, Wff]),
        phrase(verb_phrase, Y df Z, [Arg, VPWff]) .
phrase(determiner, [every | List] df List, [X, Reswff, Predwff, Wff]) :-
        gensym(x, X),
        Wff =.. [(∀ X), (Reswff → Predwff)] .
phrase(determiner, [a | List] df List, [X, Reswff, Predwff, Wff]) :-
        gensym(x, X),
        Wff =.. [(∃ X), (Reswff & Predwff)] .
phrase(noun_phrase, X df Z, [Arg, Predwff, Wff]) :-
        phrase(determiner, X df Y, [Arg, Reswff, Predwff, Wff]),
        phrase(c_noun_phrase, Y df Z, [Arg, Reswff]) .
phrase(noun_phrase, [Name | X] df X, [Name, Wff, Wff]) :-
        proper_name(Name) .
phrase(c_noun_phrase, [Word | X] df X, [Arg, Word(Arg)]) :-
        common_noun(Word) .
phrase(c_noun_phrase, [Wd, C | X] df Y, [Arg, (Wd(Arg) & Wff)]) :-
        common_noun(Wd),
        comp(C),
        phrase(verb_phrase, X df Y, [Arg, Wff]) .
phrase(verb_phrase, [Verb | X] df Y, [Subj, Wff]) :-
        transitive(Verb),
        phrase(noun_phrase, X df Y, [Obj, Verb(Subj, Obj), Wff]).
phrase(verb_phrase, [Verb | List] df List, [Arg, Verb(Arg)]) :-
        intransitive(Verb) .
common_noun(farmer) .
comp(who) .
proper_name(john) .
det(every) .
transitive(beats) .
intransitive(walks) .
```

Figure **5.11**   Parsing to logical form

The parser has an impressive ability to keep track of the recursive formation of phrases within its fragment - assuming it knows the vocabulary, a sentence such as 7) will be parsed to the logical form 8)

7)   Every university which owns a mainframe which communicates accesses every institution which accesses a network that has a gateway,

8)   ($\forall$ x0)(university(x0) & ($\exists$ x1)(mainframe(x1) & communicates(x1) & owns(x0, x1)) → ($\forall$ x2)(institution(x2) & ($\exists$ x3)(network(x3) & ($\exists$ x4)   (gateway(x4) & has(x3, x4)) & accesses(x2, x3)) → accesses(x0, x2))).

But one should not play down its shortcomings. It shies away from even the simplest examples of pronominal anaphora. The treatment of 'every' and 'some' follows Montague's PTQ, although it does not contain Montague's rule which allows for quantifier scope ambiguities (cf. example 8, section 4.5.2); the logical ordering of the quantifiers always follows their syntactic order. And it suffers from whatever linguistic disadvantages are inherent in Montague's system.

5.5.4 Extracting semantic information (ii): a simple case grammar

In this sub-section we shall consider a slightly different representation of the semantic content of sentences. Instead of the standard formalization of

9)   Brutus stabbed Caesar at noon,

in terms of a three place relation - stabbed_at(brutus, caesar, noon) - we can see it as reporting the existence of a certain kind of event: an event of a stabbing, which was at noon. The agent - or more generally, the *subject* - of this event was Brutus, and its object was Caesar:

$$(\exists e)(subj(e, brutus) \ \& \ stabbed(e) \ \& \ obj(e, caesar) \ \& \ at(e, noon)).$$

The linguistic notion of *case* was originally introduced to classify certain surface syntactic features of words (cf. the discussion of **pronoun**, in section 5.3.1). Those surface features nevertheless reflect different possible semantic roles, such as subject or direct object, and in modern *case grammars* case is intended as an essentially semantic notion. Categories such as subject, direct object, location, direction, time, duration, manner, indirect object, instrument, and objective provide ways of characterizing an event. (In terms of the notion of frame, mentioned in section 3.3.1, they provide the slots of a frame, a case frame, for a typical event.) For certain kinds of event, some of the cases may be inappropriate. For instance, with an event of a falling - of a tree, say - in which the subject is not an intentional agent, there will be no objective or goal for which it was performed. A given sentence may fill in some of the relevant characteristics, but not others.

The grammar developed here will ignore quantificational structure and tense. Instead of $\exists$ we shall use Skolem constants (cf. section 4.6.4), so that 9) will be parsed into this wff:

$$subj(e0, brutus) \ \& \ stabbed(e0) \ \& \ obj(e0, caesar) \ \& \ at(e0, noon)$$

9) contains a prepositional phrase acting as an adverbial modifier; a significant feature of this construction is that it is iterable:

A king shot a tiger with a revolver in India in 1938.

However, the most obvious treatment of this construction,

verb phrase --> verb phrase, prep phrase.

is *left recursive*. That is, the concept being defined is mentioned first in the defining condition, which threatens to send the parser into loops. Using difference lists: to see if **[Word | X] df Y** is a verb phrase, see if **[Word | X] df Z** is a verb phrase (followed by **Z df Y** a prepositional phrase). To avoid this looping, we could revert to the inefficient approach of using **append** - to split the word list into two smaller lists. But an alternative is to re-locate the recursion on prepositional phrases. This requires us to make what is, linguistically, an unmotivated distinction between a solitary prepositional phrase, such as 'with a revolver' - call this a 'PP' - from one involving iteration, such as 'with a revolver in India':

prep phrase --> pp.
prep phrase --> pp, prep phrase.
pp --> prep, noun phrase.

The advantage of this approach is that we reduce the question of what a VP is to more basic concepts (e.g. IV), before the recursion is encountered:

verb phrase --> intrans.
verb phrase --> trans, noun phrase.
verb phrase --> intrans, prep phrase.
verb phrase --> trans, noun phrase, prep phrase.

This involves some rather inelegant repetition. The repetition can be removed - that is, the first pair of these rules can be removed - if we allow that a prep phrase can be realized as nothing:

prep phrase --> .

Because prepositional phrases can also act as adjectival modifiers, this fragment contains significant structural ambiguity. A sentence such as

John saw a man who beat a donkey with a telescope,

is three ways ambiguous (compare Thurber's discussion of the Forster example, section 2.1.3). It could be that the telescope was with the donkey (on its back, presumably):

subj(e1, john) & saw(e1) & (man(o0) & (subj(e0, o0) & beat(e0) & (donkey(o1) & (telescope(o2) & with(o1, o2)) & obj(e0, o1))) & obj(e1, o0)),

it could be that the beating was with a telescope:

subj(e3, john) & saw(e3) & (man(o0) & (subj(e2, o0) & beat(e2) & (donkey(o4) & obj(e2, o4)) & (telescope(o3) & with(e2, o3))) & obj(e3, o0)),

or it could be that the telescope was the instrument of the seeing:

subj(e5, john) & saw(e5) & (man(o6) & (subj(e4, o6) & beat(e4) & (donkey(o7) & obj(e4, o7))) & obj(e5, o6)) & (telescope(o5) & with(e5, o5)).

(Uniformity with the treatment of VPs suggests that we should allow a common noun phrase to be a common noun followed by a possibly empty prep phrase.)

This example also serves to make another important point. No-one supposes that it is possible in general to recover a complete semantic representation of a sentence, as uttered on some occasion, from its syntactic structure alone. What a semantic parser of the sort we shall consider can offer, in general, is a number of logical structures, it being a matter for further pragmatic factors to select the most likely of them as the correct interpretation for a given discourse context. With a slight change in the example,

> John shot a man who beat a donkey with a telescope,

the third reading is almost certainly ruled out, because telescopes are not the sort of thing you can use to shoot with. A semantic theory which was augmented by a theory of lexical decomposition or conceptual analysis - of words like 'shoot' and 'telescope' - would have some chance of making this ruling.

In the present system we abstract from quantificational structure, using Skolem constants in place of existential quantifiers. The system is multi-sorted - a sort of events, and a sort of objects - so we need to initialize **gensym** twice at the outset:

```
parse(List, Wff) :- init_gensym(e),
                    init_gensym(o),
                    phrase(sentence, List df [],  Wff) .
```

The rule for sentence formation is much as before, except that we must now keep track of two terms: the subject entity **Ent**, and the event described by the VP, **Evt**:

```
phrase(sentence,  X df Z, Wff) :-
       phrase(noun_phrase, X df Y, [Ent, Evt, VPWff, Wff]),
       phrase(verb_phrase,  Y df Z, [Ent, Evt, VPWff]) .
```

If the subject NP is a proper name, the **Name** it supplies will unify with **Ent**, which will be substituted into the part of the **VPWff** which states that **Ent** is the subject or agent of that event, **subj(Evt, Ent)**.

```
phrase(noun_phrase, [Name| List] df List, [Name, Evt, Wff, Wff]) :-
       proper_name(Name) .
```

The rules for prepositional phrases serve both their adverbial and adjectival roles. The semantically significant category is the pp - it takes the **Wff** supplied by either a VP or CN, and the **Arg** (an event or entity, respectively), and adjoins to the **Wff** the relevant qualification **AdWff**:

phrase(pp, [Wd | X] df Y, [Arg, Wff, Wff & AdWff]) :-
    prep(Word),
    phrase(noun_phrase, X df Y, [Ent, Arg, Wd(Arg, Ent), AdWff]).

In the case of 'with a telescope', **AdWff** will be the result of conjoining **with(Arg, Ent)** and the instantiation of **telescope(Ent)** supplied by 'a telescope'. This is a wff which can qualify an **Arg** which is either an event or an object. Since, for example, both physical objects and events have spatial location, it seems quite right that the same formula can in principle qualify both sorts, as with **in(X, india)**. But notice that this grammar is austere in its treatment of cases. Because it makes no attempt at lexical analysis, it does not recognize that (most probably) **in(X, india)** describes spatial location and **in(X, 1938)** temporal location. So it does not distinguish them into **place(X, india)** and **time(X, 1938)**, as might be expected of a full case system. For a preposition like 'with', a lexical analysis might distinguish between the sense in which an object is with something (possessing, accompanying, etc.), from the sense in which an event is with something (manner, instrument). The rules for prep phrases handle the recursion. The rule for the empty difference list **X df X** returns the Wff unmodified:

phrase(prep_phrase, X df X, [Arg, Wff, Wff]) .

The rule for the prep phrase which is a single pp returns whatever semantics that pp has:

phrase(prep_phrase, Df, Semantics) :-
    phrase(pp, Df, Semantics).

Otherwise, the relevant qualifying phrase is constructed recursively:

phrase(prep_phrase, X df Z, [Arg, Wff1, Wff3]) :-
    phrase(pp, X df Y, [Arg, Wff1, Wff2]),
    Y \= Z,
    phrase(prep_phrase, Y df Z, [Arg, Wff2, Wff3]).

The rules for NP construction are much the same as those from the preceding sub-section. The significant changes are to the treatment of VPs. Consider the clause for intransitive verbs.

```
phrase(verb_phrase, [Verb | X] df Y, [Ent, E, Wff]) :-
    intransitive(Verb),
    phrase(prep_phrase, X df Y, [E, Verb(E) & subj(E, Ent), Wff]),
    gensym(e, E).
```

The **gensym** at the end generates the event name (which may not be the main event of the sentence, if the VP is in a relative clause), which is instantiated to **E**. Notice that the structure which will be the semantics of the verb, **Verb(E) & subj(E, Ent)**, gets handed to the prepositional phrase (if there is one) for modification. This has a slot for the subject of the sentence; the case frame for a transitive verb additionally includes the event's having a direct object, which the rule for TVs must therefore provide.

Exercise 5

A.   The following are examples of simple imperatives in English:

>   Walk!
>   Hit John!
>   Shoot a tiger!
>   Find the king of France!

That is, an imperative can be a list consisting of an infinitive verb phrase followed by an exclamation mark. Formulate a grammar using difference lists, which defines a predicate **imperative**, which will recognize and generate these sentences.

B.   Write a D.C.G. for simple English questions such as these:

>   What killed Jones?
>   Who loves London?
>   Which dog barks?
>   Which man hates a woman?

Write a program based on your grammar. Formulate it so that it can parse each interrogative into a structural description, a syntactic analysis.

C.   Modify the case grammar to allow for auxiliary modification of VPs, as in 'John did not walk':

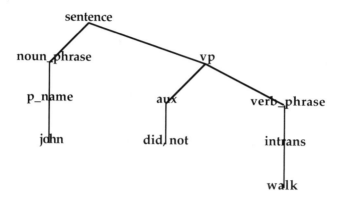

The grammar should be capable of parsing a sentence such as 'A dog did bark' into the underlying form:

dog(o1) & (past(e0) & (subj(e0, o1) & bark(e0))),

and a negated sentence, such as 'Brutus will not stab Caesar at noon' into the appropriate wff:

¬ (future(e0) & (subj(e0, brutus) & stab(e0) & obj(e0, caesar) & at(e0, noon))).

Auxiliary modification can of course affect a subsidiary VP:

John did see a man who did not beat a donkey with a telescope.

D.   Adapt the parser in section 3 above to translate into Prolog, rather than first order logic, and use the parser to enable a database to be queried in natural language. Choose a program to provide the database - e.g. the nutritional advice or dating agency example. For instance, sentence 1) could be translated into 2):

1)   every person who likes jazz likes cinema
2)   **forall((person(X), likes(X, jazz)), likes(X, cinema))**

That is, you need to revise the rule for 'every' so that it translates in terms of **forall** and a Prolog variable, rather than ∀ and logical variable. The program should take an indicative sentence like 1), translate it into an appropriate formula like 2), evaluate this against the database, and then print out some kind of response. Obviously, the lexicon will need to be adapted to the vocabulary appropriate to the database chosen, and the database itself may need to be extended (e.g. to infer **person(X)** from **man(X)** or **woman(X)**). You might extend the system to include adjectives, and the 'is' of predication:

3)   some shy man who likes cinema suits jane
4)   **((shy(X), man(X), likes(X, cinema)), suits(X, jane))**
5)   jane is a small extrovert woman who likes travel
6)   **((small(X), extrovert(X), woman(X), likes(X, travel)), jane=X)**

Appendices

Appendix 1: logical status

X is *necessarily true* iff it is true in all possible states of affairs.
X is *logically impossible* iff it is true in no possible state of affairs.
X is *logically possible* iff there is at least one state of affairs in which it is or would be true.
X is *contingent* iff both X and ¬X are logically possible.
X is *contingently true* iff it is contingent and actually true.

X, Y, Z, ... are mutually *consistent* iff there is at least one state of affairs in which they are all true.
X, Y, Z, ... are *inconsistent* iff in no state of affairs are they all true.
X and Y are *contrary* iff in no possible state of affairs are they both true.
X and Y are *contradictory* iff in no state of affairs are they both true, but in no state of affairs are they both false.
X, Y, Z ... *entail* W iff in no state of affairs in which X, Y, Z ... are all true is W false.
X, Y, Z ... do *not entail* W iff it is possible for W to be false when all of X, Y, Z ... are true.

In propositional logic, these properties and relations can be tested for using truth tables. We might add that two sentences X and Y are *logically independent* iff all four combinations are possible: both true, both false, and one true and the other false. When we take any two atomic wffs A, B and draw up four lines for their truth table, we show that we treat each atomic wff as logically independent of the next.

Appendix 2: the grammar of logic

Syntax (1) - Classification of basic symbols.

A, B, C, ... are **sentences** (atomic wffs).
¬ is a **unary** sentence **connective** (negation).
&, v, →, ↔ are **binary** sentence **connectives** (conjunction, disjunction, the material conditional, the material biconditional).
a, b, c, ... are **names** or constants, which refer to specific individuals.
x, y, z, x_1, x_2, ... are **variables**, which range over individuals.

Names and variables are **terms**.

P, Q, R, S, ... are **predicates**, which express properties and relations.
= is the **identity** relation.
∃, ∀ are **quantifiers** (existential and universal).

Syntax (2) - Acceptable ways of combining these symbols. (Formation rules)

If *pred* is a one place predicate, and *term* is a term, then *pred(term)* is a wff. Examples: P(a), P(x), Q(b), etc.

If *pred* is a two place predicate, and *term1* and *term2* are terms, then *pred(term1, term2)* is a wff. Examples: R(c, c), S(x, y), R(z, a), etc. Exception: identity. We write *term1 = term2* instead of *=(term1, term2)*.

More generally: If *pred* is an n place predicate, and *term1, ..., termN* are n terms, then *pred(term1, ..., termN)* is a wff.

If *wff* is a wff, and * is a unary sentence connective, then * *wff* is a wff. Examples: ¬A, ¬¬Q(y), ¬¬¬R(a, b), etc.

If *wff1* and *wff2* are wffs, and * is a binary sentence connective, then *wff1 * wff2* is a wff. Examples: A & ¬B, P(x) v R(a, x), a = b → b = a, etc.

If *quant* is a quantifier, *var* is a variable, and *wff* a wff, then *(quant var) wff* is a wff. Examples: (∃x)A, (∀x)R(x, x), (∀z)(P(z) v (∃y)R(y, z)), etc.

Nothing else is a wff of standard first order logic.

Syntax (3) - Variations and alternatives

Various extensions of the language are possible, e.g. modal logic adds the non truth functional □ and ◊ to the category of unary sentence connective (cf. section 4.6.2). If we allow function symbols f, g, h, ..., (cf. section 5.3.1), then the category of term must be expanded to include complex terms:

If *func* is an n place function symbol, and *term1*, ..., *termN* are terms, then *func(term1 , ..., termN)* is a term. Examples: f(x), g(a, b), f(f(y)), h(c, f(a)), etc. (Exceptions: arithmetical functions - we write, for example, x + y instead of +(x, y).)

With a description operator ι, complex terms can also be definite descriptions: (ιx)P(x) - the unique x such that P(x). The combination (∃!x)P(x) means: there exists exactly one x such that P(x), i.e. (∃x)(P(x) & (∀y)(P(y) → y = x).

A ***many-sorted*** logic allows for more than one sort of variable, e.g. t_1, t_2, t_3, ..., over times (cf. exercise 4.6 D), e_1, e_2, e_3, ..., over events.

Alternative notations for the logical constants include:

~ (tilde) for ¬;

⊃ (horseshoe) for →;

∧ or . for &;

≡ for ↔;

∧ for ∀ (i.e. a large ∧. ∀ is like a generalized version of conjunction. For if all things have property P, then this thing has P, AND that thing has P, AND the next thing has P, AND ... etc). Also (x) is used in place of (∀x), etc.

∨ for ∃ (i.e. a large ∨ - ∃ is like a generalized version of ∨; cf. example 10 of exercise 2.1 C.)

For Polish propositional notation, see section 2.4; Σ for ∃; ∏ for ∀.

Appendix 3: the grammar of Prolog

Syntax (1). Classification of single characters

Category	Type	Examples
i	Uppercase letters	A B C ...
ii	Underscore	_
iii	Lowercase letters	a b c ...
iv	Arabic numerals	0 1 2 3 ...
v	Symbol characters	+ - * / ^ < > @ # $ & ? ...
vi	Single quote	'
vii	Double quote	"
viii	Round brackets	( )
ix	Square brackets	[ ]
x	Space	

Syntax (2). Basic terms

Cat.	Type	Initial character	Other characters	Examples
α	Variable	One from categories i or ii	Any (or none) from i, ii, iii or iv.	X NEXT _1234 X2 List _list New_Tail
β	Atoms - names and predicates	From iii	Any (or none) from i, ii, iii or iv.	london e213 the_moon fact
		From v	Any (or none) from v .	==> $@?&
γ	Quoted atoms	vi, and final character vi	Any sequence of i, ii, iii, iv, v, vii, viii, ix, x.	'The result: ' ' ---> '
δ	Numerals	From iv	Any sequence of iv (possibly with decimal point).	42 0.793
	Floating point	From iv	Any sequence of iv, followed by e, followed by integer.	42e200 0.793e-341

Syntax (3). Compound terms

Cat.	Type	Description	Examples
ε	List term	List brackets (category ix), enclosing a sequence of 0, 1 or more terms (i.e. from categories α, β, γ, δ, ε, or ζ). If more than 1 term: each must be separated from next by a comma. List brackets enclosing 1 or more terms (each separated from the next by a comma) followed by |, followed by a list term, or variable.	**[ ] [london]** **[a, b, c, d]** **['This', costs, £, N]** **[sentence, [np, [john]] , [vp, [walks]]]** **[Head | Tail]** **[a, b, c | [d]]** **[X, Y | _]**
ζ	N place term		
i	0 place	Atoms (category β).	**go ! fail**
ii	1 place	Any atom (category β) followed by (followed by any term (categories α, β, γ, δ, ε, ζ) followed by). Note: the combination *atom term* is an acceptable alternative to *atom(term)*, if *atom* has been declared a **prefix** operator, and *term atom* if *atom* has been declared a **postfix** operator.	**var(X)** **son_of(john)** **male(son_of(john))** **print([a, b, c])** **assert(write(stop))** **son_of john** **show [a, b, c]** **john s_father** **[a, b, c] ==>**
iii	2 place	Any sequence of the form: *atom (term1 , term2)* Note: the combination *term1 atom term2* is an acceptable alternative to *atom(term1, term2)*, if *atom* has been declared an **infix** operator. (See section 5.3.1 for operator declarations.)	**abs(-3, 3)** **loves(X, son_of X)** **[] reverses_to X** **high_pressure ->** **clear_skies** **2 + (3 * 5)**
iv	N place	An atom followed by (followed by a sequence of N terms, each separated from the next by a comma, followed by).	**max(73, 59, M)** **substitute(This, That, List1, List2)**

Note: a combination such as **substitute This for That in List1 =>
List2** is permissible if the atoms **for, in** and **=>** have been declared
as infix operators, and **substitute** a prefix operator.

Syntax (4).   Clauses

The sentences or clauses of Prolog are certain kinds of terms. To
understand the classification, it helps to distinguish a class of
formulae on essentially semantic grounds - the test formulae. These
are possibly complex formulae which Prolog can *test* for truth - either
posed directly as queries, or as the bodies (antecedents) of rules.
Variables in test formulae are basically existential in force - Prolog
is testing to see if it can find *some* instance which satisfies the term.
Basically, N place terms (category ζ) are test formulae. Note that
this includes formulae of the form 'X , Y', '**not** X' and 'X ; Y', i.e.
Prolog can check whether a conjunctive condition holds, etc. But an
important component of the definition is negative: terms of the form
'X :- Y' are *not* test formulae (Prolog can use rules, but it cannot test
whether a rule as a whole is true).

The clauses: the sentences which one may *assert* to be true, in
a program. Basically, variables in clauses are universal in force, i.e.
clauses with variables are asserted to hold for *all* instances.

N place terms are clauses (atomic sentences, asserted
unconditionally).

If X is an N place term and Y a test formula, then 'X :- Y' is
a clause (rules).

Again, an important part of the definition is negative: **:-** can occur at
most once in a clause (you cannot nest conditionals within
conditionals); **not** can only figure in a test formula (i.e. to the right
of **:-**).

Appendix 4: natural deduction rules

	Introduction	**Elimination**

Conjunction

Introduction:
$$\frac{X,\ Y}{X\ \&\ Y}$$

(& Y)

Elimination:
$$\frac{X\ \&\ Y}{X} \qquad \frac{X}{Y}$$

Disjunction

Introduction:
$$\frac{X}{X\ v\ Y} \qquad \frac{Y}{X\ v\ Y}$$

(Y, ¬Y)   (X)

Elimination:
$$\frac{X\ v\ Y,\ \neg X}{Y} \qquad \frac{X\ v}{}$$

Conditional

Introduction:
$$\begin{array}{c} X \qquad \text{ASS} \\ \vdots \\ Y \\ \hline X \to Y \end{array}$$

Elimination:
$$\frac{X,\ X \to Y}{Y}$$

Negation

Introduction:
$$\begin{array}{c} X \qquad \text{ASS} \\ \vdots \\ \frac{Y,\ \neg Y}{\neg X} \end{array}$$

Elimination:
$$\begin{array}{c} \neg X \qquad \text{ASS} \\ \vdots \\ \frac{Y,\ \neg Y}{X} \end{array}$$

Biconditional

Introduction:
$$\frac{X \to Y,\ Y \to X}{X \leftrightarrow Y}$$

Elimination:
$$\frac{X \leftrightarrow Y}{X \to Y} \qquad \frac{X \leftrightarrow Y}{Y \to X}$$

Some Derived Rules:

Double Negation

$$\frac{X}{\neg\neg X} \qquad \frac{\neg\neg X}{X}$$

Modus Tollens
$$\frac{X \to Y,\ \neg Y}{\neg X}$$

Z

Proof by Cases
$$\frac{X\ v\ Y,\ X \to Z,\ Y \to}{Z}$$

There are important constraints on the use of all the quantifier rules. But roughly - for any name n, any predicate P (simple or complex), and almost any variable v:

Introduction   **Elimination**

Universal Quantifier

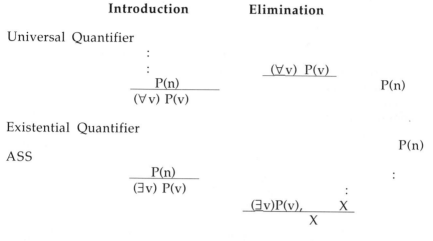

$$\frac{\vdots}{\underline{P(n)}}$$
$$(\forall v)\ P(v)$$

$$\frac{(\forall v)\ P(v)}{}$$
$$P(n)$$

Existential Quantifier

ASS

$$P(n)$$

$$\frac{P(n)}{(\exists v)\ P(v)}$$

$$\vdots$$

$$\frac{(\exists v)P(v),\qquad X}{X}$$

N.B. The rules →I, RAA and ∃E all involve the discharge of an assumption.

Identity

$$\frac{}{a = a}$$

$$\frac{P(a),\ a = b}{P(b)}$$

$$\frac{P(a),\ b = a}{P(b)}$$

Appendix 5: partial glossary for Edinburgh Prolog

(Inevitably, the nomenclature chosen, and mix of predicates defined, will vary from one implementation to another. This can only be a rough guide - consult the manual for your implementation.)

Special characters

. (full stop) - each complete sentence added to a program must be terminated by a period (to let Prolog know when one ends and the next begins.)

:- (colon and hyphen) - 'if'. So B :- A is 'If A then B', A → B.

, (comma) - conjunction. So B :- A, C is 'If A and C then B', (A & C) → B.

; (semi-colon) - disjunction. So B :- A; C is 'If A or C then B', (A v C) → B.

?- the query prompt: requests input from user.

_ (underscore) - occurring on its own, the anonymous or 'don't care' variable. Prefixed to a letter or word, makes it a Prolog variable.

= (identity) - checks whether two terms are identical. Will unify structures but not evaluate arithmetical functions.

== (double equality sign) - checks whether two terms are identical, but will not unify.

\= (back slash and equals) - non-identity.

! (exclamation mark) - the cut. Control feature preventing Prolog tracking back to look for solutions to goals which precede it.

=.. (univ) - X =.. L holds when L is the list consisting of the functor of X followed by its arguments.

/* - start comment. Must be paired with:

*/ - end comment; Prolog ignores all material in between.

% - Single line comment mark - Prolog ignores everything to end of line.

< - if X and Y are numbers, X < Y holds iff X is less than Y.

- if X and Y are constants, X < Y holds iff X is alphabetically before Y.

[and] - list brackets; members of list must be separated by commas.

| (vertical bar) - the list constructor: [Head | Tail] will match any list with first member Head and remaining list Tail.

' (single quote) - quotation mark, must be in pairs. (Overrides variable convention: 'X' is a constant, not a variable.)

" (double quote mark) - string quotation, must be in pairs. A double quoted string denotes the sequence of underlying ASCII codes.

+ - addition; typically used in the context X is Y + Z, or X is (Y + Z). Cf. **is** below.

- (minus sign) - subtraction.
* - multiplication.
/ or ÷ - division.
≤ or =< - $X \leq Y$ and $X =< Y$ hold iff $X \leq Y$.

Some fairly common predefined predicates

abolish(X) - deletes all clauses of the form specified by its argument X.

abs(X, Y) - holds iff Y is the absolute value of X (i.e. it knocks off the minus if X is a negative number).

append(X, Y, Z) - holds iff Z is the list which results by appending list X to the front of list Y.

arg(N, X, Y) - Y is the Nth argument of the structure X. E.g. **arg(2, between(b, a, c), X)** assigns **X** the value **a**.

assert(X) or **assertz(X)** - if X is an Edinburgh syntax wff, whether atomic or conditional, this adds X as the last clause in the definition of the predicate it concerns. A two place **assert(X, Y)** will assert a rule of the form X :- Y.

asserta(X) - as **assert(X)**, but adds X as *first* clause.

atom(X) - Type predicate: checks if X is a constant.

atomic(X) - Type predicate: checks if X is either a constant or a number.

bagof(X, C, B) - B is the bag of all Xs such that condition C is true.

bye (or **end**) - to finish current session at terminal.

call(X) - will call X as a goal; X must be assigned an Edinburgh syntax wff.

charof(X, Y) - holds iff Y is the ASCII code number of character X.

clause(X, Y) - searches for a rule of the form X :- Y. Can be used in form **clause(X, _)** to search for unconditional clause X.

concat(X, Y, Z) - holds iff Z is the result of concatenating expressions X and Y, e.g. **concat(uni, corn, unicorn)**.

consult(X) - loads file (or perhaps list of files) of name X.

cos(X, Y) - holds iff Y is the cosine of angle X.

def(X) - Type predicate: checks if the predicate X is defined, i.e. there is at least one clause for X within the current program.

fail - evaluation will fail when Prolog reaches this goal.

findall(X, Y, L) - holds iff L is the list of all Xs which satisfy Y (given any way of making Y true, i.e. by assigning its variables values.)

float(X) - Type predicate: checks if X is a floating point non-integer number.

forall(P, Q) - holds true iff $(\forall x_1) \ldots (\forall x_n)(P \rightarrow Q)$ (where $x_1 \ldots x_n$ are all the variables that occur in both P and Q).

functor(X, Y, N) - if structure X is supplied, functor Y and arity N are returned; if Y and N are supplied, X will be a structure with that functor and arity.

gensym(Word**, X)** - generates series of symbols Word0, Word1, Word2, ..., for any word Word. Each time it is called it assigns the next one to **X**.

get(X) - read in the next character typed, and assign it to **X**.

init_gensym(Word**)** - initializes word Word for **gensym**.

integer(X) - checks if X is an integer (whole number, positive or negative).

int(X, Y) - holds iff Y is the integer nearest to X - below it if X is positive, above it if X is negative.

is - numerical evaluation: **X is Y** evaluates numerical term **Y**, and is true iff **X** = the value of **Y**. Thus **X is 5 + 7** will assign **X** the value 12.

kill(P**)** - deletes all clauses defining predicate P from program.

length(L, X) - holds iff X is the number of things on list L.

list(X) - type predicate: is true iff X is a list.

listing - lists all clauses in current program.

listing(X) - lists all clauses defining predicate X.

map(X, Y, Z) - holds iff each thing on list Y bears relation X to each thing on list Z; i.e. X maps list Y onto list Z.

member(X, L) - X is one of the things on the list L, i.e. a top-level member of L.

name(X, L) - L is the list of ASCII codes of the letters of atom X.

nl - stands for New Line: puts a carriage return in Default Output Window, thus putting cursor on a new line.

nonvar(X) - Type predicate: checks if X is not an unassigned variable.

nospy(P**)**, or **nospy** P - switches off the spy point on predicate P. Cf **spy**.

not(A**)** - negation of A; brackets required if A complex. **not(**A**)** succeeds if A fails to be proved, and fails if A can be proved.

number(X) - Type predicate: checks if X is a number.

on(X, L) - same as **member**.

op(P, S, X) - declare word X to be an operator with precedence P and syntax S (infix, prefix or postfix, and left/right associativity.)

put(N) - prints the character with ASCII code N.

pwr(X, Y, Z) - holds iff $Z = X^Y$.

read(X) - reads in term typed from keyboard and assigns it to **X**.

repeat - a goal which succeeds, and succeeds on backtracking.

retract(X) - deletes first occurrence of clause X from database, if one can be found which matches X. Backtracking across the **retract** will cause next matching X to be deleted.

retractall(X) - deletes from database all clauses which match X.

save(X) - saves all of current database as file X.

see(X) - switch to make X the current input stream, opening it if not already opened.

setof(X, C, S) - S is the set of all Xs such that condition C true (given some way of assigning values to its unbound variables.) S is a list with no repetitions.

sign(X, Y) - Y is the sign of X: Y is 1 if X is a positive number, 0 if X is 0, and -1 if X is negative.

sin(X, Y) - holds iff Y is the sine of angle X.

sort(X, Y) - Y is the list of terms in list X sorted in < order.

spy(P), or **spy** P - allows any predicate, including predefined ones, to be spied on. Should be set as a query, prior to running query to be spied on.

sqrt(X, Y) - holds iff Y is the square root of X, i.e. Y times Y is X.

struct(X) - checks whether X is a structure (rather than an atom).

tab(X) - X spaces are printed in Default Output Window (i.e. same as tabulation on a typewriter - helps display by separating out text.)

tan(X, Y) - holds iff Y is the tangent of angle X.

tell(X) - switch the output stream to X.

var(X) - checks if X is a variable which is currently not assigned a value.

write(X) - writes any term X to screen.

writeq(X) - same as **write**, except that atoms in single quotes are displayed as such.

Selected references, and further reading

1   Smullyan uses knights and knaves examples not as an informal prelude to formal logic, but as a means to present, informally, some of the deepest results in metalogic. See *What is the Name of This Book?* (Prentice-Hall, 1978), or *The Lady or the Tiger* (Penguin, 1983). Hat exercises are developed by Mitsumasa Anno and Akihiro Nozaki in *Anno's Hat Tricks* (Bodley Head).

2.1   Thurber's 'Wild Bird Hickok and his Friends' is in his *Let Your Mind Alone!* (Hamish Hamilton, 1937). His 'What a Lovely Generalization!' (see section 2.5) is in *Thurber Country* (Hamish Hamilton, 1953).

2.3   The quotation from Sextus Empiricus is by permission of Oxford University Press, from William and Martha Kneale *The Development of Logic* (OUP, 1962). For Grice on implicature, see 'Logic and Conversation', in D. Davidson and G. Harman (eds) *The Logic of Grammar* (Dickenson, 1975).

2.4   Tests for distinguishing names and quantifiers on the basis of scope interactions are discussed in detail by Dummett, *Frege* Ch 4 (Duckworth, 1973). Gettier's 'Is Justified True Belief Knowledge?', *Analysis*, **23** (1963), pp. 121-123, is also in A. Phillips Griffiths, (ed) *Knowledge and Belief* (Oxford University Press, 1967).

2.5   Goodman's 'grue' paradox is presented in his *Fact, Fiction and Forecast* (Bobbs-Merrill, 1963).

3.1   For other books on Prolog, see, for example, W. Clocksin and C. Mellish *Programming in Prolog* (Springer, 1981), and L. Sterling and E. Shapiro *The Art of Prolog* (MIT Press, 1986). See also R. Kowalski's *Logic for Problem Solving* (North Holland, 1979).

3.3   Quine's collection *From a Logical Point of View* (Harper and Row, 1963) contains some of his papers on ontology, e.g. 'On What There Is', and 'Logic and the Reification of Universals'. For books treating consistency, completeness and decidability, see e.g. G. Boolos and R. Jeffrey *Computability and Logic* (Cambridge University Press, 1974), or E. Mendelson *Introduction to Mathematical Logic* (Van Nostrand, 1964).

3.5   The problem of the farmer and the river was discussed by Bas van Fraassen in a lecture on Symmetry given at the London School of Economics.

3.6   D.C.G.s are presented in F. Pereira and D. Warren 'Definite Clause Grammars for Language Analysis', *Artificial Intelligence*, **13** (1980), pp. 231-278, reprinted in B. Grosz, K. Sparck Jones and B. Webber (eds) *Readings in Natural Language Processing* (Morgan Kaufmann, 1986).

4.1   Many logic texts present some version of natural deduction, for example, S. Guttenplan, *The Languages of Logic* (Blackwell, 1986).

4.2   Ayer's original formulation of weak verifiability was in the first edition of *Language, Truth and Logic* (Gollancz, 1936); the reformulation in his Introduction to the second edition.   Church's review was in the *Journal of Symbolic Logic*, **14** (1949).

4.3   The blocks example of Moore's is in his article 'The Role of Logic in Knowledge Representation and Commonsense Reasoning', which can be found in R. Brachman and H. Levesque (eds) *Readings in Knowledge Representation* (Morgan Kaufmann, 1985).

4.6   The classical statement of Russell's theory of descriptions is his 'On Denoting', *Mind*, **14** (1905).   One discussion of it is Kaplan's 'What is Russell's Theory of Descriptions?', in Davidson and Harman (eds) *The Logic of Grammar*.   See S. Kripke *Naming and Necessity* (Blackwell, 1980) for some of the issues concerning necessity. For a more detailed discussion of the relation between 'means that' and 'true', see Martin Davies *Meaning, Necessity and Quantification* (Routledge, 1981).   For a more detailed treatment of resolution, see, for example, A. Bundy *The Computer Modelling of Mathematical Reasoning*, (Academic Press, 1983).

5.1   For a detailed presentation of set theory, see, for example, P. Suppes *Axiomatic Set Theory* (Dover, 1972).

5.2   For Connectionist models, see, for example, D.E. Rumelhart, J.L. McClelland, and the PDP Research Group: *Parallel Distributed Processing: Explorations in the Microstructure of Cognition* (2 volumes, MIT Press, 1986).   On the interactive activation and competition model, see also McClelland and Rumelhart *Explorations in Parallel Distributed Processing* (MIT Press, 1988), Chapter 2.

5.3   H. Levesque and R. Brachman 'A Fundamental Tradeoff in Knowledge Representation and Reasoning', in R. Brachman and H. Levesque (eds).   This collection also contains R. Davis, B. Buchanan and E. Shortliffe 'Production Rules as a Representation for a Knowledge-Based Consultation Program' (originally in *Artificial Intelligence*, **8**, 1977, pp. 15-45), which discusses MYCIN, one of the most   important   systems   to   include   a   measure   of confidence/uncertainty in its rules and data.

5.4   For a more sophisticated production system approach to theorem proving, see A. Newell and H. Simon 'GPS, A Program that Simulates Human Thought', in E. Feigenbaum and J. Feldman (eds) *Computers and Thought* (Oldenbourg, 1963).   Nilsson's *Principles of Artificial Intelligence* (Springer Verlag) contains an extended treatment of different production system strategies.

5.5   The semantic programs follow two important semantic programmes.   The treatment of quantifiers follows Montague's 'The Proper Treatment of Quantification in Ordinary English', in R. Thomason (ed) *Formal Philosophy* (Yale, 1974).   The case for treating event-describing sentences in terms of explicit quantification over events is presented in Davidson's 'The Logical Form of Action

Sentences', in N. Rescher (ed) *The Logic of Decision and Action* (Univ. Pittsburgh Press, 1967). G. Gazdar and C. Mellish *Natural Language Processing in Prolog* (Addison Wesley, 1989) provides a more detailed treatment of computational linguistics.

Index